THE BOOK ®

Rover 213 & 216
Service and Repair Manual

Peter G Strasman

(1116-224-2AA9)

Models covered

All Rover 213 & 216 saloons, including special/limited edition models
1342 cc & 1598 cc

Does not cover Rover 214 & 216 introduced October 1989

© Haynes Publishing 1997

A book in the **Haynes Service and Repair Manual Series**

ABC

2

ISBN **1 85960 232 0**

British Library Cataloguing in Publication Data
A catalogue record for this book is available from the British Library.

Printed by **J H Haynes & Co. Ltd, Sparkford, Nr Yeovil, Somerset BA22 7JJ**

Haynes Publishing
Sparkford, Nr Yeovil, Somerset BA22 7JJ, England

Haynes North America, Inc
861 Lawrence Drive, Newbury Park, California 91320, USA

Editions Haynes S.A.
147/149, rue Saint Honoré, 75001 Paris, France

Haynes Publishing Nordiska AB
Fyrisborgsgatan 5, 754 50 Uppsala, Sverige

Contents

LIVING WITH YOUR ROVER

Contents

Introduction to the Rover 200 Series

The cars in the range are economical and well constructed but, of course, show much evidence of their Japanese influence in design.

There is a sufficiently large number of model variations to suit most demands in respect of engine, transmission and trim specifications. It will be realised that the performance of the smaller-engined versions, especially with automatic transmission, must be limited with such a large body.

From the points of view of servicing and repair, the car should present no problems to the home mechanic.

For modifications, and information applicable to later models, refer to the Supplement at the end of this manual.

Acknowledgements

Thanks are due to Champion Spark Plug who supplied the illustrations showing spark plug conditions. Sykes-Pickavant provided some of the workshop tools. Lastly special thanks are due to all those people at Sparkford who helped in the production of this manual.

We take great pride in the accuracy of information given in this manual, but vehicle manufacturers make alterations and design changes during the production run of a particular vehicle of which they do not inform us. No liability can be accepted by the authors or publishers for loss, damage or injury caused by errors in, or omissions from, the information given.

Rover 216 Vitesse EFi

Rover 216 Vanden Plas EFi

Working on your car can be dangerous. This page shows just some of the potential risks and hazards, with the aim of creating a safety-conscious attitude.

General hazards

Scalding

• Don't remove the radiator or expansion tank cap while the engine is hot.
• Engine oil, automatic transmission fluid or power steering fluid may also be dangerously hot if the engine has recently been running.

Burning

• Beware of burns from the exhaust system and from any part of the engine. Brake discs and drums can also be extremely hot immediately after use.

Crushing

• When working under or near a raised vehicle, always supplement the jack with axle stands, or use drive-on ramps. *Never venture under a car which is only supported by a jack.*
• Take care if loosening or tightening high-torque nuts when the vehicle is on stands. Initial loosening and final tightening should be done with the wheels on the ground.

Fire

• Fuel is highly flammable; fuel vapour is explosive.
• Don't let fuel spill onto a hot engine.
• Do not smoke or allow naked lights (including pilot lights) anywhere near a vehicle being worked on. Also beware of creating sparks (electrically or by use of tools).
• Fuel vapour is heavier than air, so don't work on the fuel system with the vehicle over an inspection pit.
• Another cause of fire is an electrical overload or short-circuit. Take care when repairing or modifying the vehicle wiring.
• Keep a fire extinguisher handy, of a type suitable for use on fuel and electrical fires.

Electric shock

• Ignition HT voltage can be dangerous, especially to people with heart problems or a pacemaker. Don't work on or near the ignition system with the engine running or the ignition switched on.

• Mains voltage is also dangerous. Make sure that any mains-operated equipment is correctly earthed. Mains power points should be protected by a residual current device (RCD) circuit breaker.

Fume or gas intoxication

• Exhaust fumes are poisonous; they often contain carbon monoxide, which is rapidly fatal if inhaled. Never run the engine in a confined space such as a garage with the doors shut.
• Fuel vapour is also poisonous, as are the vapours from some cleaning solvents and paint thinners.

Poisonous or irritant substances

• Avoid skin contact with battery acid and with any fuel, fluid or lubricant, especially antifreeze, brake hydraulic fluid and Diesel fuel. Don't syphon them by mouth. If such a substance is swallowed or gets into the eyes, seek medical advice.
• Prolonged contact with used engine oil can cause skin cancer. Wear gloves or use a barrier cream if necessary. Change out of oil-soaked clothes and do not keep oily rags in your pocket.
• Air conditioning refrigerant forms a poisonous gas if exposed to a naked flame (including a cigarette). It can also cause skin burns on contact.

Asbestos

• Asbestos dust can cause cancer if inhaled or swallowed. Asbestos may be found in gaskets and in brake and clutch linings. When dealing with such components it is safest to assume that they contain asbestos.

Special hazards

Hydrofluoric acid

• This extremely corrosive acid is formed when certain types of synthetic rubber, found in some O-rings, oil seals, fuel hoses etc, are exposed to temperatures above 400°C. The rubber changes into a charred or sticky substance containing the acid. *Once formed, the acid remains dangerous for years. If it gets onto the skin, it may be necessary to amputate the limb concerned.*
• When dealing with a vehicle which has suffered a fire, or with components salvaged from such a vehicle, wear protective gloves and discard them after use.

The battery

• Batteries contain sulphuric acid, which attacks clothing, eyes and skin. Take care when topping-up or carrying the battery.
• The hydrogen gas given off by the battery is highly explosive. Never cause a spark or allow a naked light nearby. Be careful when connecting and disconnecting battery chargers or jump leads.

Air bags

• Air bags can cause injury if they go off accidentally. Take care when removing the steering wheel and/or facia. Special storage instructions may apply.

Diesel injection equipment

• Diesel injection pumps supply fuel at very high pressure. Take care when working on the fuel injectors and fuel pipes.

⚠ *Warning: Never expose the hands, face or any other part of the body to injector spray; the fuel can penetrate the skin with potentially fatal results.*

Remember...

DO

• Do use eye protection when using power tools, and when working under the vehicle.
• Do wear gloves or use barrier cream to protect your hands when necessary.
• Do get someone to check periodically that all is well when working alone on the vehicle.
• Do keep loose clothing and long hair well out of the way of moving mechanical parts.
• Do remove rings, wristwatch etc, before working on the vehicle – especially the electrical system.
• Do ensure that any lifting or jacking equipment has a safe working load rating adequate for the job.

DON'T

• Don't attempt to lift a heavy component which may be beyond your capability – get assistance.
• Don't rush to finish a job, or take unverified short cuts.
• Don't use ill-fitting tools which may slip and cause injury.
• Don't leave tools or parts lying around where someone can trip over them. Mop up oil and fuel spills at once.
• Don't allow children or pets to play in or near a vehicle being worked on.

For modifications, and information applicable to later models, see Supplement at end of manual

Dimensions

Overall length	4.156 m (163.8 in)
Overall width	1.623 m (63.8 in)
Overall height (at kerb weight)	1.377 m (54.0 in)
Ground clearance (at kerb weight)	165.0 mm (6.5 in)
Wheelbase	2.45 m (96.5 in)
Track-front	1.4 m (55.0 in)
Track-rear	1.415 m (55.5 in)

Kerb weights up to 1987 (with oil, coolant and full fuel tank)

213 (manual)	860 kg (1896 lb)
213 S:	
Manual	865 kg (1907 lb)
Automatic	876 kg (1932 lb)
213 SE (automatic)	886 kg (1954 lb)
213 Vanden Plas	945 kg (2084 lb)
216 S	940 kg (2073 lb)
216 SE	945 kg (2084 lb)
216 Vanden Plas:	
Manual	954 kg (2104 lb)
Automatic	976 kg (2152 lb)
216 Vitesse	945 kg (2084 lb)

Kerb weights from 1987 (with oil, coolant and full fuel tank)

213	895 kg (1975 lb)
213S:	
Manual	900 kg (1985 lb)
Automatic	910 kg (2010 lb)
213 SE Automatic	925 kg (2040 lb)
213 EX	945 kg (2084 lb)
216 S	975 kg (2150 lb)
216 SE	970 kg (2139 lb)
216 SE EFi and EX:	
Manual	990 kg (2185 lb)
Automatic	1010 kg (2230 lb)
216 Vanden Plas:	
Manual	995 kg (2194 lb)
Automatic	1020 kg (2249 lb)
216 Vitesse	1000 kg (2205 lb)
216 Sprint	960 kg (2117 lb)

Capacities

Engine oil with filter change:	
1.3 models	3.5 litres (6.25 pints)
1.6 models	3.6 litres (6.30 pints)
Manual transmission:	
1.3 models	2.3 litres (4.0 pints)
1.6 models	2.2 litres (3.75 pints)
Automatic transmission (service fluid change):	
Three speed	2.4 litres (4.25 pints)
Four-speed	2.0 litres (3.5 pints)
Refill from dry (includes torque converter):	
Three speed	5.0 litres (8.75 pints)
Four-speed	5.75 litres (10.0 pints)
Cooling system:	
1.3 models up to VIN 800 000 (1985 model year)	4.5 litres (8.0 pints)
1.3 models from VIN 800 000 (1985 model year)	6.4 litres (11.0 pints)
1.6 models	6.4 litres (11.0 pints)
Fuel tank	46.0 litres (10.0 gals)

Jump starting

HAYNES HiNT *Jump starting will get you out of trouble, but you must correct whatever made the battery go flat in the first place. There are three possibilities:*

1 The battery has been drained by repeated attempts to start, or by leaving the lights on.

2 The charging system is not working properly (alternator drivebelt slack or broken, alternator wiring fault or alternator itself faulty).

3 The battery itself is at fault (electrolyte low, or battery worn out).

When jump-starting a car using a booster battery, observe the following precautions:

✔ Before connecting the booster battery, make sure that the ignition is switched off.

✔ Ensure that all electrical equipment (lights, heater, wipers, etc) is switched off.

✔ Make sure that the booster battery is the same voltage as the discharged one in the vehicle.

✔ If the battery is being jump-started from the battery in another vehicle, the two vehcles MUST NOT TOUCH each other.

✔ Make sure that the transmission is in neutral (or PARK, in the case of automatic transmission).

1 Connect one end of the red jump lead to the positive (+) terminal of the flat battery

2 Connect the other end of the red lead to the positive (+) terminal of the booster battery.

3 Connect one end of the black jump lead to the negative (-) terminal of the booster battery

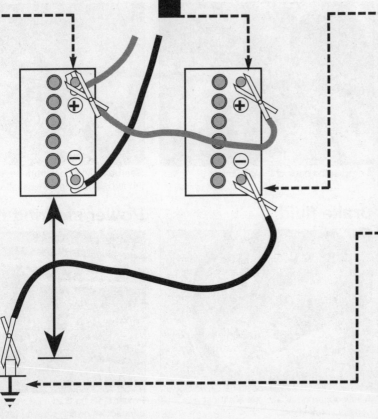

4 Connect the other end of the black jump lead to a bolt or bracket on the engine block, well away from the battery, on the vehicle to be started.

5 Make sure that the jump leads will not come into contact with the fan, drive-belts or other moving parts of the engine.

6 Start the engine using the booster battery, then with the engine running at idle speed, disconnect the jump leads in the reverse order of connection.

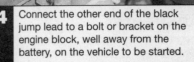

Identifying leaks

Puddles on the garage floor or drive, or obvious wetness under the bonnet or underneath the car, suggest a leak that needs investigating. It can sometimes be difficult to decide where the leak is coming from, especially if the engine bay is very dirty already. Leaking oil or fluid can also be blown rearwards by the passage of air under the car, giving a false impression of where the problem lies.

> ⚠ **Warning: Most automotive oils and fluids are poisonous. Wash them off skin, and change out of contaminated clothing, without delay.**

> **HAYNES HiNT** *The smell of a fluid leaking from the car may provide a clue to what's leaking. Some fluids are distinctively coloured. It may help to clean the car carefully and to park it over some clean paper overnight as an aid to locating the source of the leak.*
>
> *Remember that some leaks may only occur while the engine is running.*

Sump oil

Engine oil may leak from the drain plug...

Oil from filter

...or from the base of the oil filter.

Gearbox oil

Gearbox oil can leak from the seals at the inboard ends of the driveshafts.

Antifreeze

Leaking antifreeze often leaves a crystalline deposit like this.

Brake fluid

A leak occurring at a wheel is almost certainly brake fluid.

Power steering fluid

Power steering fluid may leak from the pipe connectors on the steering rack.

Front jacking bracket

Rear jacking bracket

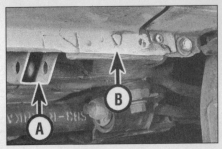

Sill jacking point

A *DO NOT jack up or support the car under this box member*

B *Correct jacking/support location point*

Jacking

To avoid repetition, the procedure for raising the vehicle, in order to carry out work under it, is not included before each relevant operation described in this Manual.

It is to be preferred, and it is certainly recommended, that the vehicle is positioned over an inspection pit or raised on a lift. Where these facilities are not available, use ramps or jack up the vehicle strictly in accordance with the following guide. Once the vehicle is raised, supplement the jack with axle stands.

To lift the front of the car (both wheels) locate the jack under the jacking bracket. Support the car with axle stands placed under the forward jacking points under the sills.

Raise the rear of the car by placing the jack under the rear jacking bracket.

Support the car with axle stands placed under the rearmost jacking points under the sills.

Towing

If the car is being towed, use the hooks provided, but have the ignition key in position (1) so that the steering does not lock. Remember that the brake pedal will require greater effort as the vacuum servo assistance will not be available.

It is permissible to tow a light vehicle using the rear towing hook.

If the car is fitted with automatic transmission it is recommended that the front wheels are raised off the ground when being towed. If this is not possible, restrict the towing speed to 48 km/h (30 mph) and the distance towed to 48 km (30 miles).

Wheel changing

To change a roadwheel, remove the spare wheel from the well in the luggage boot.

Remove the jack, wheelbrace and trim removal lever from the container ahead of the spare wheel.

Prise off the hub cap or roadwheel trim according to model.

Make sure that the handbrake is fully applied and chock the wheel opposite to the one being removed.

Release but do not remove the wheel nuts.

Locate the jack from the tool kit under the reinforced jacking point below the sill nearest to the roadwheel being changed. Do not jack up under the tubular bars adjacent to the jacking points. The correct points of lift are marked with a triangle.

Raise the car, remove the wheel nuts and roadwheel.

Fit the spare wheel, tighten the nuts until the roadwheel cannot be held against rotation.

Lower the jack and tighten the roadwheel nuts fully. Fit the wheel trim or hub cap.

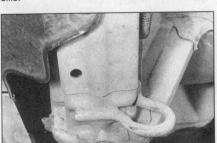

Front towing hook

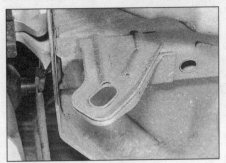

Rear towing hook

Spare wheel stowage

Tool and jack stowage

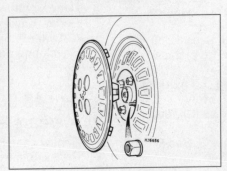

Roadwheel trim plate

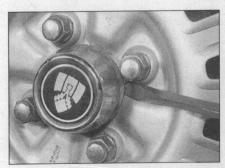

Prising off wheel centre cap

Maintenance is essential for ensuring safety, and desirable for the purpose of getting the best in terms of performance and economy from your car. Over the years the need for periodic lubrication has been greatly reduced if not totally eliminated. This has unfortunately tended to lead some owners to think that, because no such action is required, the items either no longer exist, or will last forever. This is certainly not the case; it is essential to carry out regular visual examination as comprehensively as possible in order to spot any possible defects at an early stage before they develop into major expensive repairs.

The following service schedules are a list of the maintenance requirements and the intervals at which they should be carried out, based on the schedule recommended by the manufacturers. Where applicable these procedures are covered in greater detail throughout this manual, near the beginning of each Chapter.

At weekly intervals or before a long journey

- ☐ Check the engine oil level
- ☐ Check the coolant level (Chapter 2, Sec 2)
- ☐ Check the brake fluid level in the reservoir (Chapter 9, Sec 2)
- ☐ Check the washer fluid level, adding a screen wash (Chapter 12, Sec 22)
- ☐ Check the operation of all lights, horn, direction indicators and wipers
- ☐ Check the tyre pressures (Chapter 8, Sec 8)

Every 6000 miles (10 000 km) or 6 months – whichever comes first

- ☐ Check wear and condition of tyres (Chapter 8, Sec 8)
- ☐ Check disc pads for wear (Chapter 9, Sec 3)
- ☐ Renew engine oil and filter (Chapter 1, Sec 3 or 35)
- ☐ Check transmission oil level (Chapter 6, Sec 2 or 13, or Chapter 7, Sec 3 or 12)
- ☐ Lubricate all controls, linkages and hinges
- ☐ Adjust clutch (Chapter 5, Sec 2) (early models only)
- ☐ Check refrigerant (air conditioned models) (Chapter 2, Sec 23)

Every 12 000 miles (20 000 km) or annually – whichever comes first

- ☐ Clean battery terminals and apply petroleum jelly (Chapter 12, Sec 2)
- ☐ Check drivebelts for tension and condition (Chapter 2, Sec 12)
- ☐ Renew spark plugs (Chapter 4, Sec 7)
- ☐ Adjust valve clearances (1.3 models) (Chapter 1, Sec 6)
- ☐ Renew air filter element (Chapter 3, Secs 3, 29)
- ☐ Top up carburettor damper piston (1.6 models) (Chapter 3, Sec 2)
- ☐ Renew automatic transmission fluid (1.3 models) at first 12 000 miles (20 000 km), then every 24 000 miles (40 000 km) or two years (Chapter 7, Sec 3)
- ☐ Check shoe linings for wear (Chapter 9, Sec 6)
- ☐ Renew wiper blades (Chapter 12, Sec 20)

Every 24 000 miles (40 000 km) or 2 years – whichever comes first

- ☐ Check condition and tension of timing belt (Chapter 1, Sec 7 or 39)
- ☐ Check valve clearances (1.6 models) (Chapter 1, Sec 38)
- ☐ Renew automatic transmission fluid (1.6 models) (Chapter 7, Sec 12)
- ☐ Check condition of exhaust system (Chapter 3, Sec 41)
- ☐ Check front wheel alignment (Chapter 10, Sec 27)
- ☐ Check ignition timing (1.3 only) (Chapter 4, Sec 3)
- ☐ Check headlamp alignment (Chapter 12, Sec 16)
- ☐ Check steering and suspension for wear (Chapter 10, Sec 2)
- ☐ Check steering and driveshaft gaiters for condition (Chapters 8 and 10)
- ☐ Renew PCV valve (Chapter 1, Sec 4)
- ☐ Renew fuel filter (1.3 models) (Chapter 3, Sec 4)
- ☐ Renew emission blow-by filter (1.3 models) (Chapter 1, Sec 4)
- ☐ Renew crankcase breather filter (Chapter 1, Sec 4)
- ☐ Check condition of all coolant and brake hoses (Chapter 2 and 9)
- ☐ Clean inside of distributor cap and check rotor for erosion (Chapter 4, Sec 2)
- ☐ Adjust idle speed and mixture (Chapter 3, Sec 15, 22 or 36)
- ☐ Adjust handbrake cable if travel excessive (Chapter 9, Sec 18)
- ☐ Drain manual transmission oil and renew (Chapter 6, Secs 2, 13)
- ☐ Renew anti-freeze coolant (Chapter 2, Sec 5)
- ☐ Renew brake hydraulic fluid by bleeding (Chapter 9, Sec 14)
- ☐ Check hub bearings for wear (Chapter 8, Sec 2)

Every 48 000 miles (80 000 km) or 4 years – whichever comes first

- ☐ Renew camshaft belt (Chapter 1, Secs 8, 40)
- ☐ Renew fuel filter (fuel injection models) (Chapter 3, Sec 31)

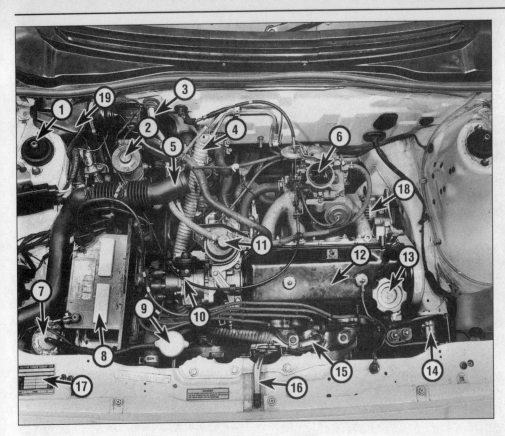

Under-bonnet view – 1.3 model

1 Suspension strut
2 Brake master cylinder
3 Brake servo
4 Air cleaner (removed) hot air intake
5 Air cleaner (removed) cold air intake
6 Carburettor
7 Coolant expansion tank
8 Battery
9 Radiator cap
10 Distributor
11 Fuel pump
12 Rocker cover
13 Oil filler cap
14 Front left engine mounting
15 Exhaust manifold
16 Bonnet lock
17 Vehicle identification plate
18 Alternator
19 Windscreen wiper motor

Under-body (rear end) – 1.3 model

1 Exhaust silencer
2 Axle beam
3 Panhard rod
4 Fuel tank
5 Trailing arm
6 Exhaust pipe
7 Handbrake cable
8 Brake hose
9 Fuel filter cover

Underbody (front end)

1 Torsion bar
2 Exhaust pipe
3 Gearbox stabiliser bar
4 Gearchange rod
5 Radius arm
6 Tie-rod balljoint
7 Lower suspension arm
8 Transmission
9 Sump pan
10 Brake caliper
11 Driveshaft
12 Cover plates
13 Anti-roll bar

**Under-bonnet view –
1.6 fuel injection model**

1 Suspension strut
2 Wiper motor
3 Throttle housing
4 Air cleaner
5 Battery
6 Coolant expansion tank
7 Camshaft cover
8 Timing belt upper cover
9 Washer fluid reservoir
10 Fuel rail
11 Fuel pressure regulator
12 Ignition electronic
   control unit (ECU)
13 Servo
14 Brake master cylinder
15 Distributor
16 Bonnet lock

Length (distance)

Inches (in)	x 25.4	= Millimetres (mm)	x 0.0394	=	Inches (in)
Feet (ft)	x 0.305	= Metres (m)	x 3.281	=	Feet (ft)
Miles	x 1.609	= Kilometres (km)	x 0.621	=	Miles

Volume (capacity)

Cubic inches (cu in; in³)	x 16.387	= Cubic centimetres (cc; cm³)	x 0.061	=	Cubic inches (cu in; in³)
Imperial pints (Imp pt)	x 0.568	= Litres (l)	x 1.76	=	Imperial pints (Imp pt)
Imperial quarts (Imp qt)	x 1.137	= Litres (l)	x 0.88	=	Imperial quarts (Imp qt)
Imperial quarts (Imp qt)	x 1.201	= US quarts (US qt)	x 0.833	=	Imperial quarts (Imp qt)
US quarts (US qt)	x 0.946	= Litres (l)	x 1.057	=	US quarts (US qt)
Imperial gallons (Imp gal)	x 4.546	= Litres (l)	x 0.22	=	Imperial gallons (Imp gal)
Imperial gallons (Imp gal)	x 1.201	= US gallons (US gal)	x 0.833	=	Imperial gallons (Imp gal)
US gallons (US gal)	x 3.785	= Litres (l)	x 0.264	=	US gallons (US gal)

Mass (weight)

Ounces (oz)	x 28.35	= Grams (g)	x 0.035	=	Ounces (oz)
Pounds (lb)	x 0.454	= Kilograms (kg)	x 2.205	=	Pounds (lb)

Force

Ounces-force (ozf; oz)	x 0.278	= Newtons (N)	x 3.6	=	Ounces-force (ozf; oz)
Pounds-force (lbf; lb)	x 4.448	= Newtons (N)	x 0.225	=	Pounds-force (lbf; lb)
Newtons (N)	x 0.1	= Kilograms-force (kgf; kg)	x 9.81	=	Newtons (N)

Pressure

Pounds-force per square inch (psi; lbf/in²; lb/in²)	x 0.070	= Kilograms-force per square centimetre (kgf/cm²; kg/cm²)	x 14.223	=	Pounds-force per square inch (psi; lbf/in²; lb/in²)
Pounds-force per square inch (psi; lbf/in²; lb/in²)	x 0.068	= Atmospheres (atm)	x 14.696	=	Pounds-force per square inch (psi; lbf/in²; lb/in²)
Pounds-force per square inch (psi; lbf/in²; lb/in²)	x 0.069	= Bars	x 14.5	=	Pounds-force per square inch (psi; lbf/in²; lb/in²)
Pounds-force per square inch (psi; lbf/in²; lb/in²)	x 6.895	= Kilopascals (kPa)	x 0.145	=	Pounds-force per square inch (psi; lbf/in²; lb/in²)
Kilopascals (kPa)	x 0.01	= Kilograms-force per square centimetre (kgf/cm²; kg/cm²)	x 98.1	=	Kilopascals (kPa)
Millibar (mbar)	x 100	= Pascals (Pa)	x 0.01	=	Millibar (mbar)
Millibar (mbar)	x 0.0145	= Pounds-force per square inch (psi; lbf/in²; lb/in²)	x 68.947	=	Millibar (mbar)
Millibar (mbar)	x 0.75	= Millimetres of mercury (mmHg)	x 1.333	=	Millibar (mbar)
Millibar (mbar)	x 0.401	= Inches of water (inH₂O)	x 2.491	=	Millibar (mbar)
Millimetres of mercury (mmHg)	x 0.535	= Inches of water (inH₂O)	x 1.868	=	Millimetres of mercury (mmHg)
Inches of water (inH₂O)	x 0.036	= Pounds-force per square inch (psi; lbf/in²; lb/in²)	x 27.68	=	Inches of water (inH₂O)

Torque (moment of force)

Pounds-force inches (lbf in; lb in)	x 1.152	= Kilograms-force centimetre (kgf cm; kg cm)	x 0.868	=	Pounds-force inches (lbf in; lb in)
Pounds-force inches (lbf in; lb in)	x 0.113	= Newton metres (Nm)	x 8.85	=	Pounds-force inches (lbf in; lb in)
Pounds-force inches (lbf in; lb in)	x 0.083	= Pounds-force feet (lbf ft; lb ft)	x 12	=	Pounds-force inches (lbf in; lb in)
Pounds-force feet (lbf ft; lb ft)	x 0.138	= Kilograms-force metres (kgf m; kg m)	x 7.233	=	Pounds-force feet (lbf ft; lb ft)
Pounds-force feet (lbf ft; lb ft)	x 1.356	= Newton metres (Nm)	x 0.738	=	Pounds-force feet (lbf ft; lb ft)
Newton metres (Nm)	x 0.102	= Kilograms-force metres (kgf m; kg m)	x 9.804	=	Newton metres (Nm)

Power

Horsepower (hp)	x 745.7	= Watts (W)	x 0.0013	=	Horsepower (hp)

Velocity (speed)

Miles per hour (miles/hr; mph)	x 1.609	= Kilometres per hour (km/hr; kph)	x 0.621	=	Miles per hour (miles/hr; mph)

Fuel consumption*

Miles per gallon (mpg)	x 0.354	= Kilometres per litre (km/l)	x 2.825	=	Miles per gallon (mpg)

Temperature

Degrees Fahrenheit = (°C x 1.8) + 32

Degrees Celsius (Degrees Centigrade; °C) = (°F - 32) x 0.56

It is common practice to convert from miles per gallon (mpg) to litres/100 kilometres (l/100km), where mpg x l/100 km = 282

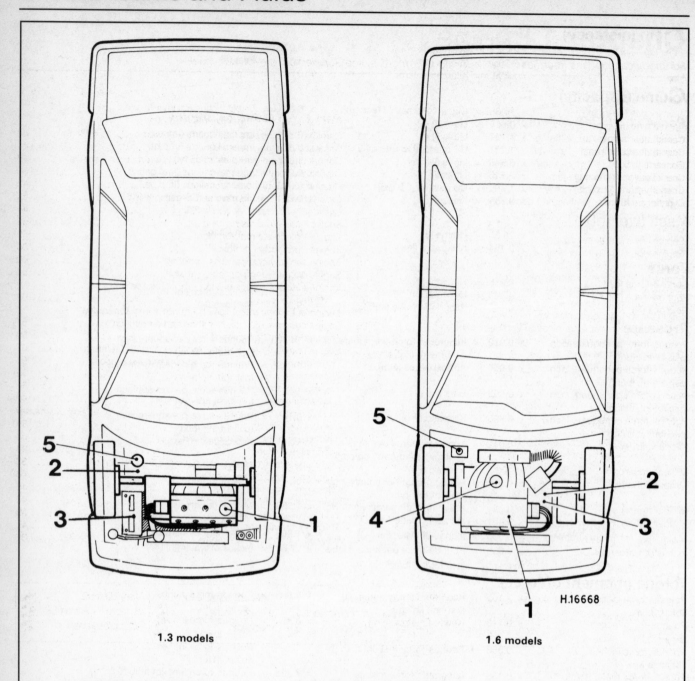

1.3 models

1.6 models

H.16668

Component or system	Lubricant type/specification
Engine (1)	Multigrade engine oil, viscosity SAE 10W/30 or 10W/40, to API SF
Manual gearbox (2)	Multigrade engine oil, viscosity SAE 10W/30 or 10W/40, to API SF
Automatic transmission (3) 1.3 models (refill and top up) 1.3 (top up only) and 1.6 models	Hondamatic Automatic Gearbox Fluid Dexron IID type ATF
SU carburettor piston damper (4)	Multigrade engine oil
Brake fluid (5)	Hydraulic fluid to FMVSS DOT 4

Chapter 1 Engine

For modifications, and information applicable to later models, see Supplement at end of manual

Contents

Degrees of difficulty

 Easy, suitable for novice with little experience

 Fairly easy, suitable for beginner with some experience

 Fairly difficult, suitable for competent DIY mechanic

Difficult, suitable for experienced DIY mechanic

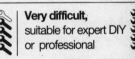 **Very difficult,** suitable for expert DIY or professional

Specifications

Part A 1.3 engine

General

Engine type	Four cylinder overhead camshaft transversely mounted
Code	EV2
Capacity	1342 cc (81.8 cu in)
Bore	74.0 mm (2.91 in)
Stroke	78.0 mm (3.07 in)
Compression ratio	8.7 : 1
Firing order	1 - 3 - 4 - 2 (No. 1 at timing belt end)
Rotational direction of crankshaft ..	Anti-clockwise (viewed from crankshaft pulley)
Maximum power	53 kW (70 bhp) at 6000 rev/min
Maximum torque	104 Nm (77 lbf ft) at 3500 rev/min
Compression pressure:	
Exceeding	10.3 bar (150 lbf/in²)
Maximum difference between cylinders ..	1.4 bar (20 lbf/in²)

Cylinder block
Material .... Light alloy with cast-iron liners
Bore .... 74.0 to 74.1 mm (2.9133 to 2.9173 in)
Maximum bore taper .... 0.05 mm (0.002 in)
Maximum out-of-round .... 0.05 mm (0.002 in)
Re-bore sizes .... 0.25 and 0.50 mm (0.010 and 0.020 in)

Crankshaft
Number of bearings .... 5 (monobloc)
Main journal diameter .... 49.976 to 50.000 mm (1.9676 to 1.9685 in)
Running clearance .... 0.024 to 0.07 mm (0.0009 to 0.003 in)
Crankpin diameter .... 39.976 to 40.000 mm (1.5739 to 1.5748 in)
Running clearance .... 0.020 to 0.07 mm (0.0008 to 0.003 in)
Maximum journal/crankpin taper or out-of-round .... 0.010 mm (0.0004 in)
Crankshaft endfloat .... 0.10 to 0.45 mm (0.004 to 0.018 in)

Connecting rods
Big-end bore diameter .... 43.0 mm (1.69 in)
Side play (on crankshaft) .... 0.15 to 0.40 mm (0.006 to 0.016 in)

Pistons
Clearance in cylinder .... 0.01 to 0.07 mm (0.0004 to 0.003 in)
Piston diameter (skirt):
   Standard .... 73.96 to 73.97 mm (2.9120 to 2.9122 in)
   0.25 mm oversize .... 74.215 to 74.248 mm (2.9218 to 2.9239 in)
   0.50 mm oversize .... 74.465 to 74.498 mm (2.9317 to 2.9330 in)

Piston rings
Number .... Two compression, one oil control
Clearance in groove (compression rings) .... 0.03 to 0.13 mm (0.0012 to 0.005 in)
End gap:
   Compression .... 0.15 to 0.6 mm (0.006 to 0.024 in)
   Oil control (rails) .... 0.30 to 1.10 mm (0.012 to 0.043 in)

Gudgeon pins
Interference fit in rod .... 0.02 to 0.04 mm (0.0008 to 0.0016 in)
All replacement pins are oversize

Camshaft
Number of bearings 5
Bearing running clearance .... 0.05 to 0.15 mm (0.002 to 0.006 in)
Shaft endfloat .... 0.05 to 0.50 mm (0.002 to 0.020 in)
Cam lobe height:
   Inlet .... 40.056 mm (1.5770 in)
   Exhaust .... 40.078 mm (1.5779 in)

Rocker gear
Rocker arm to shaft clearance .... 0.018 to 0.08 mm (0.0007 to 0.003 in)

Cylinder head
Material .... Light alloy
Thickness (new) .... 90.0 mm (3.54 in)
Thickness (minimum after re-surfacing) .... 89.8 mm (3.53 in)
Maximum surface distortion .... 0.05 mm (0.002 in)

Valves
Stem diameter:
   Inlet .... 6.55 to 6.59 mm (0.258 to 0.259 in)
   Exhaust .... 6.52 to 6.56 mm (0.257 to 0.258 in)
Stem to guide clearance:
   Inlet .... 0.02 to 0.08 mm (0.0008 to 0.003 in)
   Exhaust .... 0.05 to 0.11 mm (0.002 to 0.004 in)
Valve seat angle .... 45°
Seat width .... 1.25 to 2.00 mm (0.049 to 0.080 in)
Valve clearances (cold):
   Inlet .... 0.17 to 0.22 mm (0.007 to 0.009 in)
   Exhaust .... 0.22 to 0.27 mm (0.009 to 0.011 in)
Valve spring free length .... 46.6 to 47.6 mm (1.83 to 1.87 in)

Valve timing

Inlet valve opens	15° ATDC
Inlet valve closes	15° ABDC
Exhaust valve opens	20° BBDC
Exhaust valve closes	15° BTDC

Lubrication system

Oil pump clearances:	
Outer rotor to body	0.1 to 0.2 mm (0.004 to 0.008 in)
Inner to outer rotor lobe gap	0.14 to 0.2 mm (0.006 to 0.008 in)
Rotor endfloat	0.03 to 0.15 mm (0.001 to 0.006 in)
Oil pressure:	
At 3000 rev/min	3.7 to 4.5 bar (54 to 65 lbf/in²)
At idle	1.45 bar (21 lbf/in²)
Oil capacity, including new filter	3.5 litre (6.25 pint)
Oil type/specification	Multigrade engine oil, viscosity SAE 10W/30 or 10W/40, to API SF
Oil filter	Champion E101

Torque wrench settings

	Nm	lbf ft
Camshaft sprocket bolt	38	28
Connecting rod big-end nuts	28	21
Crankshaft main bearing cap bolts	50	37
Crankshaft pulley bolt	115	85
Cylinder head bolts and nuts:		
Stage 1	30	22
Stage 2	60	44
Flywheel bolts	120	89
Oil drain plug	45	33
Oil pressure switch	18	13
Oil pump bolts	12	9
Oil pump cover screws	5	3
Oil pump pick-up bolts	12	9
Oil pump pick-up nuts	25	18
Rocker cover nuts	10	7
Rocker shaft bolts	22	16
Spark plugs	18	13
Sump pan nuts and bolts	12	9
Timing belt tensioner bolt	45	33
Timing belt cover bolts	10	7
Rear mounting bracket bolts to engine	65	48
Transmission bracket bolts to body	39	29
Engine rear mounting bracket to body nuts	22	16
Left-hand mounting to engine nut	39	29
Clutch cover bolts	25	18
Lower suspension arm balljoint to hub carrier nut	44	32
Fuel pump nuts	24	18
Carburettor mounting nuts	20	15
Inlet manifold nuts	24	18
Inlet manifold support bracket bolt	22	16
Exhaust manifold nuts	39	29
Exhaust manifold bracket bolt	24	18
Exhaust downpipe flange nuts	22	16
Flywheel housing to engine bolts	68	50
Gear selector rod bolt	22	16
Torque rod to transmission bolt	9	7
Torque rod bracket to body bolts	22	16
Transmission to engine torque bracket bolts	45	33
Coolant pump bolts	12	9
Starter mounting bolts	45	33
Distributor mounting bolts	24	18
Alternator mounting bolts	45	33
Alternator belt adjuster bolt	24	18
Roadwheel nuts	81	60

1

Part B 1.6 engine

General

Engine type .... Four cylinder, overhead camshaft, transversely mounted
Code 16H
Capacity .... 1598 cc (97.5 cu in)
Bore .... 76.20 mm (3.0 in)
Stroke .... 87.58 mm (3.448 in)
Compression ratio .... 9.6 : 1
Firing order .... 1 - 3 - 4 - 2 (No. 1 at timing belt end)
Rotational direction of crankshaft .... Clockwise (viewed from crankshaft pulley)
Maximum power .... 76 kW (104 bhp) at 6000 rev/min
Maximum torque .... 139 Nm (102 lbf ft) at 3500 rev/min
Compression pressure:
    Exceeding .... 10.3 bar (150 lbf/in^2)
    Maximum difference between cylinders .... 1.4 bar (20 lbf/in^2)

Cylinder block

Material .... Cast-iron
Bore .... 76.20 to 76.30 mm (3.000 to 3.006 in)
Maximum bore taper .... 0.05 mm (0.002 in)
Maximum out-of-round .... 0.05 mm (0.002 in)
Re-bore size .... 0.50 mm (0.020 in)

Crankshaft

Number of bearings 5
Main journal diameter .... 57.19 to 57.20 mm (2.2516 to 2.2520 in)
Running clearance .... 0.05 to 0.08 mm (0.002 to 0.003 in)
Minimum regrind diameter .... 56.19 mm (2.2122)
Crankpin diameter .... 47.62 to 47.64 mm (1.8748 to 1.8756 in)
Running clearance .... 0.04 to 0.08 mm (0.0015 to 0.003 in)
Minimum regrind diameter .... 46.63 mm (1.8359 in)
Maximum journal/crankpin taper or out-of-round .... 0.010 mm (0.0004 in)
Crankshaft endfloat .... 0.10 to 0.18 mm (0.004 to 0.007 in)
Endfloat thrust washer thicknesses .... 2.26 mm (0.089 in), 2.28 mm (0.090 in), 2.31mm (0.091 in),
                                           2.34 mm (0.092 in)

Connecting rods

Length between centres .... 148.07 mm (5.830 in)

Pistons

Clearance in cylinder:
    At top .... 0.07 to 0.11 mm (0.0028 to 0.0044 in)
    At bottom .... 0.03 to 0.05 mm (0.001 to 0.002 in)
Piston oversize .... 0.51 mm (0.020 in)

Piston rings

Number .... Two compression, one oil control
Clearance in groove (compression) .... 0.03 to 0.08 mm (0.0012 to 0.0032 in)
End gap:
    Compression .... 0.30 to 0.56 mm (0.012 to 0.022 in)
    Oil control (rails) .... 0.38 to 1.14 mm (0.015 to 0.045 in)

Gudgeon pins

Interference fit in rod .... 0.02 to 0.04 mm (0.0008 to 0.0015 in)

Cylinder head

Material .... Cast-iron
Thickness (new) .... 84.13 to 84.38 mm (3.312 to 3.322 in)
Thickness (minimum after re-surfacing) .... 83.87 mm (3.302 in)
Maximum surface distortion .... 0.05 mm (0.002 in)

Camshaft

Number of bearings 3
Bearing running clearance .... 0.025 to 0.056 mm (0.001 to 0.0022 min)
Camshaft endfloat .... 0.05 to 0.18 mm (0.002 to 0.007 in)
Cam lobe height:
    Inlet .... 8.68 to 9.5 mm (0.342 to 0.374 in)
    Exhaust .... 8.58 to 9.5 mm (0.338 to 0.374 in)

Cam followers

Outside diameter	30.14 mm (1.1865 in)
Adjustment shim thicknesses:	
Mark:	**Thickness**
97	2.47 mm (0.097 in)
99	2.52 mm (0.099 in)
01	2.56 mm (0.101 in)
03	2.62 mm (0.103 in)
05	2.67 mm (0.105 m)
07	2.72 mm (0.107 in)
09	2.77 mm (0.109 in)
11	2.83 mm (0.111 in)
13	2.87 mm (0.113 in)
15	2.93 mm (0.115 in)
17	2.98 mm (0.117 in)
19	3.03 mm (0.119 in)
21	3.08 mm (0.121 in)
23	3.13 mm (0.123 in)
25	3.18 mm (0.125 in)
27	3.23 mm (0.127 in)

Valves

Stem diameter:	
Inlet	7.91 to 7.93 mm (0.3115 to 0.3120 in)
Exhaust	7.89 to 7.92 mm (0.3109 to 0.3114 in)
Oversize	8.46 to 8.47 mm (0.331 to 0.336 in)
Stem to guide clearance	0.038 mm (0.0015 in)
Valve seat angle	45° 15'
Valve head diameter:	
Inlet	38.0 mm (1.5 in)
Exhaust	31.0 mm (1.218 in)
Valve clearances (cold)*:	
Inlet 1	0.35 to 0.38 mm (0.014 to 0.015 in)
Exhaust	10.43 to 0.46 mm (0.017 to 0.018 in)
*Adjust only if clearance below	0.30 mm (0.012 in)
Valve spring free length	46.6 to 47.6 mm (1.83 to 1.87 in)

Valve timing

Inlet valve opens	17° BTDC
Inlet valve closes	59° ABDC
Exhaust valve opens	57° BBDC
Exhaust valve closes	19° ATDC

Lubrication system

Oil pump clearances:	
Outer rotor to body	0.18 to 0.27 mm (0.007 to 0.011 in)
Inner to outer rotor lobe gap	0.03 to 0.15 mm (0.001 to 0.006 in)
Rotor endfloat	0.03 to 0.08 mm (0.001 to 0.003 in)
Oil pressure:	
At 3000 rev/min	3.7 to 4.5 bar (54 to 65 lbf/in²)
At idle	1.4 bar (21 lbf/in²)
Oil capacity, including new filter	3.6 litre (6.30 pint)
Oil type/specification	Multigrade engine oil, viscosity 10W/30 or 10W/40, to API SF
Oil filter	Champion C104

Torque wrench settings

	Nm	lbf ft
Brake servo pipe union	50	37
Camshaft belt tensioner bolt	25	18
Camshaft carrier bolts	25	18
Camshaft cover bolts	8	6
Camshaft pulley bolt	57	42
Connecting rod big-end nuts	45	33
Coolant temperature sender	15	11
Crankshaft pulley bolt	45	33
Cylinder head bolts:		
Stage 1	40	30
Stage 2	81	60
Stage 3	Tighten 1/4 turn (90°)	

Torque wrench settings (continued)

	Nm	lbf ft
Flywheel bolts (new)	58	43
Transmission adaptor plate bolts:		
M8 bolts	25	18
M10 bolts	45	33
M12 bolts	90	66
Knock sensor	12	9
Main bearing cap bolts	90	66
Oil pump bolts	26	19
Oil pressure switch	25	18
Spark plugs	18	13
Sump pan drain plug	25	18
Sump pan bolts	8	6
Coolant inlet elbow bolts	25	18
Coolant outlet elbow bolts	25	18
Manifold bolts and nuts	22	16
Flywheel housing to engine	90	66
Torque converter housing to engine:		
M10 bolts	45	33
M12 bolts	90	66
Driveplate to crankshaft	110	81
Driveplate to torque converter	32	24
Suspension arm balljoint nut	44	32
Roadwheel nuts	81	60
Alternator mounting bracket bolts	45	33
Alternator belt adjuster link bolt	24	18
Reverse lamp switch	25	18
Starter motor mounting bolts	45	33
Engine/transmission mountings:		
Right-hand:		
Bracket to engine bolts	45	33
Bracket nuts	40	30
Through-bolt	120	89
Left-hand:		
Bracket to transmission bolts	45	33
Mounting to body bolts	40	30
Through-bolt	120	89
Rear mounting:		
Bracket to transmission	90	66
Support plate to bracket	75	55
Mounting to bracket bolts	60	44
Mounting through-bolts	60	44

Part A 1.3 (1342 cc) engine

1 General description

The engine is of four cylinder overhead camshaft type mounted transversely with the transmission at the front of the car.

The cylinder block, crankcase and cylinder head are of light alloy construction with cast-iron cylinder liners.

The crankshaft is supported in five main bearings the caps for which are in the form of a monobloc casting.

Crankshaft endfloat is controlled by semi-circular thrust washers at number four journal.

The pistons are fitted with two compression rings and one oil control ring. The gudgeon pin is of press fit type in the connecting rod small end.

The cylinder head incorporates two inlet valves and one exhaust valve per cylinder. The valves are operated by individual rockers from the single belt-driven camshaft.

The oil pump is driven directly from the crankshaft while the distributor is driven from a dog on the end of the camshaft.

The fuel pump is driven from an eccentric cam on the camshaft.

Crankshaft rotation is anti-clockwise when viewed from the pulley end .

2 Lubrication system

1 The oil pump is of trochoid type and supplies oil under pressure to a full-flow cartridge type oil filter which incorporates a bypass valve.

2 Oil then flows through the galleries and drillings to all the engine bearings and moving parts. Oil flow from the cylinder block to the cylinder head is regulated by a control orifice.

3 Engine oil and filter

1 At the intervals specified in Routine Maintenance, the engine oil and filter should be renewed.

2 With the engine hot, place a container under the sump pan, remove the dipstick and oil filler cap.

3 Unscrew the sump pan drain plug and allow the oil to drain completely. While this is happening, unscrew and discard the oil filter cartridge. Be prepared for some oil to run out (photo).

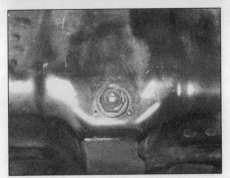

3.3 Sump pan oil drain plug

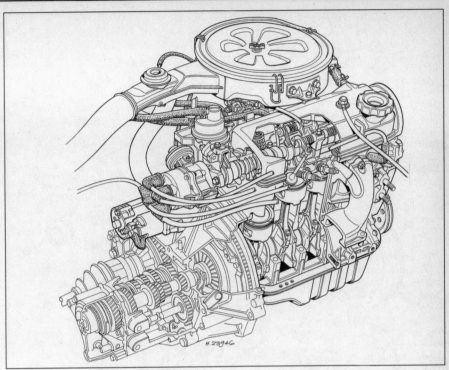

Fig. 1.1 Cutaway view of 1.3 engine and transmission (Sec 1)

**Fig. 1.2 External components –
1.3 engine (Sec 1)**

1 Distributor holder
2 Fuel pump and insulator
3 Rocker cover and gasket
4 Coolant temperature transmitter
5 Camshaft rear bearing upper bracket
6 Camshaft No.4 bearing upper bracket
7 Camshaft No.3 bearing upper bracket
8 Camshaft No.2 bearing upper bracket
9 Camshaft front bearing upper bracket
10 Crankcase breather
11 Thermostat and seal
12 Coolant outlet housing
13 Thermostat housing
14 Inlet manifold and gasket
15 Coolant connecting pipe
16 Oil pressure switch
17 Cylinder block drain plug
18 Coolant pump
19 Oil pump cover plate
20 Oil pump rotors
21 Oil pump
22 Timing belt cover seal
23 Oil filter
24 Timing belt upper cover
25 Timing belt lower cover
26 Belt tensioner access plug
27 Oil pressure relief valve
28 Crankshaft front oil seal
29 Oil drain plug
30 Oil pump pick-up strainer
31 Engine oil dipstick
32 Sump pan
33 Dipstick guide tube
34 Cover plate
35 Sump pan gasket
36 Cylinder block/crankcase
37 Crankshaft rear oil seal retainer
38 Exhaust manifold and gasket
39 Cylinder head and gasket
40 Crankshaft rear oil seal
41 Heater hose connection
42 Coolant inlet housing
43 Cooling system bleed screw
44 Fuel pump cover
45 Hot air cover

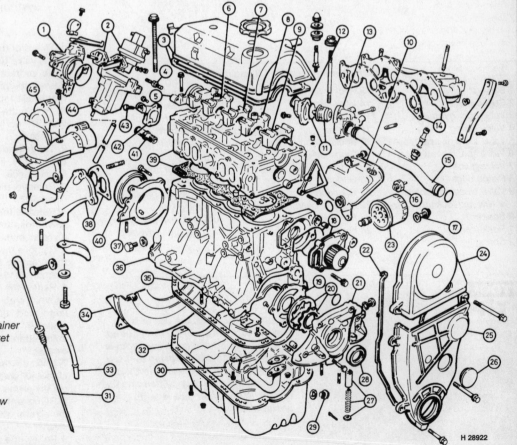

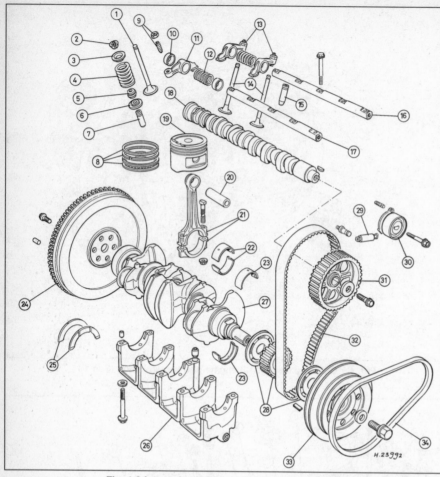

Fig. 1.3 Internal components – 1.3 engine (Sec 1)

1 Exhaust valve
2 Split cotters
3 Valve spring retainer
4 Valve spring
5 Valve stem oil seal
6 Valve spring seat
7 Valve guide
8 Piston rings
9 Valve clearance adjuster
  screw and locknut
10 Spacer
11 Rocker arm
12 Spring

13 Rocker arm
14 Inlet valves
15 Valve guide
16 Rocker shaft – inlet
17 Rocker shaft – exhaust
18 Camshaft
19 Piston
20 Gudgeon pin
21 Connecting rod and cap
22 Big-end bearing shells
23 Main bearing shell
24 Flywheel

25 Crankshaft thrust washers
26 Main bearing caps and oil
  gallery – monobloc
27 Crankshaft
28 Timing belt sprocket and
  guide plates
29 Tensioner spring
30 Timing belt tensioner
31 Camshaft sprocket
32 Timing belt
33 Crankshaft pulley
34 Alternator drivebelt

TOOL TiP

To remove the filter, the use of a removal tool will probably be required. Alternatively, drive a large screwdriver right through the filter casing (not too close to its base otherwise the threaded connecting sleeve may be damaged) and use the screwdriver as a lever to unscrew it.

3.4 Fitting a new oil filter

4 Clean the filter mounting ring on the crankcase and smear the rubber seal on the filter with engine oil. Screw on the new filter using hand pressure only, not a tool (photo).
5 Wash the filler cap in petrol or paraffin to clean its gauze and shake it dry.
6 Refit and tighten the sump pan drain plug.
7 Refill the engine with the correct quantity of specified oil.
8 Start the engine, the oil warning lamp will take a few seconds to go out. This is normal and is due to the new filter filling with oil.
9 Switch off, check the oil level and top up to the MAXIMUM notch on the dipstick.

4 Crankcase ventilation system

1 This is of the positive crankcase ventilation (PCV) valve type. The purpose of the system is to extract blow-by gases which have passed the piston rings and collected in the crankcase together with oil fumes and draw them into the intake manifold where they are burned during the normal combustion processes.
2 The following servicing should be carried out at the intervals specified in Routine Maintenance.
3 Remove the air cleaner as described in Chapter 3.
4 Release the clip which secures the PCV valve hose to the carburettor insulator and disconnect the hose.
5 Remove the valve and hose assembly from the breather chamber, release the clip and disconnect the hose from the valve.
6 Renew the valve and connect the hose to its small end. Fit the securing clip and fit the large end of the valve in the breather chamber. Fit the other end of the hose to the carburettor insulator. Refit the clip and the air cleaner.
7 Unscrew the wing nut and disconnect the clips and remove the air cleaner cover and lift out the element.
8 Remove the blow-by filter after extracting the screws which hold it to the side of the air cleaner.
9 Renew the filter and fit it by reversing the removal operations.

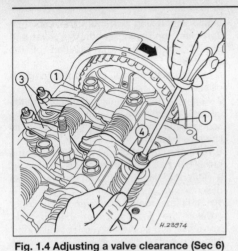

Fig. 1.4 Adjusting a valve clearance (Sec 6)

1 Camshaft sprocket timing marks
3 Inlet valve rocker arm
4 Exhaust valve rocker arm

5 Major operations possible without removing the engine

1 All major operations can be carried out with the engine in the car except for removal and refitting of the crankshaft and main bearings.
2 Attention to the flywheel and to the crankshaft rear oil seal is possible once the transmission has been removed as described in Chapter 6.

6 Valve clearances - adjustment

1 Disconnect the spark plug leads, the earth lead and the rocker cover breather hose. Remove the rocker cover.
2 Apply a spanner to the crankshaft pulley bolt and turn the crankshaft in an anti-clockwise direction. Alternatively, engage top gear, raise one front roadwheel and turn it in the forward direction of travel. Keep turning until the UP mark on the camshaft sprocket is uppermost and the marks on the sprocket are

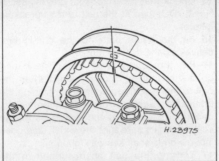

Fig. 1.5 Camshaft sprocket timing mark and belt cover notch (Sec 6)

parallel with the upper surface of the cylinder head.
3 Check the valve clearances on number one cylinder. Viewed from the camshaft sprocket, inlet valves are on the right and exhaust valves on the left. Remember that the inlet and exhaust valve clearances are different.
4 Insert the feeler blade of appropriate thickness between the end of the valve stem and the rocker arm. It should be a stiff sliding fit, if not, release the adjuster screw locknut and turn the screw as necessary. Tighten the locknut.
5 Rotate the crankshaft through 180° anti-clockwise and align the mark on the camshaft sprocket with the notch in the top of the timing belt cover.
6 Check the valve clearances for number three cylinder, adjust if necessary.
7 Rotate the crankshaft through 180° anti-clockwise and align the camshaft sprocket marks with the upper surface of the cylinder head.
8 Check the valve clearances for number four cylinder, adjust if necessary.
9 Rotate the crankshaft through 180° anti-clockwise and align the mark on the camshaft sprocket with the notch in the top of the timing belt cover.
10 Check the valve clearances for number two cylinder, adjust if necessary.
11 Refit the rocker cover using a new gasket if necessary, connect the leads and breather hose.

7 Timing belt - tensioning

1 This is not a routine operation and it should only be required if the belt becomes noisy. Adjust when the engine is cold.
2 Remove the alternator drivebelt (Chapter 12).
3 Remove the timing belt adjuster bolt access plug (photo).
4 Remove the rocker cover.
5 Turn the crankshaft by means of its pulley bolt in an anti-clockwise direction until No. 1 piston is at TDC on its compression stroke. This will be indicated when the UP mark on the camshaft sprocket is uppermost and the timing marks parallel with the top face of the cylinder head (photo).
6 Slacken the timing belt tensioner adjuster bolt (photo).
7 Turn the crankshaft pulley bolt in an anti-clockwise direction to move the timing belt the distance of three teeth of the sprocket. This action will tension the belt automatically by means of the spring-loaded tensioner.
8 Tighten the tensioner bolt to the specified torque.
9 Refit the tensioner bolt access plug.
10 Fit the alternator drivebelt and tension it.

8 Timing belt - removal and refitting

1 Disconnect the battery.
2 Remove the air cleaner (Chapter 3).
3 Disconnect the spark plug leads, the earth lead and breather hose from the rocker cover.
4 Remove the rocker cover and timing belt upper cover.
5 Remove the alternator drivebelt (Chapter 12).
6 Raise the car and securely support the front end. Remove the left-hand front roadwheel and the splash panel.
7 Set No. 1 piston to TDC as described in the preceding Section.

7.3 Removing timing belt adjuster bolt plug

7.5 Camshaft sprocket TDC marks

7.6 Slackening timing belt tensioner

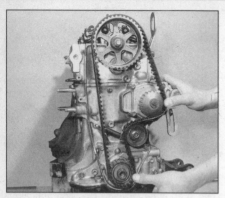

8.14 Fitting timing belt

8 Engage a low gear and with an assistant fully applying the footbrake, unscrew the crankshaft pulley bolt. If the bolt fails to unscrew, or if the car is fitted with automatic transmission, it will be necessary to remove the starter motor and temporarily lock the starter ring gear, in order to prevent the crankshaft from turning.

9 Withdraw the crankshaft pulley and key.

10 Remove the timing belt lower cover.

11 Slacken the belt tensioner bolt, retract the tensioner and re-tighten the bolt.

12 Remove the timing belt and the guide plate from the front of the crankshaft. *Do not turn the sprockets while the belt is off or the valve heads will contact the pistons.*

13 If the belt is to be used again, mark it with the direction of rotation.

14 Check that the sprockets are still set at No. 1 TDC, then fit the belt to the sprockets (photo).

15 Fit the guide plate to the crankshaft, convex side to the belt (photo).

16 Fit the belt lower cover, key and crankshaft pulley. Screw in and tighten the bolt to the specified torque again holding the crankshaft against rotation as previously described. Note that the key is of wedge section. Make sure that the wider face goes into the crankshaft key way (photos).

17 Tension the belt as described in the preceding Section.

18 Fit the splash guard panel, roadwheel and lower the car to the floor.

19 Refit the belt upper cover, rocker cover, leads, hose and alternator drivebelt (photos).

20 Refit the air cleaner and connect the battery.

9 Camshaft front oil seal - renewal

1 Remove the rocker cover.

2 Remove the timing belt upper cover.

3 Hold the camshaft sprocket still with a tool or rod passed through its spokes and release its retaining bolt.

4 Slacken the belt tensioner bolt and retract the tensioner.

5 Slip the timing belt from the camshaft sprocket, then withdraw the sprocket and key. Do not move the position of the camshaft.

6 Using a suitable tool, extract the camshaft oil seal.

7 Apply a smear of jointing compound to the oil seal recess in the housing, apply oil to the seal lips and drive it squarely home so that its lips face inwards.

8 Refit the key and sprocket. Tighten the pulley bolt to the specified torque.

9 Refit the timing belt and tension it as described in Section 7.

10 Refit the rocker cover and belt upper cover.

10 Crankshaft front oil seal - renewal

1 Remove the timing belt as described in Section 8. Do not rotate the crankshaft while the belt is off.

2 Using two screwdrivers, remove the crankshaft sprocket and inner guide plate. Prise out the oil seal.

3 Smear the inside of the oil seal housing recess with gasket cement and the seal lips with oil and drive the seal squarely into position. Fit the belt guide plate and sprocket.

4 Fit the timing belt and tension it as described in earlier Sections.

8.15 Timing belt outer guide plate

8.16A Tightening timing belt lower cover bolt

8.16B Crankshaft pulley and Woodruff key

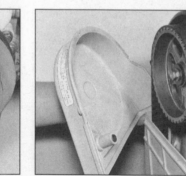

8.16C Tightening crankshaft pulley bolt

8.19A Fitting belt upper cover

8.19B Tightening timing belt upper cover bolts

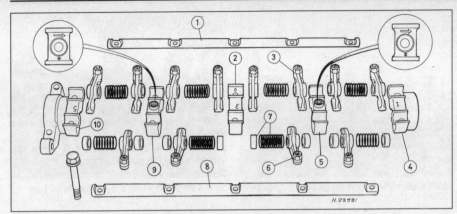

Fig. 1.6 Rocker gear components (Sec 11)

1 Inlet valve rocker shaft (eight oil holes)
2 Camshaft centre bearing upper bracket
3 Rocker arm
4 Camshaft front bearing upper bracket
5 Camshaft No.2 bearing upper bracket

6 Rocker arm
7 Spacer and spring
8 Exhaust valve rocker shaft (four oil holes)
9 Camshaft No 4 bearing upper bracket
10 Camshaft rear bearing upper bracket

11 Rocker shafts - removal and refitting

1 Remove the air cleaner.
2 Disconnect the spark plug leads, the earth lead and breather hose. Then remove the rocker cover.
3 Set No. 1 piston to TDC as described in Section 7.
4 Unscrew and remove the rocker shaft bracket bolts and lift the rocker assemblies from the cylinder head.
5 Dismantling may be carried out as necessary for the renewal of worn components.
6 Unscrew the rocker shaft lockbolts and slide off the springs, arms and collar.
7 Refitting is a reversal of removal. Check that the shaft collars are not trapped in the shaft bearing caps.
8 Before tightening the rocker shaft fixing bolts, slacken the valve clearance screw locknuts and the screws.
9 Tighten the shaft bolts to the specified torque working in diagonal sequence from the centre bolts towards each end.
10 Check and adjust the valve clearances as described in Section 6.
11 Refit the rocker cover, air cleaner and reconnect the leads and hoses.

12 Camshaft - removal and refitting

1 Remove the rocker shafts as described in the preceding Section.
2 Remove the fuel pump (Chapter 3).
3 Remove the distributor (Chapter 4) and its holder.
4 Detach the timing belt from the camshaft sprocket as described in Section 9.

5 Remove the camshaft sprocket.
6 Unbolt the camshaft rear bearing upper bracket. Remove all the upper brackets (bearing caps), keeping them in order and the right way round.
7 Lift the camshaft from the cylinder head.
8 Refitting is a reversal of removal. Note that the camshaft bearing caps are numbered 1 to 5 from the timing end of the engine. Numbers 2 and 4 should have their arrows pointing to the timing cover. Read all numbers from the inlet manifold side. Apply RTV sealant at the cylinder head joint faces of Nos 1 and 5 camshaft pedestals.
9 Fit a new camshaft oil seal, tension the timing belt (Section 7) and adjust the valve clearances (Section 6).

13 Cylinder head - removal and refitting

1 The cylinder head should only be removed from a cool engine, below 38°C (100°F) .
2 Disconnect the battery negative lead.
3 Drain the cooling system, retaining the coolant for further use.
4 Remove the air cleaner (Chapter 3).
5 Disconnect the brake servo vacuum hose

from the inlet manifold. Also remove the coolant bypass hose.
6 Disconnect the radiator top hose from the cylinder head.
7 Disconnect the hoses from the fuel pump and plug them.
8 Disconnect the throttle and choke controls from the carburettor.
9 Unscrew the bolts which secure the support bracket to the inlet manifold and the crankcase (photo).
10 Disconnect the leads from the carburettor, ignition coil and coolant sender unit.
11 Detach the air cleaner hot air duct.
12 Remove the radiator heat baffle plate.
13 Remove the centre splash guard panel.
14 Remove the hot air collector cover from the exhaust manifold.
15 Disconnect the exhaust downpipe and unbolt the exhaust manifold steady brackets.
16 Remove the rocker cover.
17 Remove the timing belt upper cover.
18 With a socket on the crankshaft pulley bolt, turn the crankshaft in an anti-clockwise direction until the UP mark on the camshaft sprocket is uppermost and the timing marks on the sprocket are parallel with the top face of the cylinder head. No. 1 piston is now at TDC on its compression stroke.
19 Remove the alternator drivebelt (Chapter 12).
20 Slacken the belt tensioner adjusting bolt, retract the tensioner and slip the timing belt from the camshaft sprocket.
21 Do not rotate the crankshaft while the belt is off the sprocket.
22 Progressively slacken the cylinder head bolts and nuts, half a turn at a time in the reverse order of tightening (Fig. 1.7).
23 Remove the bolts and nuts and lift the cylinder head from the block. It is permissible to lever the head up if it is stuck, but use a suitable tool only between the lugs provided not in the gasket joint. Positioning dowels are fitted so lift the head straight up when removing it (photo).
24 Dismantling and decarbonising of the cylinder head is covered in Section 24.
25 Before refitting the cylinder head, make sure that all carbon and old gasket material has been removed from the cylinder head and block mating surfaces.

13.9 Inlet manifold support bracket

13.23 Cylinder head prising lug on block

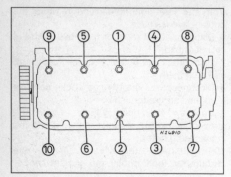

Fig. 1.7 Cylinder head bolt tightening sequence (Sec 13)

13.27 New cylinder head gasket in position

13.28 Tightening a cylinder head bolt

26 Check that the positioning dowels are fully located in the top of the block.

27 Place a new gasket on the cylinder block. Check that the timing marks are set as described in paragraph 18 (photo).

28 Carefully lower the head onto the block, insert the bolts (threads clean and lightly oiled) and screw the nuts onto the studs (photo).

29 Tighten the bolts and nuts to the specified torque working in the sequence shown in Fig. 1.7. First tighten to half the tightening torque and then to full tightening torque.

30 Connect the timing belt to the camshaft sprocket with the timing marks correctly positioned as described in paragraph 18.

31 Tension the belt as described in Section 7.

32 If the valve gear has not been disturbed,

then the valve clearances will not require checking or adjusting.

33 Fit the rocker cover and the timing belt upper cover.

34 Reconnect all hoses, control cables and electrical leads.

35 Reconnect the exhaust pipe, refit the hot air collector cover, radiator heat baffle plate and splash guard plate.

36 Fill and bleed the cooling system.

14 Sump pan - removal and refitting

1 Drain the engine oil.

2 Disconnect the exhaust downpipe from the manifold.

3 Refer to Chapter 8 and disconnect the left-hand driveshaft from the transmission.

4 Unbolt and remove the stiffener bracket from between the engine and transmission (photo).

5 Progressively unscrew the six nuts and twelve bolts which hold the sump pan to the crankcase.

6 Remove the cover plate from the lower part of the flywheel housing (photo) .

7 Remove the sump pan and peel off the one-piece gasket.

8 Before refitting, wipe the crankcase and sump pan mating surfaces clean and apply a bead of gasket cement between the studs

and the main bearing cap, also to both sides of the gasket where it seats at the main bearing cap.

9 Position the new gasket and then offer the sump pan onto the studs and tighten all nuts and bolts to the specified torque. Refit the flywheel housing cover (photos).

10 Refit the stiffener bracket, reconnect the driveshaft and the exhaust downpipe, and refill the engine with oil.

15 Oil pump - removal and refitting

1 Remove the air cleaner and rocker cover.

2 Remove the timing belt upper cover.

3 Remove the alternator drivebelt (Chapter 12).

4 Drain the engine oil.

5 Disconnect the exhaust downpipe from the manifold.

6 Raise and support the front end of the car, remove the left-hand roadwheel and the centre and left-hand splash guard panels.

7 Refer to Chapter 8 and disconnect the left-hand driveshaft from the transmission.

8 Set No. 1 piston to TDC with the camshaft sprocket timing marks aligned as described in Section 13.

9 Select a low gear and with an assistant applying the brakes fully, unscrew the crankshaft pulley bolt. If the bolt fails to

14.4 Engine/transmission stiffener bracket

14.6 Flywheel housing cover plate

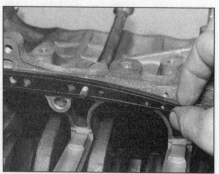

14.9A Sump pan gasket

14.9B Tightening sump pan bolts

unscrew, or if the car is fitted with automatic transmission, it will be necessary to remove the starter motor and temporarily lock the starter ring gear, in order to prevent the crankshaft from turning. Remove the pulley and Woodruff key.

10 Remove the crankshaft sprocket timing belt guide plate, the timing belt and then pull off the crankshaft sprocket with the inner belt guide plate. Note that the Woodruff key is combined with the sprocket.

11 Remove the stiffener bracket from between the engine and transmission.

12 Unbolt and remove the flywheel housing cover plate and the sump pan.

13 Extract the split pin, withdraw the collar spring and oil pressure relief valve.

14 Remove the oil pump strainer.

15 Extract the oil pump fixing screws and withdraw the pump from the front end of the crankshaft.

16 Before refitting the oil pump, smear gasket cement to the mounting face. All other operations are a reversal of removal. Always renew the O-ring seal (photos).

17 Note that the crankshaft pulley key is of tapered section. Make sure that the widest face is in the crankshaft key-way.

18 Refer to Section 14 for details of refitting the sump pan.

19 Refer to Section 7 for details of tensioning the timing belt.

20 Make sure that the driveshaft is fully engaged in the differential side gear with the spring clip positively locked.

21 Refill the engine with oil.

16 Connecting rod big-end bearings and piston rings - renewal

1 These operations will normally be carried out at the time of complete engine overhaul, but the work may be done without removing the engine from the car where it is necessary to reduce oil consumption and to improve the oil pressure.

2 Refer to Section 14 and remove the sump pan.

3 Inspect the big-end caps for identification. They should be marked 1 to 4 from the

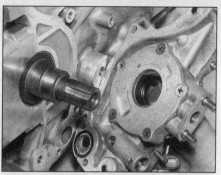
15.16A Fitting oil pump

15.16B Tightening the oil pump bolts

crankshaft pulley end of the side nearest to the exhaust manifold. If not, mark them with a centre punch on the cap and the adjacent surface of the connecting rod. Do not confuse the bearing shell code numbers (see Section 25).

4 Unscrew the big-end cap nuts, remove the cap with its shell bearing. This is difficult owing to the monobloc construction of the main bearing caps. It can be done however if the crankshaft is rotated gently in both directions and the big-end cap removed through the monobloc apertures.

5 Push each connecting rod slightly upwards and remove the upper shell half. Only move the connecting rod upwards when the big-end is at the lowest point of its throw, otherwise if the piston is at TDC it might be possible for the top piston ring to pop out of the top of the cylinder.

6 If only new shells are to be fitted, fit them in matched pairs making sure that their recesses in both the rod and cap are perfectly clean (see Section 25 regarding shell coding).

7 If the piston rings are to be renewed owing to heavy oil consumption, it is recommended that proprietary oil control sets are fitted.

8 Remove the cylinder head as described in Section 13.

9 Push the piston connecting rod assembly up and out of the top of the cylinder bore. If a heavy wear ridge is evident at the top of the bore, it will have to be carefully removed with a ridge reamer or by scraping in order to allow the ring to pass.

10 Remove the piston rings from the top of the piston. To avoid breaking a ring either during removal or refitting, slide two or three

old feeler blades at equidistant points behind the top ring and slide it up them. Remove the other rings in a similar way (photo).

11 Clean carbon from the ring grooves, a segment of old piston ring is useful for this purpose.

12 Clean out the oil return holes in the piston ring grooves and fit the new piston rings. The top ring will be supplied stepped so that it does not impinge on the wear ridge.

13 Insert each piston ring in turn squarely into its bore and check the ring end gap. If it is not within the specified tolerance, carefully grind the end-face of the ring.

14 Now check each compression ring in its groove and measure the clearances with a feeler gauge. If it is tight the ring may be rubbed flat on a sheet of wet and dry paper laid flat on a piece of plate glass (photo) .

15 Fit the rings to the piston using the feeler blade method as described for removal. Work from the top of the piston, fitting the oil control ring first.

16 Locate the compression ring gaps at 90° to each other on the thrust side (towards the dipstick guide tube). The expander of the oil control ring should have its gap on the opposite side to the gap in the second compression ring. The gaps in the rails of the oil control ring should be on either side of the expander gap. Repeat all the operations on the remaining pistons.

17 The cylinder bore should now be de-glazed using a glaze buster or fine glasspaper to enable the new rings to bed in.

18 Take care to remove all debris and then oil the bores and piston rings liberally.

16.10 Method of removing and refitting piston rings

16.14 Checking piston ring clearance in groove

16.19 Fitting a piston into cylinder bore

1

16.22A Fitting a big-end cap

16.22B Tightening a big-end cap nut

17.1A Right-hand front engine mounting bracket

17.1B Rear engine mounting bracket

17.1C Left-hand front engine mounting bracket

17.1D Rear engine mounting

19 Fit a piston ring compressor to the first piston and insert the rod complete with shell bearing into the bore so that the compressor stands flat on the block (photo).
20 Check that with the oil hole in the connecting rod towards the inlet manifold side of the block, the valve head cut-outs in the piston crowns are on the exhaust valve side of

the engine, irrespective of the fact there are two inlet valves in the combustion chamber.
21 Place the wooden handle of a hammer on the piston crown and tap the hammer head with the hand to drive the piston into the cylinder bore. The compressor will remain on the face of the block.
22 Lubricate the shell in the cap, fit the cap

to its correctly numbered rod, and screw on the cap nuts to the specified torque (photos).
23 Fit the remaining piston/connecting rods in a similar way.
24 Refit the cylinder head (Section 13) refit the sump pan (Section 14).
25 Refill the engine with oil and coolant. Avoid high engine speeds during the first few hundred miles to allow the components to bed in.

17 Engine/transmission mountings - renewal

1 The mountings may be renewed with the engine/transmission in the car provided the weight of the engine or transmission is taken on a hoist or using a workshop jack with a block of wood as an insulator (photos) .

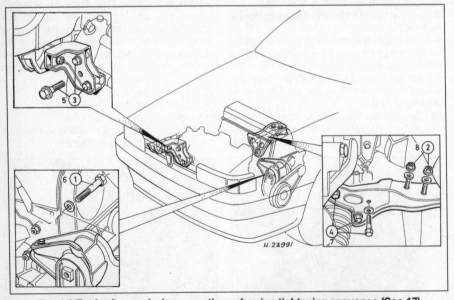

Fig. 1.8 Engine/transmission mountings showing tightening sequence (Sec 17)

Stage 1: Lightly tighten nuts/bolts 1 to 4 (encircled) in numerical sequence
Stage 2: Fully tighten the nuts/bolts 5 to 8 in numerical sequence to their specified torque wrench settings

17.1E Right-hand front engine mounting

2 Before removing the rear mounting, disconnect the rear gearchange (selector) rod from the transmission.
3 Tighten all nuts and bolts to the specified torque.

18 Engine - method of removal

The engine should be removed upwards from the engine compartment complete with the transmission.

19 Engine/manual transmission - removal and separation

1 Open the bonnet. Mark the position of the hinges with masking tape.
2 Unbolt the hinges and with the help of an assistant, lift away the bonnet and place it in a safe place where it will not be scratched.
3 Remove the battery and its tray.
4 Drain the engine oil.
5 Remove the air cleaner (Chapter 3).
6 Disconnect the brake servo vacuum hose from the inlet manifold.
7 Disconnect the carburettor controls, the leads from the ignition coil, the engine wiring harness multi-plug connector and the engine and transmission earth cables. Also disconnect the leads from the oil pressure and temperature switches (photo).
8 Disconnect the leads from the starter motor, the tachometer drive, speedometer drive cable and the reverse lamp switch leads. Take care not to remove the speedometer pinion housing or the pinion may drop into the gearbox.
9 Disconnect the clutch release cable from the release lever.
10 Disconnect the fuel feed hose from the fuel pump and plug the hose.
11 Drain the cooling system.
12 Disconnect the radiator top hose from the engine, followed by the lower hose.

13 Disconnect the heater hoses.
14 Raise the front of the car and support it securely and remove the front roadwheels. Place stands under the body members.
15 Using a hoist or other suitable lifting gear, attached to the engine and transmission lifting hooks, take the weight of the engine.
16 Support the suspension lower arms, unscrew the balljoint taper pin nuts and using a suitable splitter tool, disconnect the balljoints from both hub carriers. Take care that the arms do not jump off the jack.
17 Remove the splash guard panels.
18 Turn the steering to full right-hand lock and then disconnect the right-hand driveshaft from the transmission. Do this by inserting a lever between the inboard driveshaft joint and the transmission casing and prising against spring pressure of the shaft retaining clip.
19 Now turn the steering to full left-hand lock and disconnect the left-hand driveshaft.
20 Disconnect the gear selector and torque rods from the transmission.
21 Disconnect the exhaust downpipe from the manifold.
22 Check that the weight of the engine is still being taken by the hoist and disconnect the engine/transmission mountings.
23 Raise the engine transmission slightly and check that everything has been disconnected.
24 Lift the unit out of the engine compartment.
25 Remove all external dirt by steam cleaning or by using a water soluble solvent.
26 Support the engine and remove the starter motor and the cover plate from the face of the flywheel housing.
27 Unscrew and remove the flywheel housing to engine connecting bolts and withdraw the transmission from the engine, supporting its weight so that it does not hang upon the input shaft while the shaft is engaged in the hub of the clutch driven plate.

19.7 Temperature switch and lead

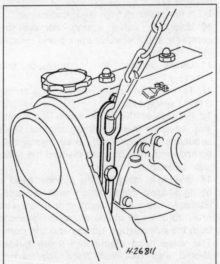

Fig. 1.9 Engine lifting lug (Sec 19)

20 Engine/automatic transmission - removal and separation

1 Removal operations are very similar to those described in the preceding Section for cars with manual transmission, but of course ignore reference to the clutch cable and gear selector. Disconnect the selector cable and kick-down cable.
2 Disconnect and plug the oil cooler pipes.
3 Disconnect the leads from the reverse lamp/inhibitor switch.
4 To separate the transmission from the engine, remove the starter and the cover plate from the face of the torque converter housing.
5 Unscrew the three bolts which hold the driveplate to the torque converter. These are accessible through the starter motor aperture, but the crankshaft will have to be rotated to bring each bolt into view.
6 Unscrew the transmission to engine connecting bolts. It will be found that some of the bolts cannot be completely removed until the transmission has been partially withdrawn.
7 With the engine supported in the vertical position, withdraw the transmission, at the same time holding the torque converter in full engagement within the converter housing otherwise there will be fluid loss and damage to the oil seal. The transmission is very heavy so carry out the work with the help of an assistant or use a trolley jack or hoist.
8 While the transmission is out of the car, make up a plate which can be bolted to the front of the torque converter housing to prevent the torque converter from falling out.

21 Engine - dismantling (general)

1 Stand the engine on a strong bench so as to be at a comfortable working height. Failing this it can be stripped down on the floor, but at least stand it on a sheet of hardboard.
2 During the dismantling process, the greatest care should be taken to keep the

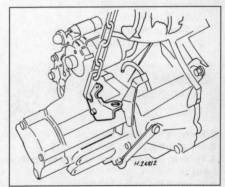

Fig. 1.10 Transmission lifting lug (Sec 19)

exposed parts free from dirt. As the engine is stripped, clean each part in a bath of paraffin.

3 Never immerse parts with oilways in paraffin, e.g. the crankshaft, but to clean, wipe down carefully with a paraffin dampened rag. Oilways can be cleaned out with a piece of wire. If an air line is available, all parts can be blown dry and the oilways blown through as an added precaution.

4 Re-use of old gaskets is false economy and can give rise to oil and water leaks, if nothing worse. To avoid the possibility of trouble after the engine has been reassembled always use new gaskets throughout.

 Do not throw old gaskets away as it sometimes happens that an immediate replacement cannot be found and the old gasket is then very useful as a template. Hang up the gaskets on a suitable nail or hook as they are removed.

5 To strip the engine, it is best to work from the top downwards. The engine oil sump proves a firm base on which the engine can be supported in an upright position. When the stage is reached where the pistons are to be removed, turn the engine on its side. Turn the block upside down to remove the crankshaft.

6 Wherever possible, replace nuts, bolts and washers finger-tight from wherever they were removed. This helps avoid later loss and muddle. If they cannot be replaced then lay them out in such a fashion that it is clear from where they came.

22 Engine ancillary components - removal

1 Before complete engine dismantling begins, remove the following ancillary components.

Distributor (Chapter 4)
Inlet manifold and carburettor (Chapter 3)
Fuel pump (Chapter 3)
Exhaust manifold and hot air collector (Chapter 3)
Alternator (Chapter 12)
Clutch (Chapter 5)
Oil filter cartridge and dipstick
Engine mounting brackets

23 Engine - complete dismantling

1 Remove the rocker cover.
2 Remove the timing belt, Section 8.
3 Refer to Section 13 and remove the cylinder head.
4 Remove the timing belt tensioner.
5 Refer to Chapter 2 and remove the coolant pump.

6 Lock the flywheel starter ring gear teeth and unbolt and remove the flywheel (or driveplate - automatic transmission). Renew the bolts and clean the threads in their holes.
7 Remove the crankcase breather.
8 Turn the engine upside down and remove the sump pan (Section 14, and the oil pump (Section 15).
9 Unbolt and remove the crankshaft rear oil seal retainer. Remove the dipstick guide tube.
10 Lay the engine on its side and remove the piston/connecting rods as described in Section 16.
11 Stand the engine on its block face and unbolt and remove the main bearing caps. These are in the form of a monobloc casting. Note the thrust washers located at No. 4 main bearing.
12 Lift the crankshaft from the crankcase. If the bearing shells are to be used again, identify them with their original crankcase or cap recesses.

24 Cylinder head - dismantling and decarbonising

1 With the cylinder head removed to the bench, dismantle in the following way.
2 Unscrew and remove the spark plugs.
3 If not already done, unbolt and remove the inlet manifold with the carburettor and the exhaust manifold with the hot air collector. Remove the thermostat housing and coolant distribution tube.
4 Remove the fuel pump.
5 Remove the distributor and distributor holder.
6 Remove the camshaft sprocket and key.
7 Extract the camshaft front oil seal (Section 9).
8 Remove the rocker shaft assemblies (Section 11).
9 Lift the camshaft from the cylinder head.
10 Using a valve spring compressor, compress the first valve spring and remove the split collets.
11 Gently release the compressor and remove it.
12 Take off the spring retainer, the spring and the spring seat.
13 Remove all the other valves in a similar way keeping them in their original fitted sequence together with their associated components. Remove and discard the valve stem oil seals.
14 Bearing in mind that the cylinder head is of light alloy construction and is easily damaged use a blunt scraper or rotary wire brush to clean all traces of carbon deposits from the combustion spaces and the ports. The valve head stems and valve guides should also be freed from any carbon deposits. Wash the combustion spaces and ports down with paraffin and scrape the cylinder head surface free of any foreign

matter with the side of a steel rule, or a similar article.
15 If the engine is installed in the car, clean the pistons and the top of the cylinder bores. If the pistons are still in the block, then it is essential that great care is taken to ensure that no carbon gets into the cylinder bores as this could scratch the cylinder walls or cause damage to the piston and rings. To ensure this does not happen, first turn the crankshaft so that two of the pistons are at the top of their bores. Stuff rag into the other two bores or seal them off with paper and masking tape. The waterways should also be covered with small pieces of masking tape to prevent particles of carbon entering the cooling system and damaging the coolant pump.
16 Press a little grease into the gap between the cylinder walls and the two pistons which are to be worked on. With a blunt scraper carefully scrape away the carbon from the piston crown, taking great care not to scratch the aluminium. Also scrape away the carbon from the surround lip of the cylinder wall. When all carbon has been removed, scrape away the grease which will now be contaminated with carbon particles, taking care not to press any into the bores. Remove the rags or masking tape from the other two cylinders and turn the crankshaft so that the two pistons which were at the bottom are now at the top. Place rag in the cylinders which have been decarbonised, and proceed as just described.

 To assist prevention of carbon build-up the piston crown can be polished with a metal polish.

17 Examine the head of the valves for pitting and burning, especially the heads of the exhaust valves. The valve seatings should be examined at the same time. If the pitting on the valve and seat is very slight, the marks can be removed by grinding the seats and valves together with coarse, and then fine, valve grinding paste.
18 Where bad pitting has occurred to the valve seats it will be necessary to recut them and fit new valves. This latter job should be entrusted to the local agent or engineering works. In practice it is very seldom that the seats are so badly worn. Normally it is the valve that is too badly worn for refitting, and the owner can easily purchase a new set of valves and match them to the seats by valve grinding.
19 Valve grinding is carried out as follows. Smear a trace of coarse carborundum paste on the seat face and apply a suction grinder tool to the valve head. With a semi-rotary motion, grind the valve head to its seat, lifting the valve occasionally to redistribute the grinding paste. When a dull matt even surface is produced on both the valve seat and the valve, wipe off the paste and repeat the process with fine carborundum paste, lifting

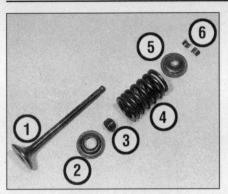

24.25A Valve components

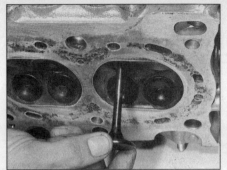

24.25B Fitting a valve

24.25C Fitting a valve stem oil seal

1 Valve
2 Valve spring seat
3 Valve stem oil seal
4 Valve spring
5 Valve spring cap
6 Split cotters

and turning the valve to redistribute the paste as before. A light spring placed under the valve head will greatly ease this operation. When a smooth unbroken ring of light grey matt finish is produced, on both valve and valve seat faces, the grinding operation is complete. Carefully clean away every trace of grinding compound, take great care to leave none in the ports or in the valve guides. Clean the valves and valve seats with paraffin soaked rag, then with a clean rag, and finally, if an air line is available, blow the valve, valve guides and valve ports clean.

20 Check that all valve springs are intact. If any one is broken, all should be renewed. Check the free height of the springs against new ones. If some springs are not within specifications, replace them all. Springs suffer from fatigue and it is a good idea to renew them even if they look serviceable.

21 The cylinder head can be checked for warping either by placing it on a piece of plate glass or using a straight-edge and feeler blades. If there is any doubt or if its block face is corroded, have it re-faced by your dealer or motor engineering works.

22 Test the valves in their guides for side-to-side rock. If this is any more than almost imperceptible new guides must be fitted, again a job for your dealer.

23 Examine the camshaft for wear or scoring of the journals or cam lobes. Any wear or scoring in the camshaft bearings will mean renewal of the cylinder head as the bearings are line-bored and cannot be replaced independently. It may be possible to have worn cam lobes reprofiled by a specialist firm.

24 Check the rocker shafts and arms and renew any components which are worn.

25 Commence reassembly by oiling the stem of the first valve and pushing it into its guide which should have been fitted with a new oil seal. The valve stem oil seals on the inlet valve guides have a bright metal clip while those for the exhaust valve guides have a black clip (photo).

26 Fit the spring seat, the valve spring so that the closer coils are towards the cylinder head and then the spring retaining cap (photos).

27 Compress the valve spring and using a little grease locate the split cotters in the valve stem cut-out (photo).

28 Gently release the compressor, checking to see that the collets are not displaced.

29 Fit the remaining valve in the same way.

30 Tap the end of each valve stem with a plastic or copper-faced hammer to settle the components.

31 Oil the camshaft bearings in the cylinder head. Lower the camshaft into position (photos).

32 Fit the camshaft bearing cap/pedestals in their numbered sequence with arrows

1

24.26A Fitting valve spring seat

24.26B Fitting valve spring

24.26C Fitting valve spring cap

24.27 Compressing valve spring and fitting split cotters

24.31 Fitting the camshaft

24.32A Fitting a camshaft bearing cap. Fuel pump eccentric arrowed

24.32B Tightening camshaft bearing cap bolt

24.33 Tightening a rocker shaft bolt

towards the timing belt. Tighten the rear bearing cap bolts (photos) .

33 Fit the rocker shaft assemblies complete with rocker arms, springs and spacers. Tighten the bolts to the specified torque (photo).

34 Fit a new camshaft oil seal, the Woodruff key and the camshaft sprocket and then tighten its bolt to the specified torque (photos).

35 Refit the distributor holder, tighten the bolts (photos).

36 Refit the fuel pump.

37 Fit the distributor (Chapter 4).

38 Screw in the spark plugs, clean and correctly gapped.

39 Bolt on the inlet and exhaust manifold using new gaskets.

25 Engine components - examination and renovation

1 With the engine stripped down and all parts thoroughly clean, it is now time to examine everything for wear. The following items should be checked and where necessary renewed or renovated as described in the following Sections.

Cylinder block and crankcase

2 Clean away all old gasket material and then examine the casting for cracks particularly about bolt holes. If any are found, specialist welding or cold repair will be required.

3 Clean out the oilways and galleries with compressed air or wire.

4 If the cylinder bores are worn, this will be evident by the emission of exhaust smoke and general deterioration in engine performance together with increased oil consumption. A good way to test the condition of the engine is to have it at normal operating temperature with the spark plugs removed. Screw a compression tester (available from most modern accessory stores) into the first plug hole. Hold the accelerator pedal fully depressed and crank the engine on the starter motor for several revolutions. Record the reading. Zero the tester and check the remaining cylinders in the same way. All four compression figures should be approximately equal and within the tolerance given in the

24.34A Camshaft oil seal

24.34B Camshaft sprocket Woodruff key

2434C Camshaft sprocket bolt

24.34D Tightening camshaft sprocket bolt

24.35A Fitting the distributor holder

24.35B Tightening distributor holder bolts

25.12 Main and big-end bearing code number and letter

Specifications. If they are all low, suspect piston ring or cylinder bore wear. If only one reading is down, suspect a valve not seating.

5 The cylinder bores must be checked for taper, ovality, scoring and scratching. Start by examining the top of the cylinder bores. If they are at all worn, a ridge will be felt on the thrust side. This ridge marks the limit of piston ring travel.

6 An internal micrometer or dial gauge can be used to check bore wear and taper against Specifications, but this is a pointless operation if the engine is obviously in need of reboring as indicated by excessive oil consumption.

Pistons and connecting rods

7 If the cylinders have been rebored, then the reconditioner will supply the oversize pistons, rings and the gudgeon pins. Give the job of fitting the new pistons to the connecting rods to him.

8 The gudgeon pin is an interference fit in the connecting rod small end and removal or refitting and changing a piston is a job best left to your dealer or engine reconditioner. This is owing to the need for a press and jig and careful heating of the connecting rod.

9 Removal and refitting piston rings is described in Section 16.

Crankshaft

10 Examine the surfaces of the journals and crankpins; if scored or when measured with a micrometer prove to be oval or tapered then the manufacturer's recommendation is to renew the crankshaft and the colour-coded bearing shells. However, by consulting a specialist crankshaft grinder it may be possible for him to recondition the original crankshaft and supply undersize shells.

11 If the crankshaft is in good condition, but it is decided to renew the main and big-end bearing shells, use the following formula to select them.

Main bearings

12 Match the letter on the cylinder block with the number on the crankshaft web adjacent to each bearing (photo).

Big-end bearings

13 Match the number on the connecting rod with the letter on the crankshaft web adjacent to each bearing.

14 The resulting main bearing or big-end shell will be colour-coded on its edge in accordance with the following table.

	A	B	C	D
1	Red	Pink	Yellow	Green
2	Pink	Yellow	Green	Brown
3	Yellow	Green	Brown	Black
4	Green	Brown	Black	Blue

Cylinder head, camshaft and rockers

15 Refer to Section 24.

Timing belt, tensioner and sprockets

16 If the timing belt shows signs of cracking or tooth wear, renew it. If it has been in operation for 80 000 km (50 000 miles) or more, it should be renewed as a matter of routine.

17 If the sprockets have tooth wear, renew them.

18 The tensioner pulley should spin smoothly and quietly. If it is rough or worn on its spindle, renew it.

Flywheel (or driveplate)

19 Check the clutch mating surface of the flywheel. If it is deeply scored (due to failure to renew a worn driven plate) then it may be possible to have it surface ground provided the thickness of the flywheel is not reduced too much.

20 If lots of tiny cracks are visible on the surface of the flywheel then this will be due to overheating caused by slipping the clutch or 'riding' the clutch pedal.

21 With a pre-engaged type of starter motor it is rare to find the teeth of the flywheel ring gear damaged or worn, but if they are, then the ring gear will have to be renewed.

22 To remove the ring gear, drill a hole between the roots of two teeth taking care not to damage the flywheel and then split the ring with a sharp cold chisel.

23 The new ring gear must be heated to 350°C (662°F). If you do not have facilities for obtaining these temperatures, leave the job to your dealer or engine reconditioner.

24 Where such facilities are available, then the ring gear should be either pressed or lightly tapped gently onto its register and left to cool naturally, when the contraction of the metal on cooling will ensure that it is a secure and permanent fit. Great care must be taken not to overheat the ring gear, as if this happens its temper will be lost. A clutch input shaft pilot bearing is not fitted on this engine.

25 If the ring gear on the driveplate is worn, renew the plate complete.

Oil pump

26 Check that the oil relief valve slides freely in its housing.

27 If the pump has been in use for a long time carry out the following checks for wear outside the specified tolerance (see Specifications).

28 Extract the pump rear plate screws. An impact driver will probably be required for this (photo).

29 Remove the rear plate, remove the inner and outer rotors, identifying the faces which are in contact with the rear plate so that they can be refitted the same way round (photos).

30 Clean all components and reassemble the rotors.

31 Check the clearance between the outer

25.28 Extracting oil pump rear plate screws

25.29A Oil pump outer rotor showing face 'up' dimple

25.29B Oil pump inner rotor showing face 'up' dimple

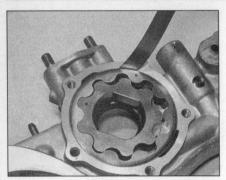

25.31 Checking oil pump outer rotor clearance

25.32 Checking oil pump rotor lobe tip clearance

25.33 Checking oil pump rotor endfloat

rotor and the oil pump body using feeler gauges (photo).

32 Check the clearance between the inner rotor lobe tip and the outer rotor lobe tip (photo).

33 Place a straight-edge across the runs of the oil pump housing and insert feeler blades between the rotors and the straight-edge (photo).

34 If any clearance is outside that specified, renew the worn components or the pump complete.

Oil seals and gaskets

35 It is recommended that all gaskets and oil seals are renewed at major engine overhaul. Sockets are useful for removing or refitting oil seals. An arrow is moulded onto some seals to indicate the rotational direction of the

component which it serves. Make sure that the seal is fitted the correct way round to comply with the arrow.

26 Engine reassembly - general

1 To ensure maximum life with minimum trouble from a rebuilt engine, not only must every part be correctly assembled, but everything must be spotlessly clean, all the oilways must be clear, locking washers and spring washers must always be fitted where indicated and all bearing and other working surfaces must be thoroughly lubricated during assembly. Before assembly begins renew any bolts or studs whose threads are in any way

damaged; whenever possible use new spring washers.

2 Apart from your normal tools, a supply of non-fluffy rag, an oil can filled with engine oil, a supply of new spring washers, a set of new gaskets and a torque wrench should be collected together.

27 Engine - complete reassembly

1 Set the cylinder block on the bench with the crankcase uppermost.

2 Wipe out the main bearing shell recesses in the crankcase and insert the selected shells or if the original ones are being used again, return them to their original locations (photo).

3 Oil the shells liberally and then stick the semi-circular thrust washers on either side of No. 4 main bearing in the crankcase using some thick grease. Make sure that the oil grooves on the thrust washers are visible when the thrust washers are fitted (photos).

4 Lower the crankshaft into the crankcase taking care not to displace the thrust washers (photo).

5 Wipe out the main bearing shell recesses in the main bearing cap monobloc and fit the selected shells or if the original ones are being used again, return them to their original locations (photo).

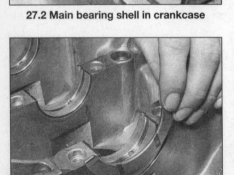

27.2 Main bearing shell in crankcase

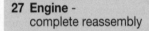
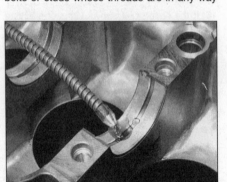

27.3A Oiling main bearing shells

27.3B Crankshaft thrust washer

27.4 Lowering crankshaft into position

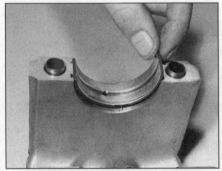

27.5 Main bearing shell in monobloc

27.6 Fitting monobloc

27.7 Tightening main bearing monobloc bolts

27.8 Checking crankshaft endfloat

6 Oil the crankshaft journals and crankpins and fit the cap monobloc (photo).
7 Fit the cap bolts and tighten to the specified torque (photo).
8 Now check the crankshaft endfloat either using a dial gauge or by inserting a feeler blade between the machined shoulder of a crankshaft web and the thrust washers. If the endfloat is outside the specified tolerance, then the thrust washer thickness must be incorrect (photo).
9 Lay the engine on its side and fit the piston/connecting rods as described in Section 16.
10 Fit the oil pump having smeared its mounting face with jointing compound.
11 Fit the oil pick-up tube and strainer using a new gasket at its mounting flange (photos).
12 Using a new gasket and seals, fit the sump pan as described in Section 14.
13 Tighten all bolts and nuts to the specified torque.
14 Bolt on the crankshaft rear oil seal retainer complete with new seal and having applied jointing compound to its mounting face (photos).
15 Fit the cylinder head complete with camshaft and rocker shaft as described in Section 13.
16 Refit the flywheel (or driveplate - automatic transmission), tightening new bolts to the specified torque and having applied locking fluid to their threads (photos).

27.11A Oil pick-up tube gasket

27.11B Oil pick-up tube and brackets

27.14A Crankshaft rear oil seal retainer

27.14B Tightening crankshaft rear oil seal retainer bolts

27.16A Applying thread locking fluid to flywheel bolts

27.16B Tightening flywheel bolts

27.17A Bolting on the thermostat housing

27.17B Coolant tube and O-ring

27.18 Timing belt tensioner

27.19A Timing belt inner guide

17 Refer to Chapter 2 and fit the coolant pump. Bolt on the thermostat housing using a new gasket. Use a new O-ring and connect the coolant tube between the pump and thermostat housing (photos).
18 Fit the timing belt tensioner (photo).
19 Fit the belt inner guide, the crankshaft sprocket and key, the timing belt and the belt outer guide, convex side to belt (photos).
20 Fit the belt lower cover, the crankshaft pulley and bolt. Set the crankshaft so that the pulley and cover timing marks are in alignment.
21 Fit the crankcase breather and the oil dipstick guide tube (photo).
22 Connect the timing belt to the camshaft and coolant pump sprockets as described in

Section 8 and tension the belt as described in Section 7.
23 Fit the timing belt upper cover triangular-shaped backing plate and then the upper cover (photo).
24 Check and adjust the valve clearances.
25 Fit the rocker cover using a new gasket (photo).
26 Tighten the domed nuts, but do not overtighten them (photo).

28 Engine ancillary components - refitting

1 Refit and centralise the clutch (Chapter 5).

2 Bolt on the engine mounting brackets.
3 Screw on a new oil filter cartridge and insert the dipstick.
4 Fit the manifolds to the cylinder head using new gaskets. Fit the hot air collector to the exhaust manifold.
5 Fit the carburettor to the inlet manifold.
6 Fit the fuel pump (Chapter 3).
7 Fit the alternator (Chapter 12).
8 Fit the distributor (Chapter 4).

29 Engine/manual transmission - reconnection

1 Support the engine in an upright position.
2 Apply a smear of grease to the gearbox input (clutch) shaft.
3 Offer the transmission to the engine and slide the input shaft through the splined hub of the driven plate until the flywheel housing mates with the rear face of the crankcase. If any difficulty is experienced, it may be due to the clutch driven plate not having been correctly centralised or the shaft and hub splines not being aligned. If the latter, have an assistant turn the crankshaft pulley bolt slightly while pushing on the gearbox (photo).
4 Insert the connecting bolts and tighten to the specified torque.
5 Bolt on the starter motor and the flywheel housing cover plate.

27.19B Crankshaft sprocket with integral key

27.21 Crankcase breather (oil separator)

27.23 Timing belt upper cover backing plate (arrowed)

27.25 Rocker cover gasket

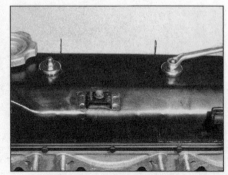
27.26 Tightening rocker cover nuts

29.3 Connecting transmission to engine

30.1 Lowering engine/transmission into engine compartment

30.17A Front splash guard panel

30 Engine/manual transmission - refitting

1 Attach the lifting gear to the engine/transmission and hoist it up, then down into the engine compartment. Take care that nothing is damaged during the lowering process particularly the radiator and brake master cylinder (photo).
2 Reconnect the engine and transmission mountings.
3 Connect the exhaust downpipe.
4 Connect the gear selector rod and the torque rod.
5 With the steering in full left-hand lock, connect the left-hand driveshaft making sure that the shaft securing clip snaps positively into engagement in the differential side gear.
6 Turn the steering to full right-hand lock and connect the right-hand driveshaft.
7 Fit the splash guard panels (photos).
8 Reconnect the suspension lower arm balljoints to the hub carriers.
9 Remove the lifting hoist.
10 Fit the front roadwheels and remove the safety stands.
11 Reconnect the heater and coolant hoses (photo).
12 Reconnect the fuel feed hose to the pump.
13 Connect the clutch cable.
14 Connect the speedometer drive cable to

the transmission, also the tachometer drive (if fitted).
15 Connect the reverse lamp switch leads.
16 Connect the leads to the rear of the alternator.
17 Connect the carburettor controls including the wiring harness plug.
18 Connect the HT and LT leads to the coil.
19 Connect the vacuum hoses.
20 Connect the brake servo vacuum hose.
21 Connect the transmission and engine earth cables (photos).
22 Fit the battery and its tray and connect the leads.
23 Fit the air cleaner and connect the vacuum hoses to it. Also fit the air intake duct to the inlet on the wing valance.

24 With the help of an assistant fit the bonnet.
25 Fill the engine with oil and the cooling system with antifreeze mixture. Refill the transmission with oil if it was drained (photo).

31 Engine/automatic transmission - reconnection and refitting

1 Support the engine in an upright position.
2 Check that the torque converter is pushed fully into its housing.
3 Offer the transmission to the engine, insert the connecting bolts and tighten them. Remember that some bolts including those at the base of the torque converter housing must

30.17B Side splash guard panel

30.11 Heater and coolant hoses at thermostat housing

30.21A Engine earth bonding cable

30.21B Transmission earth bonding cable

30.25 Filling the engine with oil

be inserted into their holes in the transmission casing before the engine and transmission are fully connected.

4 Insert the driveplate to torque converter bolts. The crankshaft will have to be turned to align the bolt holes and screw in the bolts one at a time through the starter motor aperture.

5 Bolt on the starter motor and converter housing cover plate.

6 The refitting operations are similar to those described in the preceding Section for cars with manual transmission, but ignoring reference to the clutch and gear selector controls.

7 Connect the transmission fluid cooler pipes.

8 Connect the reverse lamp/inhibitor switch leads.

9 Connect the kickdown cable and selector cable and check their adjustment (Chapter 7).

10 Check and top up the transmission fluid.

32 Initial start up after major overhaul

1 Before starting the engine, check that all hoses, controls and electrical leads have been connected.

2 Make sure that tools and rags have been removed from the engine compartment.

3 Starting may take a little longer than usual as the fuel pump and carburettor must first fill with fuel.

4 Have the throttle speed screw turned in an extra turn to increase the engine idle speed. This will help to offset the stiffness of the new engine components.

5 Check the ignition timing.

6 If the majority of internal components have been renewed, treat the engine as a new one and restrict speed for the 1000 km (600 miles).

7 It is recommended that the engine oil is renewed at the end of the first 1000 km (600 miles). Also the tension of the drivebelts should be checked and the idle speed and mixture adjusted if necessary.

Part B 1.6 (1598 cc) engine

33 General description

The engine is of four-cylinder, in-line camshaft type, mounted transversely at the front of the car.

The crankshaft is supported in five shell-type main bearings. Thrust washers are fitted to the centre main bearing in the crankcase to control crankshaft endfloat.

The connecting rods are attached to the crankshaft by horizontally split shell-type big-end bearings, and to the pistons by interference fit gudgeon pins. The aluminium alloy pistons are of the slipper type and have their gudgeon pins offset to the thrust side to reduce piston slap. Two compression rings and a three-piece oil control ring are fitted to each piston.

The overhead camshaft is mounted in a carrier attached to the cylinder head and is driven via a toothed belt by the crankshaft. The camshaft operates the valves through inverted bucket type tappets which are also housed in the camshaft carrier. Tappet adjustment is by shims fitted between the valve stems and the tappet buckets.

The inlet and exhaust valves are mounted at an angle in the cylinder head and are each closed by a single valve spring.

The oil pump, pressure relief valve and full-flow oil filter are located in a housing attached to the front of the cylinder block. The rotor type oil pump is driven directly by the crankshaft.

The distributor rotor is driven directly by the camshaft whereas the fuel pump is operated by an eccentric camshaft lobe. The toothed timing belt also drives the coolant pump and a separate drivebelt is used for the alternator, driven by a sprocket on the crankshaft.

34 Lubrication system

1 The oil pump is of rotor type and the oil pump housing incorporates an oil pressure relief valve.

2 The full-flow canister type oil filter is screwed onto the oil pump housing.

3 Pressurised oil is supplied to the crankshaft and camshaft bearings through oil galleries and drillings.

35 Engine oil and filter

Refer to Part A, Section 3.

36 Crankcase ventilation system

Refer to Part A, Section 4.

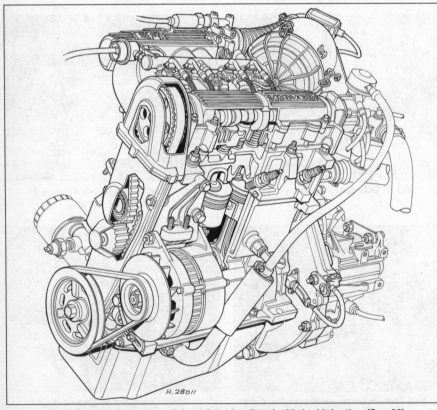
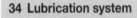
Fig. 1.11 Cut-away view of the 1.6 engine fitted with fuel injection (Sec 33)

Fig. 1.12 External components – 1.6 engine (Sec 33)

1 Camshaft cover
2 Camshaft cover
3 Camshaft cover gaskets
4 Camshaft carrier
5 Coolant outlet elbow
6 Thermostat
7 Coolant thermistor
8 Thermostat housing
9 Oil filler cap
10 Oil filler tube
11 Coolant inlet elbow
12 Spark plug
13 Crankshaft rear oil seal
14 Dipstick guide tube
15 Oil dipstick
16 Transmission adaptor plate
17 Crankshaft sensor
18 Knock sensor
19 Main bearing cap
20 Sump pan gasket
21 Sump pan
22 Oil separator
23 Main bearing shells
24 Coolant pump
25 Oil pressure relief valve
26 Oil pump
27 Oil pick-up strainer
28 Crankshaft front oil seal
29 Drive belt
30 Crankshaft pulley
31 Oil pressure switch

32 Timing belt lower cover
33 Timing belt upper cover
34 Oil filter
35 Timing belt tensioner
36 Cylinder block/crankcase
37 Cylinder head gasket
38 Cylinder head
39 O-ring seal
40 Hollow dowel
41 Cylinder head bolt with threaded extension
42 Gasket
43 Drain plug
44 Cylinder head bolt

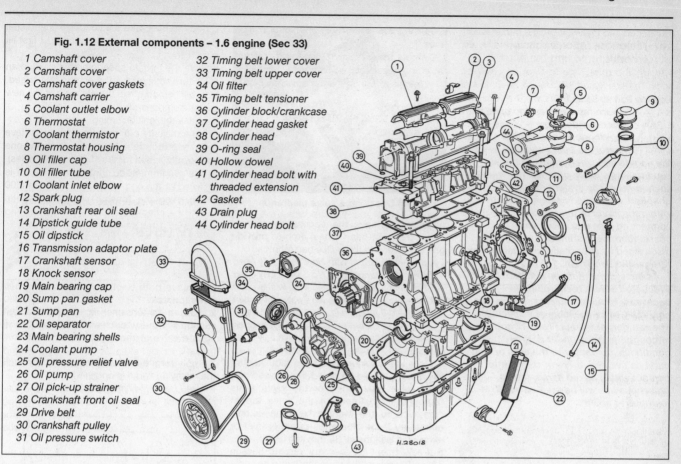

Fig. 1.13 Internal components (1.6 engine) (Sec 33)

1 Timing belt
2 Camshaft sprocket
3 Camshaft front oil seal
4 Camshaft locating plate
5 Camshaft
6 Gudgeon pin
7 Pistons rings and piston
8 Connecting rod and cap
9 Big-end bearing shell
10 Crankshaft
11 Main bearing shell
12 Woodruff key
13 Belt guide plate
14 Crankshaft sprocket
15 Crankshaft pulley
16 Pulley bolt and washer
17 Timing belt tensioner
18 Tappet (cam follower) and shim
19 Inlet valve, oil seal, spring, cap, cotters
20 Exhaust valve
21 Piston/ connecting rod
22 Crankshaft thrust washers

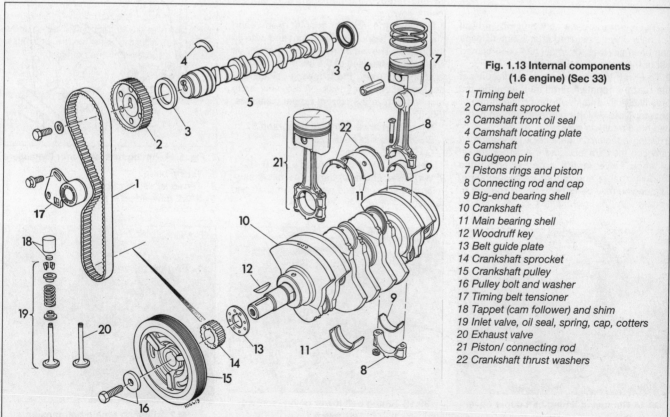

37 Major operations possible without removing the engine

Refer to Part A, Section 5.

⚠️ *Warning: vehicles equipped with air conditioning:*

Whenever overhaul of a major nature is being undertaken to the engine and components of the air conditioning system obstruct the work and such items of the system cannot be unbolted and moved aside sufficiently far within the limits of their flexible connecting pipes, to avoid such obstruction the system should be discharged by your dealer or a competent refrigeration engineer.

As the system must be completely evacuated before recharging, the necessary vacuum equipment to do this is only likely to be available at a specialist. The refrigerant fluid is Freon 12 and although harmless under normal conditions, contact with the eyes or skin must be avoided. If Freon comes into contact with a naked flame, then a poisonous gas will be created which is injurious to health.

38 Valve clearances - adjustment

1 This is not a routine servicing job and will normally only be required after a high mileage has been covered, overhaul has been carried out or the engine becomes noisy.
2 To check the valve clearances, disconnect the battery negative terminal then undo the retaining bolts and lift off the camshaft carrier covers. Note which bolts also secure cable and hose retaining clips.
3 Using a feeler gauge, check the clearance between the cam lobe and the tappet bucket of each valve in the order given in the following table and record each clearance. The engine may be turned using a spanner or socket on the crankshaft pulley bolt. If

38.3 Checking a valve clearance

necessary remove the access panel from under the right-hand wheel arch to provide greater access to the pulley bolt (photo).

Check No 1 tappet with No 8 valve fully open
Check No 3 tappet with No 6 valve fully open
Check No 5 tappet with No 4 valve fully open
Check No 2 tappet with No 7 valve fully open
Check No 8 tappet with No 1 valve fully open
Check No 6 tappet with No 3 valve fully open
Check No 4 tappet with No 5 valve fully open
Check No 7 tappet with No 2 valve fully open

4 Once the readings have been tabulated for all valves it should be noted that, unless new parts have been fitted or the valve seats reground, adjustment of the valve tappet clearance to the standard setting is only necessary if the clearance of either inlet or exhaust is less than 0.30 mm (0.012 in).
5 If adjustment is necessary, refer to Section 43 and remove the camshaft and tappets (cam followers).
6 Remove the adjusting shim from each maladjusted tappet bucket in turn and note its thickness. The shim reference number is engraved on the face of the shim - see Specifications. By using the following calculation, determine the thickness of the new shim required to give the correct tappet clearance: (photo)

A = clearance measured in paragraph 3
B = thickness of existing shim
C = correct clearance
New shim thickness required = $A + B - C$

7 With new shims obtained as necessary, refer to Section 43 and refit the camshaft and tappets.

38.6 Valve clearance adjusting shim

39 Timing belt - tensioning

1 Remove both Sections of the timing belt cover (photos).
2 Slacken the tensioner fixing bolts and then engage a torque wrench with a 9.5 mm (3/8 in) square drive in the tensioner bracket hole (photo).
3 Apply torque in a clockwise direction until the following figure is obtained:

Used belt   14 Nm (10.3 lbf ft)
New belt   20 Nm (15 lbf ft)

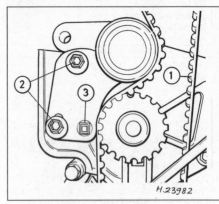

Fig. 1.14 Timing belt tensioner (Sec 39)

1 Timing belt
2 Tensioner securing bolts
3 3/8in. drive adjuster hole

39.1A Removing timing belt upper cover

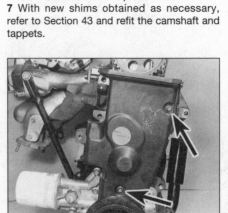

39.1B Timing belt lower cover (screws arrowed)

39.2 Adjusting timing belt tension

40.4 Alternator drivebelt

40.6A Camshaft sprocket timing marks

40.6B Crankshaft pulley timing marks

4 Keep the specified torque applied while the tensioner bracket bolts are tightened.

5 If there is any possibility that the timing sprockets were rotated while the belt was slack, check that when the crankshaft pulley timing marks are in alignment, the camshaft sprocket marks are in alignment. If this is not the case, slacken and reposition the belt and then retension it again.

40 Timing belt -
removal and refitting

1 Jack up the front of the car and support it on axle stands.
2 Remove the right-hand front roadwheel and the access panel under the wheel arch.
3 Disconnect the battery negative terminal.
4 Slacken the alternator pivot mounting bolt and the adjustment arm bolts. Move the alternator towards the engine and remove the drivebelt from the pulleys (photo).
5 Lift off the timing belt upper cover then undo the screws and remove the lower cover.
6 Using a socket or spanner on the crankshaft pulley bolt, turn the engine over until the dimple on the rear face of the camshaft sprocket is aligned with the notch on the camshaft carrier. Check also that the notch on the crankshaft pulley is aligned with the timing mark on the oil pump housing (photos).

7 Slacken the two timing belt tensioner retaining bolts and move the tensioner away from the engine (photo).
8 Slip the timing belt off the three sprockets and remove it from the engine (photo). Do not turn the camshaft sprocket while the belt is off.
9 If the original belt is to be re-used, mark it with chalk to indicate its direction of rotation and also its outer facing edge. Store the belt on its edge while off the engine.
10 Refitting the timing belt is a reversal of removal. Tension the belt as described in the preceding Section.

41 Camshaft oil seals -
renewal

Front oil seal

1 Remove the timing belt upper cover.
2 Remove the timing belt lower cover.
3 Turn the crankshaft pulley bolt in a clockwise direction until the pulley TDC marks are in alignment. Also check that the camshaft sprocket dimple aligns with the notch.
4 Retract the belt tensioner and slip the belt from the camshaft sprocket.
5 Lock the camshaft sprocket and unscrew its securing bolt. Remove the sprocket.
6 Using a suitable tool, prise out the oil seal.

40.7 Timing belt tensioner bolts (arrowed)

7 Oil the lip of the new seal and fit it so that the lip is inwards.
8 Refit the sprocket and tighten the bolt.
9 Check that the timing marks are in alignment and fit the belt.
10 Adjust the belt tension as described in Section 39.
11 Refit the belt covers.

Rear oil seal

12 Remove the distributor cap, rotor arm and shield (Chapter 4).
13 Prise out the oil seal and discard it.
14 Oil the lip of the new seal and fit it with its lip inwards (photo).
15 Refit the distributor, rotor arm and shield.

40.8 Slipping timing belt from camshaft sprocket

41.7 Fitting camshaft front oil seal

41.14 Fitting camshaft rear oil seal

42.2 Crankshaft pulley bolt and washer

42.3 Removing crankshaft pulley

42.4A Removing crankshaft sprocket

42 Crankshaft front oil seal - renewal

1 Remove the timing belt as described in Section 40.
2 Engage a low gear and have an assistant apply the brakes hard. Unscrew the crankshaft pulley bolt (photo). If the bolt fails to unscrew, or if the car is fitted with automatic transmission, it will be necessary to remove the starter motor and temporarily lock the starter ring gear, in order to prevent the crankshaft from turning.
3 Remove the crankshaft pulley and belt guide plate (photo).

42.4B Crankshaft sprocket inner belt guide plate

4 Remove the crankshaft sprocket and inner guide plate (photos).
5 Using a suitable tool, extract the oil seal.
6 Grease the seal lips and tape the shoulder on the crankshaft to prevent damage to the lips and press it into its seat. Remove the tape.
7 Fit the belt inner guide plate, the crankshaft sprocket, the outer guide plate and pulley.
8 Prevent the crankshaft from rotating and tighten the pulley bolt.
9 Refit the timing belt (Section 40).
10 Tension the belt (Section 39).

43 Camshaft and tappets (cam followers) - removal and refitting

1 Disconnect the battery negative lead.
2 Remove the air cleaner.
3 Remove the timing belt (Section 40).
4 Remove the fuel pump (Chapter 3).
5 Remove the distributor cap, rotor arm and shield.
6 Undo the retaining bolts and lift off the two camshaft carrier covers. Note the position of the cable and hose clips on the cover bolts (photo).
7 Using a suitable socket, or spanner, undo the camshaft sprocket retaining bolt. Engage a stout screwdriver or bar through the sprocket holes and in contact with the carrier to prevent the camshaft turning.

8 Remove the sprocket retaining bolt and washer then withdraw the sprocket from the camshaft. Carefully ease it off using two levers if it is tight.
9 Using pliers, withdraw the camshaft locating plate from the carrier (photo).
10 Progressively slacken the camshaft carrier retaining bolts and, when all tension on the bolts has been relieved, remove them.
11 Raise the camshaft carrier slightly and push down the tappet buckets until the cam lobes are clear.
12 Move the camshaft towards the rotor arm end until sufficient clearance exists to enable the oil seal at the sprocket end to be removed. Hook the seal out using a screwdriver.
13 Now move the camshaft towards the sprocket end and remove the remaining oil seal in the same way.
14 The camshaft can now be carefully removed from the rotor arm end of the carrier (photo).
15 Lift out each of the tappet buckets in turn and keep them in strict order. Make sure that the small adjustment shim has remained in place inside the bucket (photo).
16 Withdraw the camshaft carrier from the cylinder head noting the location of the O-ring oil seal (photo).

Refitting

17 Smear the tappet shims with petroleum jelly and then locate the shims in the recesses of their respective tappet buckets.

43.6 Camshaft carrier cover

43.9 Camshaft locating plate

43.14 Removing camshaft from carrier

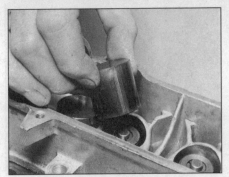

43.15 Removing cam follower

43.16 Removing camshaft carrier from cylinder head

43.21 Camshaft flats (arrowed) for turning with spanner

18 Place the camshaft carrier in position on the cylinder head and fit the tappet buckets to their locations in the carrier.

19 Lift the carrier slightly, push the tappet buckets down and carefully insert the camshaft. Fit the camshaft locating plate to the carrier front bearing journal.

20 Fit the camshaft carrier retaining bolts and progressively tighten them to the specified torque.

21 Before proceeding further the valve clearances should be checked and adjusted using the procedure described in Section 38. For the purpose of valve clearance checking the camshaft may be turned using an adjustable wrench on the square protrusion between No 6 and 7 camshaft lobe (photo).

22 With the tappet clearance checked and the correct new shims obtained as necessary, remove the camshaft, camshaft carrier and the tappet buckets (if not already done).

23 Locate a new O-ring seal in the carrier recess then fill the carrier peripheral groove with Loctite 574 sealant (photo).

24 Place the carrier in position on the cylinder head once more and insert the tappet buckets in their respective locations (photos).

25 Lift the carrier slightly, push down the tappet buckets and slide the camshaft into the carrier. Refit the camshaft locating plate.

26 Fit the camshaft carrier retaining bolts and progressively tighten them to the specified torque.

27 Thoroughly lubricate the lips of new camshaft front and rear oil seals and carefully locate them over the camshaft journals and into their position in the carrier. Tap the seals squarely into the carrier.

28 Place the camshaft sprocket on the camshaft and use the retaining bolt and washer to draw the sprocket fully home. Tighten the retaining bolt to the specified torque (photo).

29 Locate the one-piece rubber gaskets in the camshaft carrier covers using new gaskets if necessary.

30 Apply a continuous bead of RTV sealant to the cover mating faces in the camshaft carrier.

31 Fit the two covers, retaining bolts and brackets, where applicable.

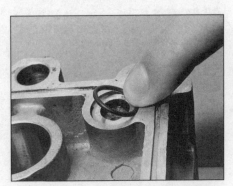

43.23 O-ring in camshaft carrier recess

43.24B Cam followers in their bores

43.28 Refitting camshaft sprocket

32 Tighten the cover bolts progressively to the specified torque.

44 Cylinder head -
removal and refitting

All models

1 Disconnect the battery negative lead.
2 Drain the cooling system (Chapter 2).

Carburettor models

3 Disconnect the fuel inlet hose from the carburettor. Unbolt the fuel pump and place it to one side with the hoses still attached (photo).

43.24A Lowering camshaft carrier onto cylinder head

44.3 Removing fuel pump with hoses attached

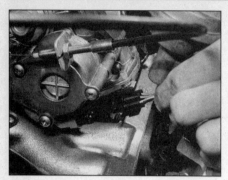

44.7 Carburettor stepping motor wiring plug

44.12A Thermostat housing hoses

44.12B Coolant inlet elbow hoses

4 Disconnect the air temperature sensor hose from the air temperature control.
5 Disconnect the brake servo vacuum hose from the inlet manifold.

Fuel injection models

6 Disconnect the fuel inlet and return hoses from the fuel rail pipes. Plug the hoses and pipes.
7 Disconnect the vacuum hoses from the inlet chamber and the multi-plug from the air valve stepper motor (photo).
8 Disconnect the multi-plugs from the fuel injectors, the fuel temperature switch and the coolant temperature thermistor.
9 Disconnect the throttle cable from the throttle lever and the abutment bracket.
10 Disconnect the air inlet hose from the throttle housing.

44.19 Manifold support strut bolt

44.21 Alternator mounting bracket bolts (arrowed)

All models

11 Release the dipstick guide tube from the camshaft front cover, and the oil filler tube support bracket from the cylinder head.
12 Disconnect the coolant hoses from the thermostat housing, the heater inlet elbow and the inlet manifold (photos).

Carburettor models

13 Disconnect the fuel drain pipe from the carburettor and manifold.
14 Disconnect the throttle control cable and the breather and vacuum pipes from the carburettor. If automatic transmission is fitted, disconnect the kickdown cable from the carburettor throttle lever.
15 Disconnect the multi-plugs from the starting and economy devices.

All models

16 Disconnect the spark plug leads and the coil HT lead from the distributor cap.
17 Extract the screws and remove the distributor cap, rotor arm and shield.

Carburettor models

18 Disconnect the inlet manifold heater, heater thermostat and coolant sensor leads.

All models

19 Disconnect the support struts and the exhaust downpipe from the manifold (photo).
20 On manual transmission models, release the clutch cable from its clips.
21 Refer to Chapter 12 and remove the

alternator and its bracket. Remove the camshaft covers (photo).
22 Set the timing marks in alignment then remove the timing belt covers. Then retract the timing belt tensioner and slip the timing belt from the camshaft sprocket.
23 Support the weight of the engine on a hoist or with a jack and block of wood placed under the sump pan and then remove the through-bolt from the right-hand engine mounting. Remove the nuts which hold the mounting to the engine and remove the mounting.
24 Unscrew the cylinder head bolts progressively starting with the centre ones and working towards each end of the head.
25 Lift the head straight up off its locating dowels. If it needs to be prised, use the lugs provided, never insert a tool in the gasket joint.
26 Peel off the gasket.
27 Refer to Section 24, Part A for details of dismantling and decarbonising.

Refitting

28 Ensure that the cylinder block and head mating faces are perfectly clean and free from any traces of oil, grease or water.
29 Place a new head gasket in position over the cylinder block dowels (photo).
30 Check that the camshaft TDC marks are aligned (all valves closed).
31 Lower the cylinder head into position and, with their threads lightly oiled, refit the retaining bolts (photo).

44.29 Cylinder head gasket in position

44.31 Lowering cylinder head onto block

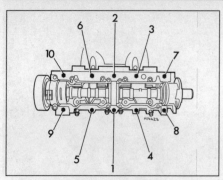

Fig. 1.15 Cylinder head bolt tightening
sequence (Sec 44)

44.38 Camshaft carrier cover and sealing
strips

44.39 Camshaft carrier covers in position
showing cable clips

32 Tighten the cylinder head bolts in the sequence shown in Fig. 1.15. Tighten to the 1st stage tightening torque, then to the 2nd stage torque. Finally tighten each bolt in sequence by a further 90° (quarter turn) .

33 Connect the right-hand engine mounting and remove the hoist or jack.

34 Fit the alternator mounting bracket, tightening the cylinder block screw before those which go into the cylinder head.

35 Fit the timing belt and tension it as described in Sections 40 and 39.

36 Fit the timing belt lower cover and then check that the camshaft locating plate is free in its slot. Turn the camshaft if necessary to free it.

37 Fit the timing belt upper cover.

38 Locate new gaskets in the camshaft cover grooves, having smeared the groove with jointing compound first (photo).

39 Fit the camshaft covers (photo).

40 Refit the alternator and tension the drivebelt (Chapter 12).

41 Connect the throttle cable, dipstick guide tube and fit the oil filler tube.

42 Reconnect the clutch cable (manual transmission models) and connect the exhaust pipe and manifold support struts.

43 Connect all electrical leads, multi-plugs, hoses and control cables according to the fuel system type fitted by reversing the removal operations described in earlier paragraphs of this Section.

44 Fill the cooling system and connect the battery.

45 Sump pan - removal and refitting

1 Drain the engine oil.

2 Disconnect the crankcase breather hose from the oil separator. Remove the oil separator from the sump pan (photo).

3 Unscrew the bolts which hold the sump connecting plate to the gearbox adaptor plate. Slacken the extension bolts then remove the manifold support stay bolt (photo).

4 Disconnect the alternator wiring harness (photo).

5 Remove the sump pan fixing screws, remove the sump pan and gasket (photo).

6 Before refitting the sump pan, make sure that the crankcase and sump pan mating faces are clean.

7 Apply a bead of RTV sealant to the centre of the semi-circular joint flanges allowing the bead to extend 12.5 mm (0.5 in) beyond the ends of the semi-circular profile (photo).

8 Fit a new gasket, offer up the sump pan and tighten the fixing screws evenly and progressively.

9 Refit and reconnect the disturbed components.

10 Refill the engine with oil.

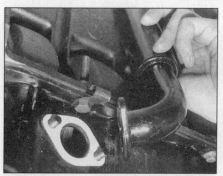

45.2 Removing oil separator from sump pan

45.3 Sump pan to adaptor plate bolts

45.4 Alternator wiring harness clips (arrowed)

45.5 Removing the sump pan

45.7 Applying RTV sealant to sump pan joint

46.6 One method of locking crankshaft

46.13 Fitting the oil pump

46.15 Oil pump fixing bolts

46 Oil pump -
removal and refitting

1 Remove the timing belt (Section 40).
2 Remove the sump pan (Section 45).
3 Disconnect the lead from the oil pressure switch.
4 Unbolt and remove the oil pick-up tube.
5 Unscrew the oil filter cartridge.
6 Undo the bolt securing the crankshaft pulley to the crankshaft, engage 1st gear (manual transmission) and firmly apply the footbrake to prevent crankshaft rotation as the bolt is undone. On automatic transmission models, or where the bolt fails to unscrew, it is necessary to remove the starter motor (Chapter 12) and prevent the crankshaft from

46.17A Oil pick-up tube O-ring

turning by inserting a suitable bar into the driveplate ring gear. If the engine is on the bench, refit two of the clutch pressure plate retaining bolts to the crankshaft and engage a stout bar between them (photo).
7 Withdraw the crankshaft pulley followed by the crankshaft sprocket and guide plate.
8 Undo the pump retaining bolts, noting their lengths and locations, and also the retaining plate fitted under the top centre bolt.
9 Withdraw the oil pump housing and recover the gasket.

Refitting

10 Make sure that the mating faces of the pump and cylinder block are clean, then place a new gasket in position on the pump housing.
11 Wrap some insulating tape around the end of the crankshaft to protect the oil seal as the pump is fitted.
12 Liberally lubricate the lips of the oil seal and the insulating tape with engine oil.
13 Position the flats of the pump inner rotor to correspond with the flats on the crankshaft and carefully fit the pump to the cylinder block (photo).
14 Remove the tape.
15 Refit the pump retaining bolts. The top centre bolt also secures the coolant pump (photo).
16 Tighten the bolts evenly to the specified torque.
17 Refit the oil pick-up tube (photos).

18 Screw on the oil filter cartridge.
19 Refit the sump pan.
20 Refit and tension the timing belt (Section 40).

47 Transmission adaptor plate -
removal and refitting

1 This operation can only be carried out after removal of the transmission.
2 Remove the clutch and flywheel (manual transmission) or driveplate (automatic transmission).
3 Remove the sump pan (Section 45).
4 Remove the oil filler tube.
5 Remove the crankshaft sensor.
6 Undo the bolts securing the adaptor plate to the cylinder block.
7 Tap the adaptor plate using a soft-faced mallet to free it from the locating dowels and remove it from the engine. Remove the two sump retaining bolts and gearbox retaining bolt from their captive recesses in the adaptor plate (photo).
8 Ensure that the mating faces of the cylinder block and adaptor plate are thoroughly clean then apply a bead of RTV sealant to the adaptor plate face (photo).
9 Make sure that the two sump retaining bolts and the gearbox retaining bolt are fitted in their adaptor plate locations and

46.17B Oil pick-up tube and strainer

47.7 Sump pan bolts in transmission adaptor plate

47.8 Applying RTV sealant to transmission adaptor plate

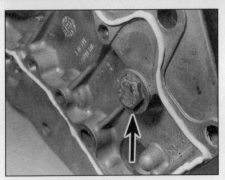

47.9 Sealant application point on gearbox retaining bolt head (arrowed)

47.10 Fitting adaptor plate to cylinder block

on a hoist or using a workshop jack with a block of wood as an insulator.
2 Tighten all nuts and bolts to the specified torque. Disconnect and renew one mounting at a time.

50 Engine - method of removal

The engine should be removed upwards from the engine compartment complete with the transmission.

51 Engine/manual transmission - removal and separation

1 With the help of an assistant, remove the bonnet as described in Chapter 11.
2 Disconnect and remove the battery and the battery tray.
3 Drain the cooling system.
4 Drain the engine oil, then unscrew and remove the oil filter cartridge.
5 Remove the air cleaner and intake duct.
6 On fuel injection models, depressurise the fuel system and then disconnect all the electrical plugs and fuel connections described in Chapter 3 and paragraphs 6 to 10 in Section 44 in this Chapter. Release the fuel pump relay connector from its bracket.
7 Disconnect the multi-plug and remove the ignition ECU from its bracket. Release the earth cable from behind the bracket.
8 Disconnect the crankshaft sensor wiring plug then undo the two starter motor retaining bolts. Remove the starter, crankshaft sensor bracket (photos).
9 Disconnect the wiring plug at the knock

apply additional sealant to their bolt heads (photo).
10 Liberally lubricate the lips of the crankshaft rear oil seal in the adaptor plate then carefully fit the adaptor plate to the cylinder block (photo) .
11 Refit the retaining bolts and tighten them evenly to the specified torque.
12 Refit the components described in paragraphs 2 to 5 of this Section .

48 Connecting rod big-end bearings and piston rings - renewal

1 These operations will normally be carried out at the time of engine overhaul, but the work may be done without removing the engine from the car where it is necessary to reduce oil consumption and to improve the oil pressure.
2 Refer to Section 45 and remove the sump pan. If new piston rings are being fitted, remove the cylinder head as described in Section 44.
3 Inspect the big-end caps for identification. They should be marked 1 to 4 from the crankshaft pulley and on the side nearest to the oil dipstick guide tube. If not, mark them with a centre-punch or a file.

4 Renewal of the bearing shells and piston ring is as described in Section 16, but ignore the reference to shell coding. As the shells are being renewed with identical ones, the size will be marked on the back of each shell.
5 The compression rings have their upper faces marked TOP.
6 Stagger the piston ring end gaps so that those for the compression rings are at 90° on the non-thrust side of the piston. The end gaps of the oil control rails and expander should be located over the gudgeon pin.
7 Check that with the piston/rod assembly in its bore, the mark on the piston crown which may be FRONT, A or an arrow is pointing to the crankshaft pulley.
8 Refit the sump pan and cylinder head (Sections 45 and 44).

49 Engine/transmission mountings - renewal

1 The mountings may be renewed with the engine/transmission in the car provided the weight of the engine or transmission is taken

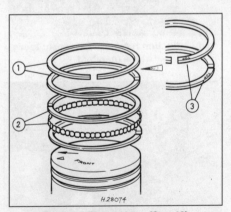

Fig. 1.16 Piston rings (Sec 48)

1 Compression ring markings
2 Compression ring end gaps (90° on non-thrust side of piston)
3 Oil control rails and expander

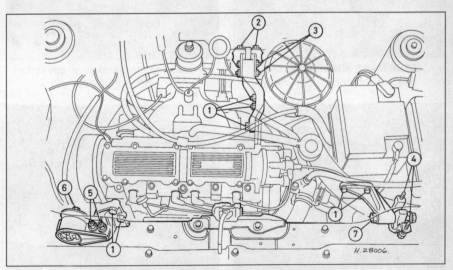

Fig. 1.17 Engine/transmission mountings (Sec 49)

1 to 7 = Bolt tightening sequence

51.8A Crankshaft sensor

51.8B Crankshaft sensor wiring plug

51.9A Knock sensor

sensor on the front face of the cylinder block (photos).

10 Spring back the clip and disconnect the wiring plug at the rear of the alternator.

11 Disconnect the wiring plug from the coolant temperature gauge sender unit in the thermostat housing (photo).

12 Disconnect the inlet manifold induction heater lead at the wiring connector and the two wires at the inlet manifold induction temperature sensor (photo).

13 Disconnect the wire at the oil pressure switch adjacent to the crankshaft pulley (photo).

14 Disconnect the wiring plug at the carburettor stepping motor and the two leads at the fuel shut-off valve solenoid (photo).

15 Release the retaining clip and remove the fuel inlet hose from the fuel pump. Plug the hose after removal.

16 Pull the float chamber vent hose off the carburettor outlet and remove the hose and pipe from the engine (photo).

17 Detach the crankcase breather hoses at the carburettor, oil filter cap and oil separator, then remove the hose assembly.

18 Disconnect the vacuum hose from the inlet manifold banjo union, undo the union bolt and recover the two washers. Place the servo vacuum hose to one side.

19 Disconnect the throttle linkage.

20 Slacken the retaining clips and disconnect the heater hoses at the inlet manifold.

21 Slacken the retaining clips and disconnect the heater hose and radiator bottom hose from the water inlet elbow followed by the expansion tank hose, radiator top hose and heater hose from the water outlet elbow and thermostat housing.

22 Refer to Chapter 5 and detach the clutch cable from the operating lever and gearbox bracket. Disconnect the reverse lamp switch leads (photo).

23 Undo and remove the bolt securing the speedometer cable to the gearbox. Withdraw the cable and pinion assembly and place them aside (photo).

24 Disconnect the gearchange linkage from the transmission.

25 Raise the front of the car and support it securely then remove the two front roadwheels.

26 Disconnect the exhaust downpipes from the manifold.

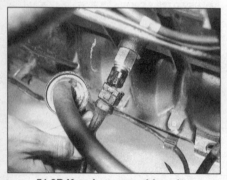

51.9B Knock sensor wiring plug

51.11 Coolant temperature gauge sender unit wiring plug

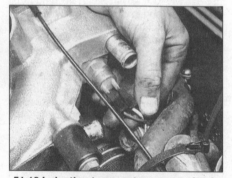

51.12 Induction temperature sensor leads at the manifold

51.13 Oil pressure switch

51.14 Fuel shut-off solenoid

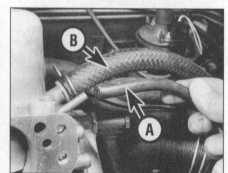

51.16 Float chamber vent hose (A) and crankcase breather hose (B)

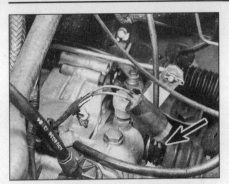

51.22 Reverse lamp switch leads

27 Fit an engine lifting bracket to the extended threads of the cylinder head studs nearest to the distributor cap.
28 Attach a suitable hoist and support the weight of the engine.
29 Place jacks under the front suspension lower suspension (track control) arms.
30 Unscrew the balljoint taper pin nuts and using a suitable splitter tool, disconnect the balljoint from the hub carrier. As they are released, take care that the car is well supported under the body members with safety stands.
31 Remove the splash guard panels.
32 Turn the steering to full right-hand lock and release the inboard end of the right-hand driveshaft by prising with a lever inserted between the transmission housing and the shaft joint.
33 Release the left-hand driveshaft in a similar way after having turned the steering to full left-hand lock.
34 Unbolt the engine rear mounting bracket from the transmission casing.
35 Remove the through-bolt from the right-hand engine mounting and the bolts which hold the mounting bracket to the engine. Remove the mounting.
36 Remove the left-hand mounting from the transmission in a similar way.
37 Lift the engine/transmission slowly to clear the rear mounting bracket and remove the engine compartment.
38 Remove all external dirt by steam cleaning or by using a water soluble solvent.

39 Remove the cover plate from the face of the flywheel housing.
40 Unscrew and remove the flywheel housing to engine connecting bolts and withdraw the transmission from the engine. supporting its weight so that it does not hang upon the input shaft while the shaft is engaged in the hub of the clutch driven plate (photo).

52 Engine/automatic transmission - removal and separation

1 Removal operations are very similar to those described in the preceding Section for cars with manual transmission, but of course ignore reference to the clutch cable and year selector.
2 Select P and release the selector cable trunnion screw and then extract the screws which hold the abutment bracket to the transmission casing.
3 Disconnect the kickdown cable.
4 Carry out the operations described in Section 20, paragraphs 3 to 8.
5 Drain the cooling system and then disconnect the coolant hoses from the fluid cooler.

53 Engine dismantling - general

Refer to Part A, Section 21.

54 Engine ancillary components - removal

If the engine has been removed from the car for major overhaul or repair, the externally-mounted ancillary components given in the following list, should first be removed. Removal is straightforward, but where

necessary reference should be made to the relevant Chapters of the manual as indicated. The removal sequence need not necessarily follow the order given.

Alternator (Chapter 12)
Timing belt covers
Fuel pump (Chapter 3)
Distributor cap and rotor arm (Chapter 4)
Oil filler tube
Thermostat, housing and coolant inlet elbow (Chapter 2)
Alternator mounting bracket
Knock sensor
Crankshaft sensor (Chapter 4)
Spark plugs (Chapter 4)
Inlet and exhaust manifolds and carburettor (Chapter 3)
Clutch and flywheel assembly (Chapter 5)
Coolant pump (Chapter 2) - after removal of the timing belt
Oil filter
Dipstick
Fuel injection equipment (Chapter 3)

1

55 Engine - complete dismantling

1 Remove the timing belt (Section 40).
2 Remove the cylinder head (Section 44).
3 Remove the camshaft and tappets (cam followers) (Section 43).
4 Remove the sump pan (Section 45).
5 Remove the oil pump (Section 46).
6 Remove the transmission adaptor plate (Section 47).
7 Check the big-end caps for identification marks. If necessary use a centre punch on the caps and rods to identify them; mark them 1 to 4 on the dipstick tube side to ensure correct refitting. **Note** that No 1 is nearest to the crankshaft pulley end of the engine (photo).
8 Turn the crankshaft so that No 1 crankpin is at its lowest point. Using a suitable socket, undo the two nuts securing the connecting rod cap to the rod.
9 Withdraw the cap, complete with bearing shell.

51.23 Speedometer drive cable and pinion

51.40 Withdrawing manual transmission from the engine

55.7 Big-end cap and rod match marks

55.14 Main bearing cap and crankcase match marks

55.16 Checking crankshaft endfloat

55.17A Removing crankshaft from crankcase

10 Using the handle of a hammer, carefully push the piston and connecting rod up through the bore and withdraw it from the top of the cylinder block.

11 If there is a severe wear ridge at the top of the cylinder bore it may require removing using a ridge reamer or scraper to enable the piston rings to pass over it.

12 Keep the bearing shells with their cap or rod if the shells are to be used again.

13 Remove the remaining pistons and rods in a similar way.

14 Check the crankcase and main bearing caps for identification marks and if no marks are present, use a centre punch to mark them (photo).

15 Undo the belts securing the main bearing caps and remove the caps, complete with bearing shells.

16 Before removing the crankshaft, check that the endfloat is within the specified limits by inserting feeler blades between No 4 crankshaft web and the thrust washers. If the clearance is not as specified, new thrust washers will be required for reassembly (photo).

17 Lift the crankshaft out of the crankcase then remove the main bearing shell upper halves and the thrust washers. Keep the main bearing shells in order with their respective caps (photos).

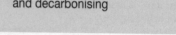

56 Cylinder head - dismantling and decarbonising

1 Remove the exhaust manifolds and carburettor (or fuel injection components).

2 Remove the distributor cap, rotor arm and shield (photos).

3 Remove the thermostat housing and coolant inlet elbow.

4 Remove the camshaft and tappets (cam followers).

5 Removal of the valves, valve grinding procedure and other renovation operations are as described in Section 24 (photos).

55.17B Crankshaft thrust washer showing oil grooves

56.2A Distributor cap and shield

56.2B Removing rotor arm screw

56.5A Valve spring compressed showing split collets

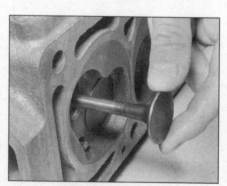

56.5B Removing a valve

56.5C Removing a valve stem oil seal

56.6A Fitting a valve stem oil seal

56.6B Valve spring and cap

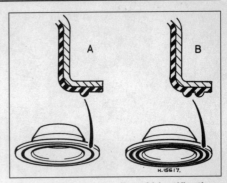

**Fig. 1.18 Valve stem oil seal identification
(Sec 56)**

A *Standard with one flange ring*
B *Oversize with two flange rings*

6 When reassembling note the valve stem oil seal identification ring (Fig. 1.18) (photos).

57 Engine components - examination and renovation

1 All oil seals, gaskets and O-rings should be renewed as a matter of course and also main and big-end shell bearings unless they have had little wear and are in perfect condition.
2 With the engine completely dismantled, clean all the components and examine them for wear. Each part should be checked and where necessary renewed or renovated, as described in Section 25, but with the following differences.

Oil pump

3 Remove the oil filter from the pump housing if not already done.
4 Undo the six screws and lift off the pump backplate (photo).
5 Lift out the two rotors from the pump body (photo).
6 Unscrew the pressure relief valve cap using a wide-bladed tool and remove the spring and plunger (photos).
7 Clean all the parts in paraffin or a suitable solvent and dry with a lint-free cloth. Examine the components for signs of scoring, wear ridges or other damage and renew the pump as a complete assembly if any of these conditions are apparent.
8 If the pump is satisfactory so far, refit the

rotors to the pump body and check the rotor lobe clearance, outer rotor-to-body clearance and the outer rotor endfloat using feeler gauges and a straight-edge (photos) .
9 Renew the pump if any of the clearances are outside the figures given in the Specifications.
10 If the pump is serviceable, renew the crankshaft front oil seal in the pump housing. Tap the old seal out from the inside using a punch and fit a new seal using a tube, block of wood or socket by tapping it squarely into the housing (photos).
11 Lubricate the pressure relief valve plunger

57.4 Oil pump backplate screws

57.5 Oil pump rotors

57.6A Unscrewing oil pump pressure relief valve cap

57.6B Relief valve components

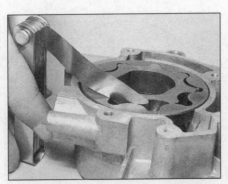

57.8A Checking the oil pump rotor lobe clearance

57.8B Checking rotor to body clearance

57.8C Checking oil pump rotor endfloat

57.10A Crankshaft front oil seal in oil pump body

57.10B Fitting a new seal to the oil pump

with clean engine oil and refit plunger followed by the spring and cap. Tighten the cap securely.

12 Liberally lubricate the two rotors with clean engine oil and place them in position in the pump housing.

13 Refit the pump backplate and secure with the six screws.

Camshaft and tappets (cam followers)

14 The camshaft itself should show no signs of wear, but if very slight score marks on the cams are noticed, they can be removed by gently rubbing down with very fine emery cloth or an oilstone. The greatest care must be taken to keep the cam profiles smooth.

15 Carefully examine the camshaft bearing surfaces for wear and, if evident, the camshaft must be renewed.

16 Check the fit of the camshaft in the carrier and if excessive bearing journal clearance is apparent, a new carrier must be obtained. The camshaft bearings run directly in the machined journals of the carrier; renewable bearings are not used.

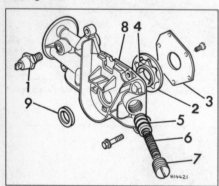

Fig. 1.19 Oil pump (Sec 57)

1 Oil pressure switch
2 Outer rotor
3 Pump backplate
4 Inner rotor
5 Pressure relief valve plunger
6 Pressure relief valve spring
7 Pressure relief valve cap
8 Oil pump body
9 Crankshaft front oil seal

17 The faces of the tappet buckets which bear on the camshaft lobes should exhibit no signs of pitting, scoring, cracks or other forms of wear and should be a smooth sliding fit in the carrier. Slight scuffing and blackening of the tappet bucket sides is normal, providing this is not accompanied by scoring or wear ridges.

18 The small shims found inside the tappet bucket should show no signs of indentation from contact with the valve stem. Renew the shim with one of an identical size if wear has taken place. Make sure that each shim is kept with its tappet bucket and not interchanged.

Crankshaft and main bearings

19 The crankshaft may be reground and undersize bearings fitted as given in the Specifications.

58 Engine reassembly - general

1 To ensure maximum life with minimum trouble from a rebuilt engine, not only must everything be correctly assembled, but it must also be spotlessly clean. All oilways must be clear, and locking washers and spring washers must be fitted where indicated. Oil all bearings and other working surfaces thoroughly with engine oil during assembly.

2 Before assembly begins, renew any bolts or studs with damaged threads.

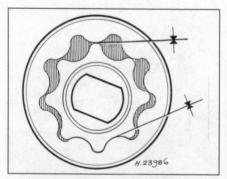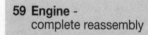

Fig. 1.20 Oil pump lobe clearance measuring point (Sec 57)

3 Gather together a torque wrench, oil can, clean rags and a set of engine gaskets and oil seals, together with a new oil filter.

4 A tube of Loctite 574 sealant will be required for the camshaft carrier to cylinder head joint face and an RTV silicone sealant for the remainder of the joint faces that do not have gaskets. These compounds, together with conventional gasket jointing compound, are available from BL dealers or motor factors.

59 Engine - complete reassembly

1 Clean the backs of the bearing shells and the bearing recesses in both the cylinder block and main bearing caps.

2 Press the main bearing shells into the cylinder block and caps and oil them liberally (photo).

3 Using a little grease, stick the thrust washers to each side of No 4 main bearing with their oilways facing away from the bearing.

4 Lower the crankshaft into position, then fit the main bearing caps in their previously noted locations (photo).

5 Insert and tighten evenly the main bearing cap bolts to the specified torque. Check that the crankshaft rotates freely, then check that the endfloat is within the specified limits by inserting a feeler blade between the crankshaft web and the thrust washers.

6 Clean the backs of the bearing shells and

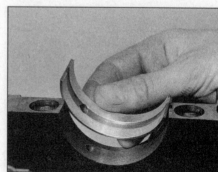

59.2 Crankcase main bearing shell

59.4 Fitting front main bearing cap

59.8A Using piston ring compressor to fit piston/connecting rod

59.8B Piston crown marking

the recesses in the connecting rods and big-end caps.

7 Fit the big-end bearing shells into their connecting rod and cap locations and oil them liberally.

8 Position a piston ring compressor around No 1 piston then insert the connecting rod and piston into No 1 cylinder. With No 1 crankpin at its lowest point, drive the piston carefully into the cylinder with the wooden handle of a hammer, and at the same time guide the connecting rod onto the crankpin. Make sure that the mark FRONT, A or an arrow on the piston crown is towards the crankshaft pulley end of the engine (photo).

9 Fit the big-end cap in its previously noted position, then screw on the nuts and tighten them to the specified torque (photos).

10 Check that the crankshaft turns freely.

11 Repeat the procedures given in paragraphs 3 to 5 for No 4 piston, then turn the crankshaft through half a turn and repeat the procedure on No 2 and No 3 piston.

12 Refit the sump and oil pick-up tube, and the cylinder head with reference to the relevant Sections and Chapters of this manual.

13 Refit the transmission adaptor plate (Section 47).

14 Refit the oil pump (Section 46).

15 Refit the sump pan (Section 45).

16 Refit the camshaft and tappets (cam followers) (Section 43).

17 Refit the cylinder head (Section 44).

18 Refit and adjust the timing belt (Sections 39, 40).

19 Adjust the valve clearances (Section 38).

60 Engine ancillary components - refitting

Reverse the removal operations for the components listed in Section 54.

61 Engine/manual transmission - reconnection and refitting

1 The operations are a reversal of those for removal and separation described in Section 51, but observe the following special points.

2 Once the engine/transmission is lowered into position, fit the left-hand mounting and the right-hand mounting. Tighten the left-hand bracket to gearbox bolts. Do not tighten the right-hand mounting to engine bracket or left-hand mounting to valance bolts nor the mounting through-bolts.

3 Check the alignment of the rear mounting bracket to the gearbox, adjusting the height of the engine/transmission as necessary, and then tighten the bracket to transmission bolts.

4 Tighten the left-hand and right-hand mounting through-bolts.

5 Check the rear mounting rubber. If it is distorted forwards or rearwards, slacken the bracket to mounting bolts, re-align the mounting rubbers and tighten the bolts.

6 Finally tighten the right-hand mounting to

engine nuts and the left-hand mounting to valance bolts.

7 Make sure that the driveshaft circlips are positively engaged in the differential side gears.

8 Refill the cooling system with antifreeze mixture and the engine with oil (photo).

62 Engine/automatic transmission - reconnection and refitting

1 Reverse the removal and separation operations described in Section 52 and Section 20 paragraphs 3 to 8.

2 When connecting the selector cable, set the hand control lever in P and press the lever on the transmission casing fully downwards (anti-clockwise). Insert the selector cable into the trunnion and secure the support bracket to the transmission casing. Tighten the trunnion screw. Check that the starter motor only operates in N or P selector positions.

3 Reconnect and adjust (Chapter 7) the kickdown cable.

4 Reconnect the coolant hoses to the fluid cooler.

5 Check and top up the transmission fluid.

63 Initial start-up after major overhaul

Refer to Part A, Section 31.

59.9A Fitting a big-end cap

59.9B Tightening big-end cap nuts

61.8 Refilling the engine with oil

Fault finding - all engines

Engine will not crank or cranks very slowly
- [ ] Discharged battery
- [ ] Poor battery connections
- [ ] Starter motor fault

Engine cranks but will not start
- [ ] No fuel
- [ ] Ignition circuit fault
- [ ] Fuel system fault
- [ ] Leak in PCV lines
- [ ] Leak in intake manifold
- [ ] Leak in hot idle compensator line

Engine stalls or rough idle
- [ ] Leak in PCV line
- [ ] Leak in intake manifold
- [ ] Leak in hot idle compensator line
- [ ] Very weak mixture
- [ ] Incorrect valve clearances

Hesitation or poor acceleration
- [ ] Incorrectly adjusted mixture
- [ ] Clogged air cleaner
- [ ] Incorrect valve clearances

Excessive oil consumption
- [ ] Worn piston rings or cylinder bores
- [ ] Worn oil seals or leaking gaskets

Excessive mechanical noise from engine
- [ ] Incorrect valve clearances
- [ ] General internal wear

Pinking on acceleration
- [ ] Ignition too advanced
- [ ] Fuel octane too low
- [ ] Overheating
- [ ] Carbon build up in engine
- [ ] Excessive oil vapour being drawn into crankcase breather system
- [ ] Upper cylinder lubricant being used
- [ ] Weak mixture

Refer also to Fault finding in Chapters 3 and 4 as 1.6 models are equipped with programmed electronic ignition and some models have a fuel injection system.

Chapter 2
Cooling, heating and air conditioning systems

Contents

Degrees of difficulty

Easy, suitable for novice with little experience	Fairly easy, suitable for beginner with some experience	Fairly difficult, suitable for competent DIY mechanic	Difficult, suitable for experienced DIY mechanic 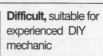	Very difficult, suitable for expert DIY or professional 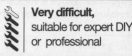

Specifications

System type .... Front mounted radiator, with expansion tank, timing belt driven coolant pump and electric fan. Fresh air heater/ventilation with air conditioner option on certain models

Pressure cap rating (1.3 models) .... 0.7 to 0.9 bar (11 to 14 lbf/in²)

Pressure cap rating (1.6 models) .... 1.035 bar (15 lbf/in²)

Thermostat (1.3 models)
Starts to open .... 76 to 78°C (169 to 173°F)
Fully open .... 91°C (196°F)
Valve lift .... 8.0 mm (0.31 in)

Thermostat (1.6 models)
Starts to open .... 76 to 80°C (169 to 176°F)
Fully open .... 88°C (190°F)
Valve lift .... 8.0 mm (0.32 in)

Fan thermoswitch
Cuts in .... 88.5 to 91.5°C (191 to 196°F)
Cuts out .... 82.0 to 88.0°C (180 to 190°F)

Coolant capacity
1.3 models up to VIN 800 000/1985 model year .... 4.5 litre (8.0 pint)
1.3 models from VIN 800 000/1985 model year .... 6.4 litre (11.0 pint)
1.6 models .... 6.4 litre (11.0 pint)

Coolant type/specification .... Soft water and ethylene glycol based antifreeze

Torque wrench settings

	Nm	lbf ft
1.3 models		
Timing belt tensioner bolt	45	33
Coolant temperature transmitter	28	20
Crankshaft pulley bolt	45	33
Cylinder block drain plug	32	23
Thermostatic switch	23	17
Thermostat housing bolts	12	9
Coolant pump bolts	12	9
1.6 models		
Thermostat housing	18	13
Coolant pump bolts	12	9
Coolant temperature transmitter	15	11
Compressor mounting bolts	45	33
Drivebelt tensioner puller nut	45	33
Pipe unions:		
5/8 in	32	23
1/2 in	22	16
3/8 in	17	12

1 Description and operation

1 The type of cooling system used will depend upon the engine and date of production.

1.3 models up to VIN 800 000/1985 model year

2 The system employs a vertical flow radiator with pressure cap, a coolant pump driven by the timing belt and a thermostat.

3 Circulation is by thermosyphon action and coolant pump impeller assistance.

4 The radiator is cooled by the ram effect of air when the car is in forward motion and has supplementary cooling by an electric fan which is actuated by a thermostatic switch.

5 The expansion tank, although not pressurised, accepts displaced coolant which is forced out past the radiator drawn back into the system as it cools. A vacuum is prevented from occurring by the opening of the vacuum valve in the radiator cap.

1.3 models from VIN 800 000/ 1985 model year and all 1.6 models

6 On these models, a crossflow aluminium radiator is fitted with an expansion tank to which is fitted a pressure cap.

7 A coolant pump is driven by the timing belt and a thermostat is incorporated in the system.

8 An electric radiator cooling fan is fitted which is controlled by a thermostatic switch.

Operation

9 On models with a vertical flow radiator the system operates in the following way. While the engine is warming up the thermostat is shut with the bypass valve open to allow coolant to circulate through the coolant pump to the cylinder block and inlet manifold. When the engine has warmed up, the thermostat opens and the bypass valve closes. Coolant is then drawn from the radiator bottom tank and circulates through the thermostat to the coolant pump and cylinder block.

10 On models with a crossflow radiator, coolant is drawn from the base of the left-hand radiator tank then passes through the coolant pump to the cylinder block. As the engine temperature increases and the thermostat opens, the coolant flows to the radiator right-hand tank and then across the radiator matrix to the left-hand tank.

11 As the coolant temperature rises, so it expands and the level in the expansion tank rises. When the system cools, a partial vacuum is created, but a valve in the expansion tank cap allows atmospheric pressure to enter thus forcing the coolant back into the system.

12 On all models a heater and ventilation system of fresh air type is fitted.

13 On certain models an air conditioner can be specified as a factory-fitted option.

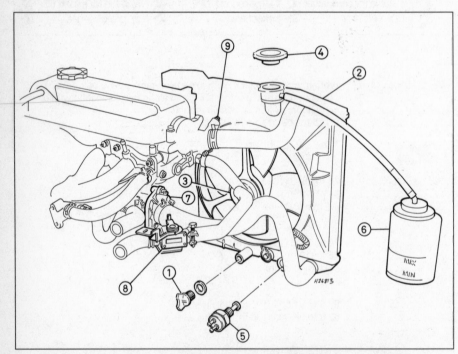

Fig. 2.1 Cooling system (1.3 models up to VIN 800 000/1985 model year) (Sec 1)

1 Radiator drain plug	4 Pressure cap	7 Thermostat housing
2 Radiator	5 Thermostatic (fan) switch	8 Coolant flow control valve
3 Fan motor	6 Expansion tank	9 Bleed screw

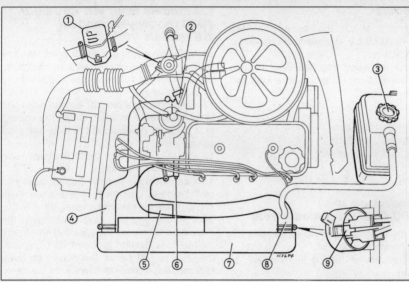

Fig. 2.2 Cooling system (1.3 models from VIN 800 000/1985 model year) (Sec 1)

1 Coolant flow control valve
2 Thermostat housing
3 Expansion tank cap
4 Radiator bottom hose
5 Fan motor
6 Bleed screw
7 Radiator
8 Radiator top hose
9 Fan thermostatic switch

Fig. 2.3 Cooling system (1.6 models with carburettor) (Sec 1)

1 Heater connection
2 Coolant pump
3 Fan thermostatic switch
4 Expansion tank filler cap
5 Radiator top hose
6 Radiator
7 Fan, motor and cowl
8 Thermostat housing

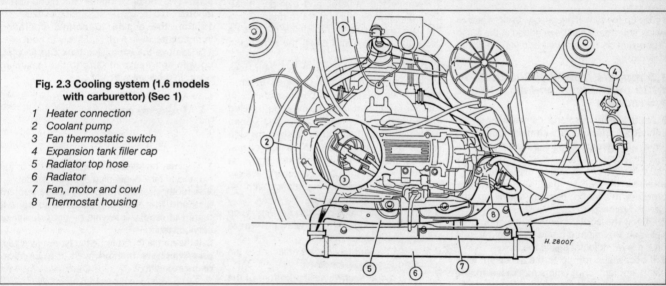

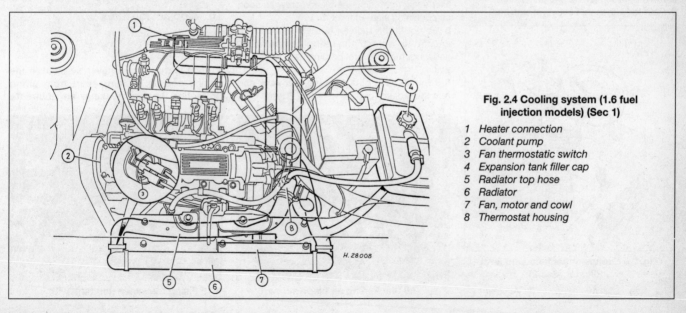

Fig. 2.4 Cooling system (1.6 fuel injection models) (Sec 1)

1 Heater connection
2 Coolant pump
3 Fan thermostatic switch
4 Expansion tank filler cap
5 Radiator top hose
6 Radiator
7 Fan, motor and cowl
8 Thermostat housing

2 Maintenance

General

1 As all models are fitted with a cooling system expansion tank, in theory, topping up should never be required.

2 If anything more than very occasional additions of coolant are required, check for a leak, probably at a hose clip. If no external leaks are evident, suspect an internal leak from a faulty cylinder head gasket. Water may show on the engine oil dipstick.

1.3 models up to VIN 800 000/1985 model year

3 At the weekly maintenance check, open the bonnet and check the coolant level in the expansion tank. This should be at or near the MAX mark.

4 Top up the tank if necessary, using water to which anti-freeze has been added in the same proportion as the original coolant. Refit the tank cap.

1.3 models from VIN 800 000/ 1985 model year and all 1.6 models

5 At the weekly maintenance check, open the bonnet and preferably with the engine cold, remove the expansion tank pressure cap.

6 If the engine is hot, cover the cap with a cloth to prevent escaping steam scalding. Unscrew the cap to the first stop to allow pressure to escape, depress again, turn the cap and remove it.

7 Check the coolant level which should be between the minimum and maximum points on the level indicator inside the tank.

8 If necessary, top up to the maximum level using coolant containing antifreeze in the same proportion as the original mixture.

9 Refit the expansion tank pressure cap.

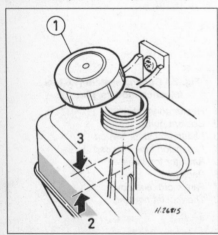

Fig. 2.5 Expansion tank coolant level indicator (Sec 2)

1 Cap   2 Minimum   3 Maximum

All models

10 Regularly check the security of the coolant hose clips and inspect the hoses for deterioration.

11 At the specified intervals (see Routine Maintenance) check the drivebelt tension and renew the coolant.

3 Cooling system - draining and refilling

1.3 models up to VIN 800 000/1985 model year

1 With the cooling system cold, remove the radiator pressure cap.

2 Set the heater temperature lever to maximum.

3 Remove the radiator and cylinder block drain plugs, allow the coolant to drain. Catch the coolant in a suitable receptacle if it is to be used again. Drain and clean the expansion tank.

4 If the cooling system has been well maintained, with regular changes of anti-freeze, then there should be no evidence of rust or sediment and it may be refilled immediately. If the system has been neglected, then it should be flushed through with a cold water hose. In severe cases, reverse flushing of the radiator may be required or even the use of a cooling system cleanser used strictly in accordance with the manufacturer's instructions.

5 Refit the drain plugs and refill the expansion tank to the maximum mark with anti-freeze mixture (see Section 5).

6 Slacken the air bleed screw adjacent to the coolant outlet elbow (photo) .

7 Fill the radiator slowly to the bottom of the filler neck, tightening the bleed screw as soon as coolant is ejected from it.

8 Do not fit the radiator cap yet, but run the engine to normal operating temperature, allowing the electric cooling fan to cut in twice.

9 Top up to the bottom of the filler neck and refit the radiator cap.

3.6 Slackening air bleed screw

1.3 models from VIN 800 000/ 1985 model year and all 1.6 models

10 With the cooling system cold, set the heater temperature control lever to maximum.

11 Unscrew and remove the cap from the expansion tank.

12 Disconnect the radiator bottom hose and allow the coolant to drain. Catch the coolant in a suitable receptacle if it is to be used again.

13 Remove, drain and clean the expansion tank. Refer to paragraph 4.

14 Reconnect the radiator bottom hose and on 1.3 models, unscrew the bleed screw. Refit and connect the expansion tank.

15 Fill the system slowly through the expansion tank using the specified anti-freeze mixture (see Section 5). Continue filling until the level is just below the maximum mark (1.6 models) or coolant flows from the bleed screw (1.3 models). Tighten the bleed screw (photo).

16 Run the engine to normal operating temperature, switch off and allow to cool.

17 Remove the expansion tank cap and top up with anti-freeze mixture to the maximum point on the level indicator.

4 Pressure cap

1 This may be fitted to either the radiator or the expansion tank depending upon the model.

2 A faulty pressure cap can cause coolant loss and it is a wise precaution to have it tested at regular intervals by your dealer or service station .

3 If the cap is found to be faulty, renew it with one which is marked with the identical pressure rating.

5 Coolant mixtures

1 Plain water should never be used in the engine cooling system. Apart from giving protection against freezing, an antifreeze

3.15 Filling the expansion tank with coolant

6.3A Removing thermostat housing cover

6.3B Removing thermostat

mixture protects the engine internal surfaces and components against corrosion. This is especially important in respect of the 1.3 all alloy engine.

2 Always use a top quality glycol based antifreeze which is suitable for mixed metal engines.

3 Ideally, a 50% mixture of antifreeze and soft or demineralised water should be used to maintain protection against freezing and corrosion. On no account use less than 30% antifreeze.

4 Renew the coolant at the specified intervals as the inhibitors contained in the antifreeze gradually lose their effectiveness.

5 Even when operating in climates where antifreeze is not necessary, never use plain water, but add a corrosion inhibitor to it.

6 Thermostat - removal, testing and refitting

1.3 models

1 Remove the radiator filler cap, taking the necessary precautions (see Section 2) if the engine is hot.

2 Drain the cooling system as described in Section 3.

3 Remove the thermostat cover and the thermostat. Extract the seal (photos).

4 To check the thermostat, its valve plate should be fully closed when cold. Now suspend the thermostat in a saucepan of water which is being heated. Prevent the thermostat from contacting the container which is being heated. Use a thermometer to check that the thermostat valve plate begins to open and is fully open at the specified temperature levels.

5 If the thermostat does not perform correctly, fit a new one.

6 Fit the thermostat using a new seal and make sure that the jiggle pin is uppermost. Bolt on the thermostat housing cover.

7 Fill the cooling system as previously described in Section 3.

1.6 models

8 The operations are very similar to those just

described for 1.3 models, but note that the opening temperatures differ slightly.

9 Always use a new gasket on clean mating surfaces when refitting the thermostat housing cover.

7 Radiator cooling fan (1.3 up to VIN 800 000/1985) - removal and refitting

The fan and motor can only be removed after the radiator has been withdrawn as described in Section 10 (photo).

8 Radiator cooling fan (1.3 from VIN 800 000/1985 and all 1.6) - removal and refitting

1 Disconnect the battery.

2 Unscrew the lower screw from the bonnet lock platform support.

3 Disconnect the wiring plug from the fan motor.

4 Unscrew the three retaining nuts and release the cowl from the radiator.

5 Withdraw the fan/cowl assembly from the engine compartment.

6 To dismantle the fan, extract the circlip and pull the fan hub from the motor shaft. The motor can be separated from the cowl after drilling out the rivets.

7 Reassembly will necessitate re-riveting the motor to the cowl. Refitting is a reversal of removal.

7.1 Radiator removed (early 1.3 model)

9 Fan thermostatic switch - testing, removal and refitting

1.3 models up to VIN 800 000/1985 model year

1 If there is any doubt about the radiator cooling fan cutting in when the coolant temperature is high, test in the following way.

2 Disconnect the leads from the thermostatic switch which is screwed into the radiator bottom tank.

3 Join the leads together and switch on the ignition. If the fan operates then the switch is faulty and must be renewed. To do this, drain the cooling system and unscrew the switch. Use a new sealing washer when refitting.

4 If as a result of the test, the motor still does not operate, first check for a blown fuse or a broken lead, otherwise the motor must be faulty and it should be renewed or repaired.

1.3 models from VIN 800 000/ 1985 model year and all 1.6 models

5 The testing operations are very similar to those just described for earlier 1.3 models but note that the switch is retained to the radiator by means of a swivel type lockplate. Always use a new sealing washer when refitting the switch.

10 Radiator (1.3 models up to VIN 800 000/1985) - removal, repair and refitting

1 Drain the cooling system as described in Section 3.

2 Disconnect the leads from the cooling fan motor and the thermostatic switch (photo).

3 Place the car over an inspection pit or raise the front end on stands, support it securely and then remove the undershield.

10.2 Cooling fan and thermostatic switch connections

2

10.4 Expansion tank hose at radiator

10.7 Removing bonnet release catch panel

10.8 Removing the radiator

4 Disconnect the expansion tank and radiator coolant hoses (photo).

5 On cars fitted with automatic transmission, disconnect the transmission fluid (cooler) pipes from the unions on the radiator side tank and plug or cap them to prevent the entry of dirt.

6 Unscrew and remove the radiator mounting bolts from the bonnet release catch panel. Also remove the lower bolt from the bonnet release catch.

7 Unscrew and remove the bolts which hold the release catch panel to the bonnet platform and move the panel aside. Remove the centre support (photo).

8 Release the radiator from the lower platform and withdraw the radiator complete with fan and cowl from the car (photo).

9 The radiator cannot be satisfactorily repaired by the home mechanic and any work should be left to specialists or an exchange unit obtained. Before parting with the old radiator remove the fan and cowling thermostatic switch, radiator mounting blocks and filler neck and cap.

10 Refitting is a reversal of removal, but use new O-ring seals at the filler neck and the thermostatic switch. Refill the cooling system as described in Section 3.

11 On cars with automatic transmission, check the transmission fluid level and top up if necessary.

11 Radiator (1.3 from VIN 800 000/1985 and all 1.6) - removal, repair and refitting

1 Disconnect the battery.

2 Drain the cooling system as previously described in Section 3.

3 Remove the radiator grille as described in Chapter 11.

4 Unscrew the bolts which hold the radiator top mounting brackets to the bonnet lock platform.

5 Remove the top rail panel.

6 On 1.6 models, remove the bolt from the bonnet lock support strut.

7 Disconnect the radiator hoses and the

electrical leads from the thermostatic switch and the cooling fan motor.

8 On 1.3 models fitted with automatic transmission, disconnect the fluid cooler hoses and plug them.

9 Remove the radiator top mounting brackets. If the car is equipped with an air conditioner, take care not to damage the condenser.

10 Lift out the radiator assembly.

11 The radiator cannot be satisfactorily repaired by the home mechanic and any work should be left to specialists or an exchange unit obtained. Before parting with the old radiator, remove the fan and cowling, the thermostatic switch, top mounting brackets and flexible blocks.

12 Refitting is a reversal of removal. Use a new seal at the thermostatic switch.

13 Refill the cooling system as described in Section 3.

14 On 1.3 models fitted with automatic transmission, check and top up the transmission fluid.

12 Drivebelts

1 The coolant pump is driven by the toothed timing belt and tensioning is covered in Section 13 and 14.

2 Tensioning and renewal of the Vee drivebelt for the alternator is described in Chapter 12.

3 Tensioning and renewal of the Vee drivebelt for the air conditioner compressor is described in Section 24 of this Chapter.

13 Coolant pump (1.3 models) - removal and refitting

1 Disconnect the battery.

2 Drain the cooling system as described in Section 3.

3 Refer to Chapter 12 and remove the alternator drivebelt.

4 Remove the air cleaner and the rocker cover. Also remove the left-hand roadwheel

and splash panel, having raised the car and supported it securely.

5 Apply a spanner to the crankshaft pulley bolt and turn the crankshaft anti-clockwise until the UP mark on the camshaft pulley is uppermost and the timing marks on the camshaft pulley rear face are aligned with the surface of the cylinder head.

6 Unscrew the crankshaft pulley bolt and withdraw the pulley. In order to prevent the crankshaft from rotating while the bolt is being unscrewed, engage a low gear and have an assistant apply the footbrake hard. Alternatively, remove the starter motor and jam the flywheel teeth with a suitable tool.

7 Unbolt and remove the two sections of the timing belt cover.

8 Slacken the belt tensioner bolt, retract the tensioner and re-tighten the bolt.

9 Mark the rotational direction of the timing belt and slip it from the sprockets together with the belt guide plate.

10 Do not rotate the camshaft or crankshaft while the belt is off.

11 Unbolt and remove the coolant pump and discard the O-ring seal.

12 Repair of the coolant pump is not possible and if the pump is leaking or faulty, it must be renewed.

13 Bolt the new pump into position using a new O-ring seal (photos).

14 Check that the camshaft sprocket timing marks are still in alignment with the cylinder head. Also, by temporarily refitting the belt lower cover and pulley, check that the

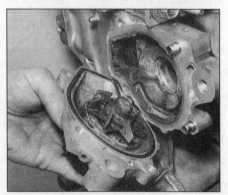

13.13A Fitting coolant pump

13.13B Tightening coolant pump bolts

crankshaft pulley timing marks are in alignment.

15 Fit the timing belt in its original rotational direction.

16 Fit the timing belt guide plate (convex side to belt) and the belt lower cover.

17 Fit the crankshaft pulley and bolt. Hold the crankshaft against rotation as previously described while the bolt is tightened to the specified torque.

18 Tension the belt by releasing the tensioner bolt and then turning the crankshaft pulley in an anti-clockwise direction so that the camshaft sprocket moves through three teeth. Tighten the tensioner bolt to the specified torque.

19 Fit the belt upper cover and rocker cover.

20 Refit and tension the alternator drivebelt.

21 Refit the air cleaner and reconnect the battery.

22 Refill the cooling system.

23 Refit the roadwheel and splash panel.

14 Coolant pump (1.6 models) - removal and refitting

1 Disconnect the battery.

2 Drain the cooling system as previously described.

3 Unbolt and remove both sections of the timing belt cover.

4 Apply a spanner to the crankshaft pulley bolt and turn the crankshaft until the timing mark on the rear face of the camshaft sprocket is in alignment with the notches on the camshaft carrier and the crankshaft pulley. The TDC notch is aligned with the cast mark on the oil pump.

5 Unbolt and remove the timing belt tensioner.

6 Move the timing belt aside and unbolt and remove the coolant pump,

7 Clean off all traces of dirt and sealant from the pump mounting face of the engine.

8 The coolant pump cannot be repaired and if it is leaking or faulty it must be renewed.

9 Apply an even bead of RTV type sealant (instant gasket) around the pump mounting face on the engine and bolt the new coolant pump into position. Tighten the bolts to the specified torque.

10 Check that the camshaft and crankshaft timing marks are still in alignment and then bolt the tensioner into position, but with the bolts finger tight.

11 Engage a suitable torque wrench with 3/8 in (9.5 mm) adaptor in the square hole of the tensioner plate, apply the specified torque of 20 Nm (15 lbf ft) and tighten the tensioner bolts while holding the applied torque.

12 Fit the timing belt covers, refill the cooling system and reconnect the battery.

15 Heating and ventilation system - description

1 The system consists of a heater matrix inside a casing, a three-speed blower and a manually-operated control unit, together with all the necessary ducting and outlet grilles. On 1.3 models, a coolant flow control valve is included in the system.

2 Fresh, outside air enters the heater casing through the grille at the base of the windscreen and passes over the matrix to either absorb heat, or not, according to the control valve setting. The air is then ducted as required according to the setting of the distribution levers on the control panel.

3 The blower motor can be set to either recirculate air inside the car or to boost the volume of outside air passing through the heater.

4 Stale air from the car interior is extracted through grilles at each side of the rear window (photo).

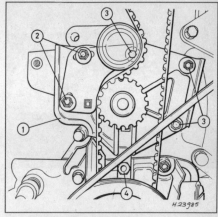

Fig. 2.6 Coolant pump bolts (1.6 models) (Sec 14)

1 Coolant pump   3 Coolant pump bolts
2 Belt tensioner bolts   4 Clamp plate

15.4 Air extraction grille

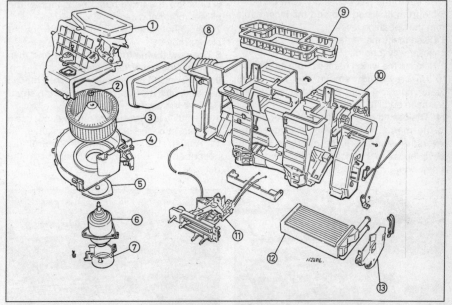

Fig. 2.7 Heater unit (Sec 15)

1 Blower casing	6 Blower motor	10 Heater casing
2 Fan fixing nut	7 Blower motor cover	11 Control unit
3 Fan	8 Duct	12 Matrix
4 Fan casing	9 Duct joint	13 Matrix cover
5 Gasket		

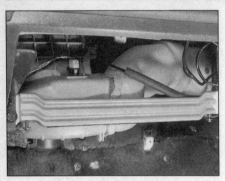

16.3 Glovebox frame

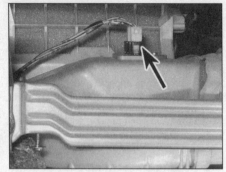

16.6 Heater blower motor plug

16.8 Heater control cables

16 Heater - removal and refitting

1 Disconnect the battery.
2 Drain the cooling system (Section 3).
3 Refer to Chapter 11 and remove the facia lower access panel, glovebox and frame and the facia panel (photo).
4 Working within the engine compartment, disconnect the heater hoses at the bulkhead.
5 Remove the nut from the large stud in the centre of the engine compartment rear bulkhead.
6 Carefully prise out the plastic pins which hold the air duct to the blower motor and heater casings and withdraw the air duct. Disconnect the blower motor wiring plug (photo).
7 Release the recirculation control outer cable from its fixing clip and the inner cable from the operating lever.
8 Disconnect the remaining control cables in a similar way (photo).
9 Release the wiring harness from its clip.
10 Unscrew and remove the two upper heater mounting bolts, pull the heater from the bulkhead and lift it away.
11 The casing may be dismantled for access to the matrix. If the matrix is clogged, try reverse flushing it. If the matrix is leaking, leave repairs to a specialist or exchange it for a new one.

12 Refitting is a reversal of removal. Adjust the control cables as described in Section 21.
13 Refill the cooling system, reconnect the battery.

17 Heater blower - removal and refitting

1 Disconnect the battery.
2 Refer to Chapter 11 and remove the glovebox and frame.
3 Carefully prise out the plastic pins which hold the air duct to the blower motor and heater casings, withdraw the air duct.
4 Disconnect the multi-plugs from the motor casings and the blower motor.
5 Disconnect the recirculation control cable.
6 Unscrew the three nuts and withdraw the blower motor and casing.
7 Disconnect the corrugated hose from the blower motor.
8 Unscrew the motor cover screws and then withdraw the motor/fan assembly.
9 If dismantling is necessary, unscrew the fan nut and pull the fan from the motor shaft. Retrieve the washer.
10 Refitting is a reversal of removal, but use a new gasket on the motor mounting flange.
11 Adjust the recirculation control as described in Section 21. Reconnect the battery.

18 Heater control panel - removal and refitting

1 Disconnect the battery.
2 Refer to Chapter 11 and remove the glovebox frame and the facia lower access panel.
3 Release the steering column upper mounting bracket and lower clamp plate and lower the column.
4 Extract the choke knob fixing screw and pull off the knob.
5 Unscrew the choke control bezel nut and release the choke control from the facia panel.
6 Prise the knobs from the blower motor and heater controls (photo).
7 Prise out the heater control escutcheon plate (photo).
8 Refer to Chapter 12 and remove the radio.
9 Unscrew the nut and release the blower motor switch from the control unit panel.
10 Release the recirculation control cable from the blower motor casing and the control arm.
11 Disconnect the other control cables in a similar way.
12 Extract the heater control panel fixing screws, withdraw the panel and disconnect the multi-plug from the rear of the panel (photo).
13 Refitting is a reversal of removal. Adjust the control cables as described in Section 21.
14 Reconnect the battery.

18.6 Pulling off heater control knob

18.7 Heater control escutcheon plate

18.12 Heater control panel screws (arrowed)

20.2 Heater coolant control valve

19 Blower motor switch - removal and refitting

1 Remove the control panel as described in the preceding Section.
2 Disconnect the leads and remove the switch.
3 Refitting is a reversal of removal.

20 Coolant flow control valve (1.3 models) - removal and refitting

1 Drain the cooling system.
2 Remove the plastic cover from the coolant control valve (photo).
3 Disconnect the cable from the valve lever.
4 Disconnect the hoses from the valve.
5 Extract the fixing screws and remove the valve from its mounting bracket.
6 Refitting is a reversal of removal.
7 Refill the cooling system.

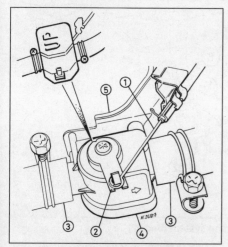

Fig. 2.8 Coolant flow control valve (1.3 models) (Sec 20)

1 Control cable   4 Valve
2 Operating lever 5 Mounting bracket
3 Heater hoses

21 Heater control rods and cables - removal, refitting and adjustment

1 The removal and refitting of all rods and cables is simply a matter of unclipping and releasing from the control lever and operating arm.
2 It is important to adjust each control rod or cable carefully in the following way if it has been disturbed or operation is incorrect.

Recirculation control cable

3 With the glovebox and frame removed (Chapter 11) to give access to the cable, disconnect the inner cable from the lever on the heater.
4 Set the facia recirculation hand control lever fully to the left and the lever on the heater fully towards the bulkhead.
5 Re-set the position of the outer cable in its clip so that the inner cable eye will drop over the lever spigot at the heater without any need to adjust either lever.

6 Check that the cable operates over its full range and the flap valve opens and closes correctly.
7 Refit the glovebox and frame.

Temperature control cable

8 Disconnect the battery and remove the facia lower access panel.
9 Release the inner cable from the spigot on the intermediate lever.
10 Move the temperature control hand lever to COLD.
11 Release the heater flap control rod from its clip on the intermediate lever and then pull the spigot on the lever fully towards the rear.
12 Adjust the position of the temperature control outer cable in its securing clip until the inner cable eye will drop over the spigot on the intermediate lever without having to move the position of either lever.
13 On 1.3 models, disconnect the coolant flow valve cable from the spigot on the flap control arm and push the arm fully towards the bulkhead.
14 Fix the heater flap control rod to the clip on the intermediate lever.

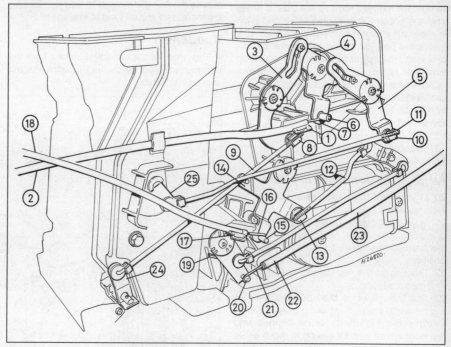

Fig. 2.9 Heater control rods and cables (Sec 21)

1 Air distribution control outer cable clip
2 Air distribution control outer cable
3 Rear intermediate lever
4 Operating lever
5 Front intermediate lever
6 Air distribution control operating lever spigot
7 Air distribution control inner cable
8 Air distribution flap control rod clip
9 Air distribution flap control rod
10 Air distribution flap control rod clip
11 Air distribution flap control rod
12 Heater flap control rod

13 Heater flap control rod clip
14 Intermediate lever
15 Intermediate lever spigot
16 Temperature control inner cable
17 Temperature control inner cable clip
18 Temperature control outer cable
19 Heater flap control arm
20 Control arm spigot
21 Heater valve inner cable (1.3 models)
22 Outer cable clip (1.3 models)
23 Heater valve outer cable (1.3 models)
24 tower flap operating lever
25 Upper flap operating lever

2

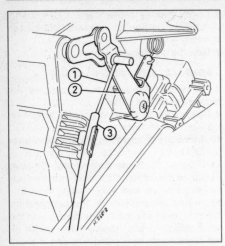

Fig. 2.10 Recirculation control cable (Sec 21)

1 Inner cable   3 Outer cable (conduit)
2 Operating lever

15 Move the temperature control hand lever to HOT.
16 On 1.3 models, remove the plastic cover from the coolant flow control valve and push the operating lever fully towards the bulkhead. Adjust the position of the valve outer control cable until the eye of the inner cable will drop over the spigot on the float control arm without having to alter the setting of lever or arm. Refit the valve plastic cover.
17 Check for correct operation of the flap valve.
18 Refit the facia lower access panel.
19 Reconnect the battery.

Air distribution control cable

20 Disconnect the battery and remove the facia lower access panel.
21 Pull the cable from spigot on the operating lever at the heater and then move the hand control lever to the left (face level position).
22 Disconnect the flap control rods from the intermediate levers.
23 Pull the spigot on the operating lever at the heater to the rear move the outer cable in its clip until the inner clip can be dropped onto the lever spigot without having to move either lever.
24 Move the air distributor control fully to the right ensuring that the lug on the operating lever is at the top of the slot in the rear instrument lever.
25 Pull the upper flap control arm forwards and connect the control rod to the clip on the rear intermediate lever.
26 With the control lever still held fully to the right, check that the lug on the operating lever is at the bottom of the slot in the front intermediate lever.
27 Pull the lower flap operating lever forwards and connect the control rod to the clip on the front intermediate lever.

28 Check the flaps open and close correctly when the control lever is operated.
29 Refit the facia lower access panel and reconnect the battery.

22 Air conditioning system - description

1 Air conditioning is an option on certain models and consists of a belt-driven compressor, a condenser mounted ahead of the radiator, a receiver dryer and an evaporator.

Compressor

2 This circulates refrigerant through the system and incorporates an electro-magnetic clutch to engage or disengage the compressor according to pressure and temperature requirements.
3 While the compressor is running, the idle control solenoid permits vacuum to be applied on the idle boost diaphragm which moves the throttle linkage to compensate for the increased engine load at idle speed .

Condenser

4 This receives vaporised refrigerant from the compressor and by cooling it, converts the vapour into liquid.

Receiver drier

5 This is located at the side of the condenser and collects moisture from the system to prevent freezing of the components.

Evaporator

6 From the receiver drier, the refrigerant flows through the sight glass to give an indication of refrigerant charge.
7 The refrigerant is then vaporised by the pressure drop as it passes through an expansion valve and passes into the evaporator. Air flow through the fins of the evaporator is cooled before it is distributed inside the car. The refrigerant is then drawn back into the compressor to start a new cycle.

23 Air conditioner - precautions and maintenance

1 Refer to *Warning* in Chapter 1, Section 37.
2 Periodically check the condition of the system hoses and for leaks at the unions.
3 During the winter or when the unit is not in regular use, run it for ten minutes every week.
4 Never switch on the air conditioner before starting the engine.
5 When ascending a long hill with the air conditioner on, if the temperature gauge starts to indicate a high reading, switch off the

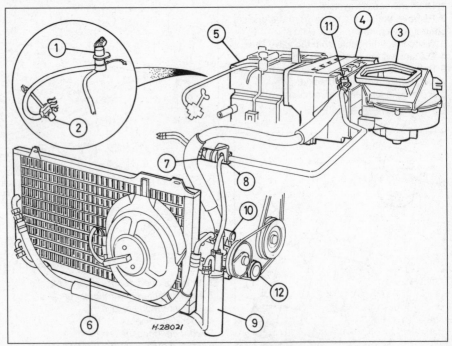

Fig. 2.11 Air conditioning system (Sec 22)

1 Idle control solenoid
2 Idle boost diaphragm
3 Blower unit
4 Evaporator, expansion valve, thermostat
5 Heater/air conditioner control panel
6 Condenser

7 Low pressure switch
8 Sight glass
9 Receiver drier
10 Compressor
11 Charge and discharge valves
12 Tensioner pulley

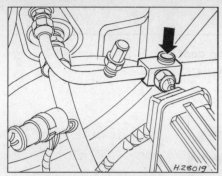

Fig. 2.12 Air conditioning sight glass (arrowed) (Sec 23)

air conditioner until the gauge shows a normal level.

6 Keep the compressor drivebelt correctly tensioned and in good condition as described in the next Section.

7 Periodically check the refrigerant charge as follows.

8 Run the engine at a fast idle for a few minutes with the air conditioning switched on. Inspect the sight glass: it should appear clear, with perhaps a few bubbles. This shows that the charge is correct.

9 If the sight glass displays a constant stream of bubbles, foam, streaking or cloudiness, switch off the air conditioning immediately and do not use it again until the system has been checked by a dealer or refrigeration specialist.

10 Gradual loss of refrigerant is a normal feature of air conditioning systems. It is recommended that the system be pro-fessionally inspected, and recharged if necessary, at least every two years.

24 Compressor drivebelt - tensioning and renewal

1 Slacken the tensioner pulley nut and move the pulley by turning the adjusting bolt until the tension is correct. This is when the total deflection at the mid-point of the longest run is between 7.0 and 9.0 mm (0.28 and 0.35 in).

2 Tighten the tensioner pulley nut to the specified torque.

3 If the compressor drivebelt is to be renewed, slacken the tensioner pulley and ease the belt over the rim of the pulley. If it is difficult to remove, apply a spanner to the crankshaft pulley bolt, turn it while prising the belt up and over the pulley rim.

4 Fit the new belt, again turning the crankshaft pulley while prising the belt over the pulley rim and into its groove.

5 Tension the belt, run the engine for five minutes and then re-tension it as described in paragraph 1.

25 Air conditioning system components - removal and refitting

> ⚠ **Warning: Before removing or refitting any component have the system discharged by your dealer or refrigerant engineer.**
> Once a component has been removed, cap the ends of open pipelines or couplings to prevent the entry of moisture.

Compressor

1 Disconnect the battery and the compressor clutch stator lead.

2 Disconnect the compressor hoses and plug all openings.

3 Remove the drivebelt as described in Section 24.

4 Unscrew and remove all the mounting bolts and lift the compressor from the engine compartment.

5 If a new compressor is being fitted, then 30 cc (1.0 fl. oz) of refrigerant oil must be added to the low pressure fitting on the compressor.

6 Refitting is a reversal of removal. Tension the drivebelt as previously described and have the system charged by your dealer or refrigeration engineer.

Condenser

7 Disconnect the battery.

8 Refer to Chapter 11 and remove the front bumper.

9 Disconnect the high pressure pipe from the receiver and the low pressure hose from the condenser. Plug the openings.

10 Disconnect the condenser fan switch leads, remove the condenser mounting bolts and lift the condenser from the car. If required, the condenser fan can be detached from the condenser.

11 If a new condenser is being fitted, pour 10 cc (0.33 fl. oz) of refrigerant oil into the condenser.

12 Refitting is a reversal of removal. Have the system charged by your dealer or refrigeration engineer.

Evaporator, expansion valve and thermostat

13 Disconnect the battery.

14 Disconnect the low pressure hose and the receiver pipe from the evaporator. Extract the O-ring seals and then plug or cap all openings.

15 Remove the protective sleeve from the low pressure hose. Also remove the grommet and retainer plate.

16 Refer to Chapter 11 and remove the glovebox and glovebox frame.

17 Refer to Section 17 and remove the blower unit. Slacken the sealing band which secures the evaporator to the heater.

18 Disconnect the drain hose and the electrical leads.

19 Unscrew the mounting bolts and lift away the evaporator assembly.

20 Release the fixing clips and remove the bottom half of the evaporator casing.

21 If the expansion valve must be removed, take off the tape and release the capillary tube from the low pressure pipe. Then remove the expansion valve and extract the O-rings. Plug or cap all openings.

22 If the thermostat must be removed, withdraw the capillary tube from the evaporator fins and remove the thermostat.

23 The evaporator can be withdrawn from its casing after extracting the screws from the casing upper section.

24 If a new evaporator is being fitted, pour 30 cc (1.0 fl oz) into it.

25 Refitting is a reversal of removal. Apply sealant around the bulkhead grommet.

26 Reconnect the battery, have the system charged by your dealer or refrigeration engineer.

26 Coolant temperature gauge and sender unit

1 If the reading on the temperature gauge is suspect, test in the following way.

2 Disconnect the lead from the transmitter unit and earth the lead.

3 Switch on the ignition. The gauge needle should move to HOT. Do not leave the ignition on for more than five seconds. If the needle does not move as indicated, check the fuse and connecting wires and if these are alright, then the gauge is faulty.

4 If the needle does move to HOT then the transmitter is faulty and should be renewed.

5 If the fuel and temperature gauges indicate FULL and HOT at the same time, then they are faulty and should be renewed.

6 To test the transmitter unit have the engine cold and disconnect the lead from the transmitter.

7 Run the engine until the coolant temperature reaches 50°C (122°F). This can be checked by inserting a thermometer in the radiator filler neck (1.3 models) or in the end of the expansion tank hose (later 1.3 and 1.6 models) after having disconnected it from the tank.

8 Using an ohmmeter, measure the resistance between the terminal of the transmitter unit and the engine (earth). The resistance should be between 135 and 176 ohms.

9 Continue running the engine until the coolant temperature reaches 80°C (176°F), at which point the resistance should be between 47.6 and 56.9 ohms.

10 If the readings are not as specified, renew the transmitter unit.

2

Fault finding - cooling

Overheating

☐ Insufficient coolant in system
☐ Radiator blocked either internally and externally
☐ Kinked or collapsed hose causing coolant flow restriction
☐ Thermostat not working properly
☐ Engine out of tune
☐ Ignition timing retarded or auto advance malfunction
☐ Cylinder head gasket blown
☐ Engine not yet run-in
☐ Exhaust system partially blocked
☐ Engine oil level too low
☐ Brakes binding

Engine running too cool

☐ Faulty, incorrect or missing thermostat

Loss of coolant

☐ Loose hose clips
☐ Hoses perished or leaking
☐ Radiator leaking
☐ Filler/pressure cap defective
☐ Blown cylinder head gasket
☐ Cracked cylinder block or head
☐ Leak into transmission fluid (automatic transmission)

Fault finding - heating

Heater gives insufficient output

☐ Engine overcooled (see above)
☐ Heater matrix blocked
☐ Heater controls maladjusted or broken
☐ Heater control valve jammed or otherwise defective

Fault finding - air conditioning

Bubbles observed in sight glass of receiver drier

☐ Leak in system
☐ Low refrigerant level

No cooling

☐ No refrigerant

Expansion valve frosted over on evaporator

☐ Faulty or clogged expansion valve
☐ Thermal bulb leaking

Insufficient cooling

☐ Faulty expansion valve
☐ Air in refrigerant circuit
☐ Clogged condenser
☐ Receiver drier clogged
☐ Faulty compressor or slack drivebelt
☐ Compressor overfilled with oil

Chapter 3
Fuel and exhaust systems

For modifications, and information applicable to later models, see Supplement at end of manual

Contents

3

Degrees of difficulty

Easy, suitable for novice with little experience	Fairly easy, suitable for beginner with some experience	Fairly difficult, suitable for competent DIY mechanic	Difficult, suitable for experienced DIY mechanic	Very difficult, suitable for expert DIY or professional

Specifications

Part A Models with carburettor

Fuel pump (1.3 models)

Type .... Mechanically operated by camshaft
Delivery pressure .... 0.19 to 0.26 bar (2.7 to 3.8 lbf/in²)

Fuel pump (1.6 models)

Type .... Electric, five vane
Delivery pressure .... 0.3 bar (4.0 lbf/in²)

Air cleaner element (1.3 models) .... Champion W183

Air cleaner element (1.6 models) .... Champion W114

Carburettor (1.3 models)

Type .... Keihin dual-barrel fixed jet with manual choke
Float level .... 35.4 to 37.4 mm (1.39 to 1.47 in)
Accelerator pump stroke .... 18.5 to 19.5 mm (0.73 to 0.77 in)
Idle speed .... 700 to 800 rev/min
CO at idle .... Not exceeding 1%
Fast idle speed .... 1500 to 2500 rev/min

Carburettor (1.6 models)

Type	SU HIF 44E with electronic mixture control
Idle speed	700 to 800 rev/min
CO at idle	2.0 to 3.5%
Fast idle speed	1150 to 1300 rev/min
Float level	1.0 to 1.5 mm (0.04 to 0.062 in)
Piston damper oil type/specification	Multigrade engine oil

Fuel tank capacity . . . . 46.0 litres (10.0 gal)

Fuel octane rating (minimum)

1.3 models	Leaded (91 RON) or Unleaded (95 RON)
1.6 models	Leaded (97 RON)

Torque wrench settings

	Nm	lbf ft
1.3 models		
Carburettor mounting nuts	20	15
Fuel pump nuts	24	18
Inlet manifold support bracket nuts	22	16
Inlet manifold fixing nuts	22	16
Manifold support bracket bolt	45	33
Exhaust manifold fixing nuts	39	29
Exhaust manifold to downpipe nuts	55	41
Fuel tank mounting strap bolts	22	16
1.6 models		
Carburettor mounting nuts	20	15
Inlet manifold fixing nuts/bolts	22	16
Manifold electric heater sensor	18	13
Exhaust manifold fixing nuts	25	18
All models		
Fuel tank mounting strap bolts	22	16

Part B Models with fuel injection system

Fuel pump

Type	Electric
Delivery pressure	4.1 bar (60 lbf/in²)
Pressure regulator range	2.5 to 1.8 bar (36 to 26 lbf/in²)

Fuel temperature switch closes . . . . 90°C (195°F)

Idle speed

Controlled by electronic control unit	710 ± 50 rev/min
With air valve closed	650 to 680 rev/min

CO at idle . . . . 1.0 to 1.5%

Air cleaner element . . . . Champion W114

Fuel tank capacity . . . . 46.0 litre (10.0 gal)

Fuel octane rating . . . . Four-star (97 RON)

Torque wrench setting	Nm	lbf ft
Fuel tank mounting strap bolts	22	16

 Warning: Many of the procedures in this Chapter entail the removal of fuel pipes and connections which may result in some fuel spillage. Before carrying out any operation on the fuel system refer to the precautions given in Safety First! at the beginning of this manual and follow them implicitly. Petrol is a highly dangerous and volatile liquid and the precautions necessary when handling it cannot be overstressed.

Part A Models with carburettor

1 General description

The fuel system on carburettor models consists of a fuel tank which is mounted forward of the rear suspension, a fuel pump mechanically operated on 1.3 models, electric on 1.6 versions and a carburettor and temperature controlled air cleaner.

The air cleaner contains a disposable paper filter element and incorporates an automatic air temperature control system. The system is controlled by a flap valve located at the junction of the air cleaner hot and cold air intakes. The flap is operated by inlet manifold vacuum acting on a thermac unit in conjunction with a temperature-sensitive thermac switch. The system allows hot or cold air to be delivered to the carburettor, depending on the position of the flap valve which varies according to engine temperature and load.

The carburettor on 1.3 models is of dual barrel fixed jet type while on 1.6 models, it is of variable venturi type with an electronic mixture control system.

2 Maintenance and inspection

1 Regularly inspect the fuel hoses for security and condition.
2 Renew the air cleaner element and (on 1.3 models) the fuel filter at the specified intervals (all Routine Maintenance).
3 The engine idle speed and mixture setting (CO content of exhaust emission) should also be checked at the specified intervals.
4 Inspect the exhaust system periodically for leaks or severe corrosion.
5 With SU carburettors keep the damper hollow piston rod topped up with engine oil.

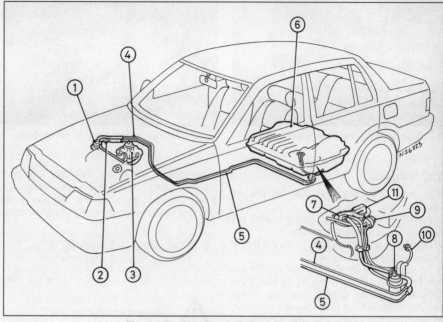

Fig. 3.1 Fuel system (1.3 models) (Sec 1)

1 Fuel pump
2 One-way valve
3 Carburettor
4 Fuel feed line
5 Fuel return line
6 Fuel tank
7 Fuel pick-up unit
8 Fuel filter
9 Two-way valve
10 Breather hose
11 Fuel transmitter unit

3 Air cleaner - servicing, removal and refitting

1.3 models

1 Unscrew the wing nut and remove the cover. Lift out the filter element (photos).
2 Wipe out the casing, fit the new element and cover.
3 To remove the air cleaner, first identify all hoses, pipes and ducts and disconnect them from the air cleaner casing (photos).
4 Unscrew the cover wing nut and the casing mounting bolt and lift the air cleaner from the engine (photo).

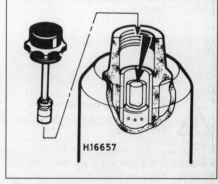

Fig. 3.2 SU carburettor damper. Oil level arrowed (Sec 2)

3.1A Air cleaner element

3.1B Air cleaner casing

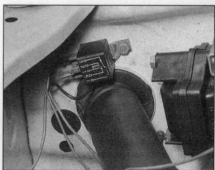
3.3A Air cleaner cold air intake. Note auxiliary lamp relay

3

3.3B Cold air intake bracket screw

3.3C Hot air intake hose at air cleaner

3.3D Crankcase vent hose at air cleaner

1.6 models

5 Release the clips and take off the air cleaner cover.
6 Remove the soiled filter element, wipe out the casing and fit the new element.
7 Refit the cover and secure it with the toggle clips.
8 To remove the air cleaner, first disconnect the cold air pipe from the air temperature control and then release the clip which secures the inlet hose to the plenum chamber.
9 Unscrew the bolts from the air cleaner mounting bracket, then disconnect the hot air pipe and vacuum hose from the air temperature control .
10 Withdraw the air cleaner and air temperature control assembly.
11 Refitting of both types of air cleaner is a reversal of removal.

4 Fuel filter (1.3 models) - renewal

 Warning: Take adequate fire precautions during this procedure

1 Disconnect the battery.
2 Raise the rear end of the car and support it securely on axle stands.
3 Remove the fuel filter cover and release the filter bracket.

3.4 Air cleaner casing mounting bracket

4 Disconnect the hoses from the filter and plug the hose ends to prevent fuel leakage.
5 Remove and discard the old filter and fit the new one by reversing the removal operations.

5 Fuel pump (1.3 models) - testing, removal and refitting

 Warning: Take adequate fire precautions during this procedure

1 Disconnect the fuel supply hose from the carburettor and insert its open end in a suitable container.
2 Disconnect the negative (blue) LT lead from the ignition coil and then have an assistant turn the ignition key to actuate the starter motor.
3 Fuel should be ejected in regular well defined spurts from the fuel hose.
4 If this is not the case then the fuel pump must be renewed as the pump is of sealed type and cannot be repaired or even cleaned.

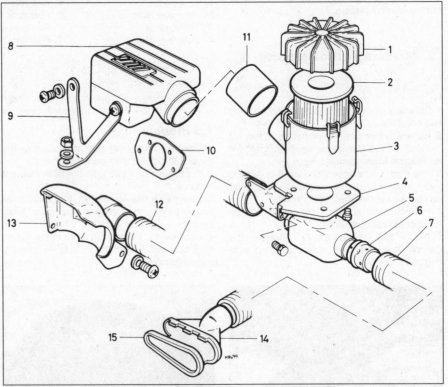

Fig. 3.3 Air cleaner (1.6 with carburettor) (Sec 3)

1 Top cover	6 Adaptor sleeve	11 Connecting tube
2 Paper element	7 Cold air intake hose	12 Hot air duct
3 Air cleaner body	8 Plenum chamber	13 Hot air box
4 Air cleaner mounting	9 Support bracket	14 Cold air intake hose
bracket	10 Gasket	adaptor
5 Thermac unit		15 Gasket

5.6 Fuel pump

5.7 Fuel pump cover and drain tube

5.8 Unscrewing fuel pump fixing nuts

5 To remove the pump, disconnect the battery.
6 Disconnect the fuel lines from the pump and plug the ends to prevent loss of fuel (photo).
7 Unscrew the bolt which secures the coolant hose support bracket and fuel pump cover and remove the cover/drain tube complete (photo) .
8 Unscrew the pump fixing nuts and remove the pump, insulator block and gaskets (photo).
9 Clean the old gasket from the flanges, locate a new gasket on each side of the insulator block and refit the pump (photo).
10 Tighten the fixing nuts to the specified torque.
11 Fit the pump cover/support bracket and locate the drain hose in its clip.
12 Reconnect the fuel lines and the battery.

6 Fuel pump (1.6 models) - testing, removal, refitting and precautions

 Warning: Take adequate fire precautions during this procedure

1 Raise the left-hand rear of the car and support it securely.
2 Disconnect the outlet hose from the pump and fit a substitute hose, the open end being inserted into a glass bottle.
3 Have an assistant turn on the ignition switch. The pump should operate and eject fuel into the bottle. If this does not happen, check the inertia switch (Section 26), then remove the pump and fit a new one in the following way.
4 Disconnect the battery.
5 Drain the fuel tank by syphoning the fuel into a container which can be sealed.
6 Disconnect the wiring plug from the pump.
7 Disconnect the two hoses from the pump.
8 Unscrew the fixing nuts and remove the pump and mounting bracket.
9 Release the fuel pump from its insulating rubber.
10 When refitting, use a new rubber insulator and locate the pump and insulator so that the wiring plug socket will be towards the outside of the car.
11 The remaining refitting operations are reversals of removal, remember to fit a rubber and flat washer under each nut.

Precautions

12 Do not leave the ignition switched on for more than a few minutes without the engine running.
13 Do not switch on the ignition (pump operational) with an empty fuel tank.

7 Fuel tank (1.3 models) - removal, repair and refitting

 Warning: Take adequate fire precautions during this procedure

1 Disconnect the battery.
2 Unscrew the tank drain plug and drain the fuel into a container which can be sealed (photo).
3 Raise the rear end of the car, support it securely and remove the left-hand rear roadwheel.
4 Remove the fuel filter cover and release the fuel filler hose access panel.
5 Disconnect the filler and vent hoses from the neck of the fuel filler.
6 Disconnect the electrical leads from the fuel level transmitter unit.
7 Support the tank on a jack with a block of wood as an insulator. Slacken the mounting strap nuts and move the straps aside (photo).

3

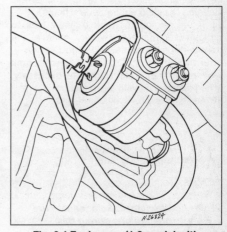

Fig. 3.4 Fuel pump (1.6 model with carburettor) (Sec 6)

5.9 Fuel pump insulator

7.2 Fuel tank drain plug

7.7 Fuel tank mounting strap

Fig. 3.5 Throttle cable at carburettor (Sec 11)

1 Cable	4 Cable deflection
2 Locknut	5 Throttle lever
3 Locknut	

8 Lower the tank slowly until the hoses can be released from the pick-up unit and the two-way valve.

9 Remove the two-way valve from the top of the tank and then withdraw the tank from under the car.

10 If the fuel tank is leaking, have it repaired by specialists. Never attempt to weld or solder a fuel tank. Residual fuel vapour cannot be satisfactorily removed unless the tank is steamed or boiled out for several hours.

11 If the reason for tank removal was to remove sediment or water, remove the transmitter unit as described in Section 9. Pour in some paraffin and shake the tank vigorously, then drain. Repeat as necessary, giving a final rinse with clean fuel.

12 Refitting is a reversal of removal.

8 Fuel tank (1.6 models) - removal, repair and refitting

⚠ **Warning: Take adequate fire precautions during this procedure**

The operations are very similar to those described in the preceding Section except that a tank drain plug is not fitted and the fuel must therefore be syphoned or pumped out.

9 Fuel level transmitter - removal, testing and refitting

⚠ **Warning: Take adequate fire precautions during this procedure**

1 Remove the fuel tank as previously described.

2 Unscrew the transmitter unit retaining ring using a suitable tool to engage with the ring lugs.

3 Carefully withdraw the transmitter unit taking care not to bend the float arm.

4 Discard the sealing ring.

5 If an ohmmeter is available, the transmitter can be tested by measuring the resistance between the terminals.

Float in fully lowered (empty) position 105 to 110 ohms

Float in half full position 25.5 to 39.5 ohms

Float fully up (full) position 2.0 to 5.0 ohms

6 If the readings are not as indicated, renew the transmitter, if they are, then the fuel gauge is faulty, refer to the next Section.

7 Refitting the transmitter is a reversal of removal, use a new sealing ring.

10 Fuel gauge - testing

1 Disconnect the leads from the fuel tank level transmitter.

2 Connect the leads together using a bridging wire.

3 Switch on the ignition. The needle of the fuel gauge should move to FULL. Do not leave the ignition switched on for more than five seconds. If the gauge does not indicate FULL and it has been established that the wiring is in good order, renew the gauge as described in Chapter 12.

4 If the gauge does operate correctly then the fault must be in the transmitter.

11 Throttle cable - adjustment and renewal

1 When correctly adjusted, the throttle cable should have a slight slackness at the carburettor. Cable deflection should be between 4.0 and 10.0 mm (0.16 to 0.40 in).

2 Adjustment is carried out using the locknuts at the cable bracket (photo) .

3 With the help of an assistant, check that idle and full throttle positions are obtainable with the accelerator pedal released or fully depressed.

4 To remove the throttle cable, release the cable bracket locknuts. If the cable inner is secured to the throttle quadrant by a clamp screw, slacken the screw.

5 Slip the cable end fitting from the carburettor throttle quadrant and the cable from its support bracket.

6 Working inside the car, disconnect the cable from the accelerator pedal by slipping the cable end fitting from the hole in the pedal arm (photo).

7 Withdraw the cable assembly through the bulkhead grommets.

8 Refitting is a reversal of removal. Adjust the cable as previously described.

12 Choke cable (1.3 models) - adjustment, removal and refitting

1 Remove the air cleaner.

2 With the choke control knob pushed fully in on the facia panel, check that the choke valve plate in the carburettor is fully open. In this position, the choke cable at the carburettor should have 5.0 mm (0.20 in) deflection under finger pressure. If not, adjust the cable setting at the choke valve plate lever connection.

3 To remove the choke cable, disconnect it from the carburettor.

4 Working inside the car, extract the choke knob retaining screw and pull off the knob (photos).

5 Unscrew the bezel nut and release the cable from the facia panel.

11.2 Throttle cable locknuts

11.6 Throttle cable at accelerator pedal arm

12.4A Extracting choke knob screw

12.4B Choke cable bezel nut

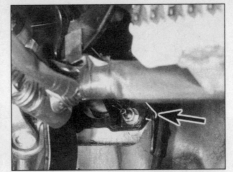

13.2 Accelerator pedal return spring

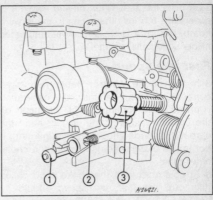

Fig. 3.6 Adjustment screws on Keihin carburettor (Sec 15)

1 Tamper proof plug
2 Mixture screw
3 Throttle speed screw

6 Lower the cable slightly until the leads can be disconnected from the choke warning lamp switch.
7 Withdraw the choke cable through the bulkhead grommet.
8 Fitting the new cable is a reversal of removal. Adjust as previously described.

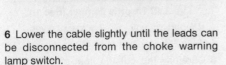

13 Accelerator pedal - removal and refitting

1 Disconnect the throttle cable as described in Section 11.
2 Working inside the car under the facia panel, extract the split pin and take off the washer from the accelerated pedal pivot rod. Disconnect the pedal return spring (photo).
3 Remove the pedal.
4 Refitting is a reversal of removal.

14 Carburettor (1.3 models) - description

1 The carburettor is of dual barrel, fixed jet type of Keihin manufacture.
2 The carburettor incorporates four inter-related systems: a primary slow-running system, a primary main system, a secondary slow and a secondary main.
3 A manually operated choke is fitted.

15.5 Keihin carburettor idle speed screw (arrowed)

4 A fuel cut-off solenoid valve is fitted to prevent running on after the ignition is switched off.
5 The accelerator pump is of diaphragm type.

15 Carburettor (1.3 models) - idle speed and mixture adjustment

1 If a tachometer is not fitted, connect a reliable instrument in accordance with the manufacturer's instructions.
2 Have the engine at full working temperature with the radiator fan cutting in.
3 Make sure that all electrical equipment is switched off.
4 Clear the intake manifold by gradually increasing the engine speed to 2500 rev/min and holding it there for thirty seconds.
5 Check the idle speed. If outside the Specification, turn the throttle stop screw (photo).
6 The mixture is set during production and will not normally require adjustment. However, after carburettor overhaul or if the engine characteristics change due to wear or carbon build up, the mixture can be adjusted in the following way.
7 Ideally, the mixture should be adjusted

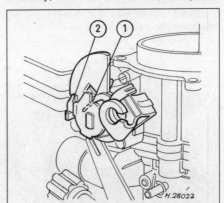

Fig. 3.7 Choke relief valve adjustment (Sec 16)

1 Forward notch (richer)
2 Rear notch (normal)

using an exhaust gas analyser. Turn the mixture screw in until the CO level in the exhaust gas is at the specified level.
8 Where an exhaust gas analyser is not available, unscrew the mixture screw until the idle speed is at its highest point and then turn the screw in until the idle speed drops by 50 rev/min.
9 Re-adjust the idle speed to the specified level.
10 During the foregoing adjustments, clear the manifold at three minute intervals as described in paragraph 4.

16 Carburettor (1.3 models) - choke adjustments

Choke relief valve

1 Normally, the hook of the tension spring should be engaged in the rear notch as shown in Fig. 3.7.
2 in severe weather, if the engine is difficult to

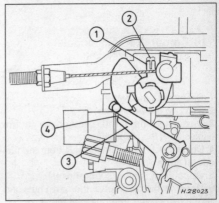

Fig. 3.8 Choke fast idle setting (Sec 16)

1 Choke lever
2 Carburettor body alignment mark
3 Fast idle lever
4 Fork gap

start or is hesitant when driving away, it is acceptable to move the spring to the forward notch. Return it to its original setting when milder conditions resume.

Fast idle speed

3 If the choke control cable has been correctly set, then when the choke cable knob is pulled out to its first detent, the marks on the choke valve plate lever and the carburettor body should be in alignment. If not, make a slight adjustment to the choke outer cable.

4 At cold start with the choke knob pulled fully out, the fast idle speed should be between 2600 and 2800 rev/min. Any adjustment required may be made by opening or closing the fork gap on the fast idle lever.

17 Carburettor (1.3 models) - accelerator pump stroke adjustment

1 Refer to Fig. 3.9 and measure the gap between the tab on the pump lever and the stop plate on the carburettor body. This represents the accelerator pump lever travel.
2 If the travel is not as shown in Specifications, carefully bend the stop plate.

18 Carburettor (1.3 models) - throttle damper adjustment

1 Have the engine running at 3500 rev/min holding it at this level by means of the carburettor throttle lever.
2 Release the throttle lever suddenly. The damper arm should fully extend during a period of between one and four seconds.
3 If the period is not as specified, small adjustments may be made to the fork slot on the opener lever (Fig. 3.10).
4 Failure to correct matters may be due to a leaking diaphragm hose or a faulty diaphragm unit.

19 Carburettor (1.3 models) - removal and refitting

1 Disconnect the battery.
2 Remove the air cleaner.
3 Disconnect the throttle and choke control cables from the carburettor.
4 Disconnect the electrical lead from the fuel cut-off solenoid valve.
5 Disconnect the fuel supply hose.
6 Unscrew the carburettor mounting nuts and lift the carburettor from the inlet manifold.
7 Refitting is a reversal of removal. Use a new flange gasket on clean mounting surfaces and adjust the throttle and choke control cables as described in Sections 11 and 12.

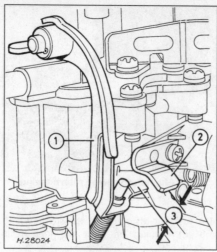

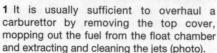

Fig. 3.9 Accelerator pump lever travel (Sec 17)

1 Pump lever   2 Stop plate
3 Pump lever travel (stroke)

20 Carburettor (1.3 models) - overhaul

1 It is usually sufficient to overhaul a carburettor by removing the top cover, mopping out the fuel from the float chamber and extracting and cleaning the jets (photo).
2 Obtain a gasket and seal set for use during reassembly.
3 If a carburettor has been in use for a long time and is obviously well worn, with slackness in the throttle valve spindle bores, it will probably be more economical to purchase a new or rebuilt unit.
4 However, for those wishing to completely dismantle the carburettor, proceed in the following way.
5 With the unit removed from the car, clean away external dirt using paraffin and a brush.
6 Disconnect the accelerator pump arm from the top cover.
7 Extract the screws and remove the top cover and the gasket (photo) .

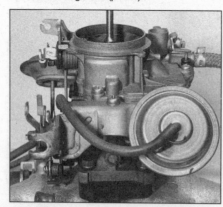

20.1 Secondary throttle opener vacuum unit on Keihin carburettor

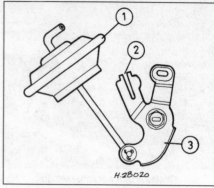

Fig. 3.10 Throttle damper (Sec 18)

1 Diaphragm unit   3 Opener lever
2 Fork slot

8 Carefully tap out the float pivot pin and remove the float.
9 Unscrew the float adjusting screw and take off the O-ring. Remove the filter gauze and the fuel inlet needle valve.
10 Remove the primary slow, main and secondary main air jets and emulsion tubes.
11 Remove the slow fuel jet plug, turn the carburettor upside down to eject the slow fuel jet.
12 Remove the main jet retainer, the power valve, the primary and secondary main jets. Take off the O-rings.
13 Remove the accelerator pump diaphragm cover, the diaphragm, spring and O-rings.
14 Clean all jets, passages and orifices with air from a tyre pump. On no account probe them with wire or this will ruin their calibration.
15 This should be the limit of dismantling.
16 Before reassembling, obtain the appropriate repair kit which will contain all the necessary seals and gaskets.
17 Reassembly is a reversal of dismantling, but adjust the float in the following way.
18 Locate the fuel inlet needle valve, O-rings and filter gauze and screw in the float adjusting screw a turn or two.

20.7 Top cover on Keihin carburettor

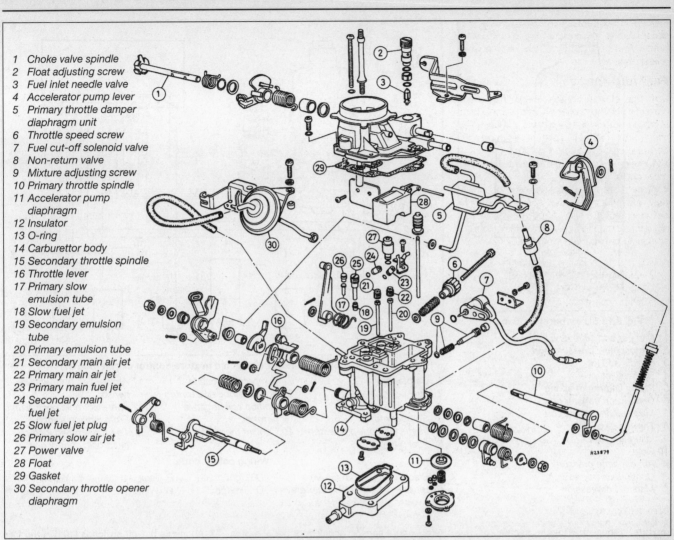

1 Choke valve spindle
2 Float adjusting screw
3 Fuel inlet needle valve
4 Accelerator pump lever
5 Primary throttle damper
   diaphragm unit
6 Throttle speed screw
7 Fuel cut-off solenoid valve
8 Non-return valve
9 Mixture adjusting screw
10 Primary throttle spindle
11 Accelerator pump
   diaphragm
12 Insulator
13 O-ring
14 Carburettor body
15 Secondary throttle spindle
16 Throttle lever
17 Primary slow
   emulsion tube
18 Slow fuel jet
19 Secondary emulsion
   tube
20 Primary emulsion tube
21 Secondary main air jet
22 Primary main air jet
23 Primary main fuel jet
24 Secondary main
   fuel jet
25 Slow fuel jet plug
26 Primary slow air jet
27 Power valve
28 Float
29 Gasket
30 Secondary throttle opener
   diaphragm

Fig. 3.11 Exploded view of Keihin carburettor (Sec 20)

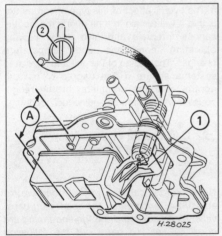

**Fig. 3.12 Keihin carburettor float setting
(Sec 20)**

1 Float arm/needle valve contact point
2 Float adjusting screw
A Float setting (measured from gasket) 35.4
   to 37.4 mm (1.39 to 1.47 in)

19 Fit the float and its pivot pin.
20 Hold the top cover vertically so that
the float hangs downwards under its own
weight.
21 With the top cover gasket in position,
measure the dimension (A) (Fig. 3.12) which
should be as given in the Specifications. Turn
the float adjusting screw in or out to achieve
this (photo).

**20.21 Float level adjusting screw on Keihin
carburettor**

21 Carburettor (1.6 models) -
description

1 The SU HIF (Horizontal Integral Float
chamber) carburettor is of the variable choke,
constant depression type incorporating a
sliding piston which automatically controls the
mixture of air and fuel supplied to the engine
with respect to the throttle valve position and
engine speed. In addition the carburettor is
equipped with an electronically-operated
mixture control device. This alters the mixture
strength and engine speed when starting and
during slow running, and also controls the
operation of a fuel shut-off valve when
decelerating or descending a hill.
2 The carburettor functions as follows. When
the engine is started and is allowed to idle, the
throttle valve passes a small amount of air.
Because the piston is in a low position it offers
a larger restriction and the resultant pressure
reduction draws fuel from the jet, and
atomisation occurs to provide a combustible

3

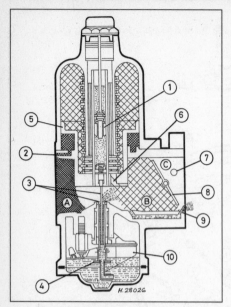

Fig. 3.13 SU carburettor (Sec 21)

1 Damper and oil reservoir
2 Atmospheric pressure port
3 Needle and jet
4 Bi-metal jet lever
5 Piston and return spring
6 Depression transfer port
7 Mixture enrichment port
8 Throttle disc
9 Idling fuel port
10 Float
A Atmospheric pressure
B Continuous depression
C Manifold depression

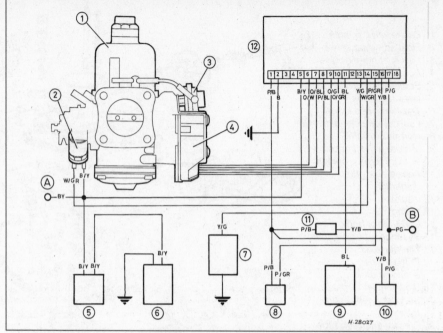

Fig. 3.14 SU carburettor electronic mixture control circuit (Sec 21)

1 Carburettor	7 Temperature gauge	11 Ambient air temperature
2 Fuel cut-off valve	8 Accelerator pedal switch	sensor
3 Vacuum switch	9 Ignition coil negative	12 Fuel electronic control unit
4 Stepper motor	terminal	A From ignition switch
5 Inertia (fuel cut-off) switch	10 Coolant thermistor	B To programmed ignition
6 Fuel pump		electronic control unit

Wiring colour code

B Black	G Green	LG Light green	P Pink	Y Yellow
BL Blue	GR Slate/grey	O Orange	W White	

mixture. Since the inside section of the tapered needle is across the mouth of the jet, a relatively small amount of fuel is passed.

3 When the throttle valve is opened, the amount of air passing through the carburettor is increased, which causes a greater depression beneath the sliding piston. An internal passageway connects this depression with the suction chamber above the piston, which now rises. The piston offers less of a restriction where the forces of depression, gravity, and spring tension balance out. The tapered needle has now been raised, and more fuel passes from the jet.

4 Incorporated in the jet adjusting (mixture) screw mechanism is a bi-metal strip which alters the position of the jet to compensate for varying fuel densities resulting from varying fuel temperatures.

5 Fuel enrichment for cold starting is by an internal valve which admits more fuel into the airstream passing through the carburettor. This valve is operated by a stepping motor which also controls the engine idling speed. An electronic control unit (ECU) which is a small microprocessor receives input from the coolant temperature sensor, ambient air

temperature sensor, accelerator pedal switch and ignition coil and adjusts the engine idle speed and mixture accordingly. The ECU also controls the operation of a fuel shut-off valve which comes into operation when decelerating or descending a hill. If, during these conditions, the engine speed is in excess of 1300 rpm, the ambient air temperature and engine temperature are above a predetermined value, and the accelerator pedal switch is closed (pedal released) the valve will be opened and closed at half second intervals. This introduces a partial vacuum to the top of the float chamber thus weakening the mixture. The fuel shut-off circuit is deactivated if the engine speed suddenly stops, ie, when declutching. When accelerating, a vacuum-operated switch acts upon the mixture control, allowing more fuel to be drawn through, resulting in the necessary richer mixture.

6 The air intake temperature is controlled by a vacuum-operated flap at the base of the air cleaner to blend the supply of hot and cold air. The flap is controlled by the thermac switch which is located in the plenum chamber adjacent to the carburettor.

7 An inertia cut-off switch is fitted in the fuse box as a means of isolating the fuel pump in the event of forward impact.

8 The overall effect of this type of carburettor is that it will remain in tune during the lengthy service intervals and also under varying operating conditions and temperature changes. The design of the unit and its related systems ensure a fine degree of mixture control over the complete throttle range, coupled with enhanced engine fuel economy.

22 Carburettor (1.6 models) - in-car adjustments

Note: *Before carrying out any carburettor adjustment ensure that the spark plug gaps, valve clearances and the ignition timing are correctly set. To carry out the following adjustments an accurate tachometer will be required. The use of an exhaust gas analyser (CO meter) is also preferable, although not essential.*

1 Remove the air cleaner and the plenum chamber.

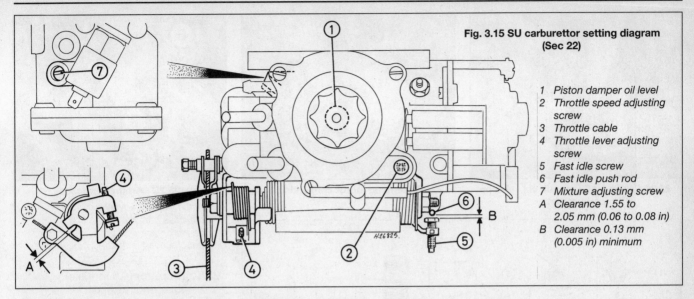

Fig. 3.15 SU carburettor setting diagram (Sec 22)

1 Piston damper oil level
2 Throttle speed adjusting screw
3 Throttle cable
4 Throttle lever adjusting screw
5 Fast idle screw
6 Fast idle push rod
7 Mixture adjusting screw
A Clearance 1.55 to 2.05 mm (0.06 to 0.08 in)
B Clearance 0.13 mm (0.005 in) minimum

2 Unscrew and remove the piston damper from the suction chamber.

3 Undo and remove the three securing screws and lift off the suction chamber, complete with piston and piston spring. After removal avoid rotating the piston in the suction chamber.

4 Invert the suction chamber assembly and drain the oil from the hollow piston rod. Check that the needle guide is flush with the piston face and is secure. Do not be concerned that the needle appears loose in the guide, this is perfectly normal.

5 Observe the position of the jet in relation to the jet guide located in the centre of the carburettor venturi. The jet will probably be slightly below the top face of the jet guide. Turn the mixture adjusting screw until the top of the jet is flush with the top of the jet guide. Now turn the adjusting screw two complete turns clockwise. If the mixture adjusting screw is covered by a small blue or red tamperproof plug, hook this out with a small screwdriver and discard it.

6 Refit the piston and suction chamber assembly, taking care not to turn the piston in the suction chamber any more than is necessary to align the piston groove with its guide. If the piston is turned excessively the spring will be wound up and the assembly will have to be dismantled, as described in Section 24.

7 Check that the piston is free to move in the suction chamber by lifting it and allowing it to drop under its own weight. A definite metallic click should be heard as the piston falls and contacts the bridge in the carburettor body. If this is not the case, dismantle and clean the suction chamber, as described in Section 24. If satisfactory, top up the damper oil with engine oil to the top of the hollow piston rod and refit the damper and plenum chamber.

8 Check that the throttle linkage operates smoothly and that there is a small amount of free play in the accelerator cable.

9 Connect a tachometer to the engine in accordance with the manufacturer's instructions, and also a CO meter if this is to be used.

10 Reconnect the vacuum hoses to the air cleaner and plenum chamber and lay the unit alongside the carburettor.

11 Start the engine and run it at a fast idle speed until it reaches its normal operating temperature. Continue to run the engine for a further five minutes before commencing adjustment.

12 Increase the engine speed to 2500 rpm for 30 seconds and repeat this at three minute intervals during the adjustment procedure. This will ensure that any excess fuel is cleared from the inlet manifold.

13 Disconnect the coolant temperature gauge sender unit wiring plug (see Chapter 2 if necessary) and join the two plug terminals together using a suitable length of wire. This will ensure that the mixture control stepping motor is not actuated during adjustment.

14 If the cooling fan is running, wait until it stops then turn the idle speed adjustment screw as necessary until the engine is idling at the specified speed.

15 Switch off the engine.

16 Check the clearance between the fast idle pushrod and fast idle adjustment screw using feeler gauges (position B in Fig. 3.15). Turn the fast idle adjustment screw as necessary to obtain the specified clearance.

17 Check the throttle lever lost motion gap using feeler gauges (position A in Fig. 3.15) and, if necessary, turn the throttle lever adjustment screw to obtain the specified clearance.

18 Start the engine and slowly turn the mixture adjustment screw clockwise (to enrich) or anti-clockwise (to weaken) until the fastest idling speed which is consistent with smooth even running is obtained. If a CO meter is being used, adjust the mixture screw

to obtain the specified idling exhaust gas CO content.

19 Reset the idling speed, if necessary, using the idle speed adjustment screw then switch off the engine once more.

20 Remove the wire connecting the coolant thermistor wiring plug terminals together, but leave the plug disconnected.

21 Start the engine again. The mixture control stepping motor should move the fast idle pushrod to the fast idle position. Compare the engine fast idle speed with the specified setting and if necessary adjust by turning the fast idle adjustment screw as required.

22 Switch off the engine and reconnect the coolant temperature gauge sender unit wiring plug. **Note:** after carrying out this adjustment, ensure that the specified minimum clearance still exists between pushrod and screw, as described in paragraph 16. Adjust the screw if the clearance is less than specified.

23 Make a final check that the idling speed and mixture are correct after refitting the air cleaner and plenum chamber, then switch off the engine and disconnect the instruments.

24 On cars equipped with an air conditioner, idle boost adjustment must be carried out in the following way after the system has been recharged with refrigerant.

25 Have the engine at normal operating temperature and idling.

26 Switch on the air conditioner and have the temperature control in the BLUE position and the air distribution and recirculation control set to the left-hand side. Set the fan switch to maximum speed.

27 When the radiator cooling fan cuts in, check the idle speed with the air conditioner switch off. Adjust to the specified speed if necessary.

28 Now turn the fan switch off and again check the idle speed. Adjust if necessary.

29 Turn the switch off and on several times, the engine idle speed should not alter.

3

23.2A Fuel cut-off (anti run on) valve on carburettors

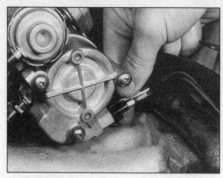

23.2B Stepping motor connecting plug

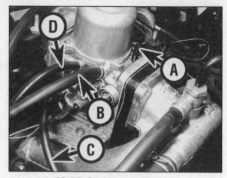

23.2C Carburettor hoses

A Ignition vacuum advance
B Crankcase breather
C Fuel inlet
D Float chamber vent

23 Carburettor (1.6 models) - removal and refitting

1 Disconnect the battery.
2 Disconnect all electrical leads, ducts and hoses from the carburettor and thermac switch (photos).
3 Disconnect the fuel supply hose and plug its open end.
4 Disconnect the throttle cable.
5 Unscrew the carburettor fixing nuts and lift the carburettor from the inlet manifold. Remove the flange insulating block and gaskets. Separate the carburettor from the plenum chamber.
6 Refitting is a reversal of removal. Use a new gasket on each side of the insulating block and adjust the throttle cable as described in Section 11.

24 Carburettor (1.6 models) - overhaul

1 Remove the carburettor, as described in the previous Section.
2 Clean off the exterior of the carburettor using paraffin, or a suitable solvent and wipe dry.
3 Unscrew the damper from the suction chamber and drain the oil from the piston rod (photo).

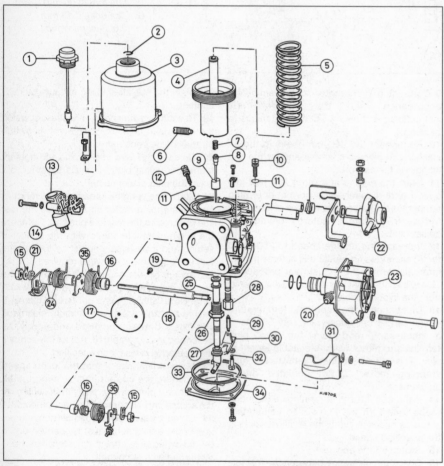

Fig. 3.16 Exploded view of SU HIF carburettor (Sec 24)

1 Damper piston
2 Jump ring
3 Suction chamber
4 Air valve piston
5 Spring
6 Needle retaining screw
7 Needle bias spring
8 Jet needle
9 Needle guide
10 Throttle adjusting screw
11 Seal
12 Mixture adjusting screw
13 Fuel cut-off valve
14 Valve solenoid
15 Spindle nut and lockplate
16 Seal
17 Throttle valve plate and screw
18 Throttle valve plate spindle
19 Carburettor body
20 Fast idle pushrod
21 Plain washer
22 Vacuum capsule
23 Mixture control stepper motor
24 Progressive throttle lever and return spring
25 Jet bearing
26 Jet bearing nut
27 Jet assembly
28 Float needle seat
29 Float needle
30 Bi-metal jet lever
31 Float
32 Jet retaining screw and spring
33 Float chamber cover seal
34 Float chamber cover
35 Lost motion link/throttle stop and spring
36 Fast idle lever and return spring

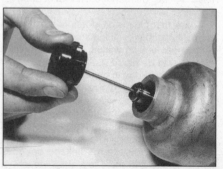

24.3 Withdrawing damper

24.4 Carburettor suction chamber and air valve piston

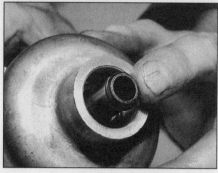

24.5A Piston rod circlip

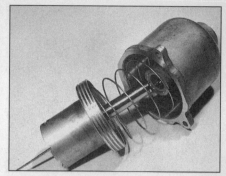

24.5B Removing air valve piston and spring

4 Unscrew the three retaining screws and lift off the suction chamber and piston assembly (photo).

5 Push the piston up to expose the retaining circlip. Extract the circlip and withdraw the piston and spring assembly (photo).

6 Unscrew the needle guide locking screw and withdraw the needle guide and spring (photo).

7 Mark the relationship of the float chamber cover to the carburettor body. Unscrew the four retaining screws and lift off the cover and O-ring seal (photo).

8 Unscrew the jet adjusting lever retaining screw and withdraw the jet and adjusting lever assembly. Disengage the jet from the lever (photo) .

9 Unscrew the float pivot screw and lift out the float and fuel needle valve. Unscrew the needle valve seat from the base of the float chamber (photos).

10 Unscrew the jet bearing locking nut and remove the jet bearing (photos) .

11 Undo the three retaining screws and remove the fuel shut-off valve and solenoid assembly. Recover the gasket (photo).

12 Dismantling the remaining components is not recommended, as these parts are not available separately. If the throttle levers, linkage or spindle appear worn, or in any way damaged, it will be necessary to renew the complete carburettor. **Do not** remove the mixture control stepping motor or vacuum

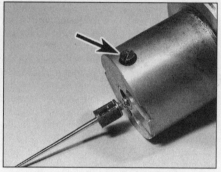

24.6 Needle locking screw (arrowed) and needle partially withdrawn

24.7 Lifting off float chamber cover

3

24.8 Jet and adjuster lever

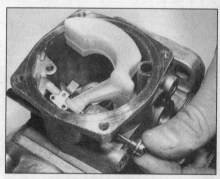

24.9A Float pivot screw

249B Fuel inlet needle valve

24.9C Unscrewing needle valve seat

24.10A Jet bearing locknut

24.10B Removing jet bearing

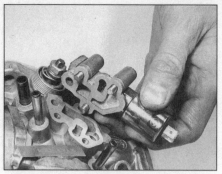

24.11 Fuel shut off (anti run on) solenoid valve

24.13 Fuel needle valve seat filter

switch. These components are set to each individual carburettor during manufacture and may not operate correctly if disturbed.

13 Check the condition of the float needle valve and seat and renew these components if there is any sign of pitting or wear ridges particularly on the needle. Ensure that the filter in the seat assembly is clean (photo).

14 Examine the carburettor body for cracks and damage, and ensure that the brass fittings and piston guide are secure.

15 Clean the inside of the suction chamber and the outer circumference of the piston with a petrol-moistened rag and allow to air dry. Insert the piston into the suction chamber without the spring. Hold the assembly in a horizontal position and spin the piston. If there is any tendency for the piston to bind, renew the piston and dashpot assembly.

16 Connect a 12 volt supply to the terminals of the fuel shut-off valve solenoid and ensure that the valve closes. If not, renew the solenoid.

17 Check the piston needle and jet bearing for any signs of ovality, or wear ridges.

18 Shake the float and listen for any trapped fuel which may have entered through a tiny crack or fracture.

19 Check the condition of all gaskets, seals and connecting hoses and renew any that show signs of deterioration.

20 Begin reassembly by refitting the jet

bearing and retaining nut to the carburettor body.

21 Refit the fuel needle valve and seat, followed by the float and float pivot screw.

22 Allow the float to close the needle valve under its own weight and measure the distance from the centre of the float to the face of the carburettor body, as shown in Fig. 3.17. If the measured dimension is outside the float level height setting given in the Specifications, carefully bend the brass contact pad on the float to achieve the required setting.

23 Engage the jet with the cut-out in the adjusting lever, ensuring that the jet head moves freely. Position the jet in the jet bearing and, at the same time, engage the slot in the adjusting lever with the protruding tip of the mixture adjustment screw. Secure the assembly with the retaining screw.

24 Turn the mixture adjustment screw as necessary to bring the top of the jet flush with the jet bearing upper face when viewed from above. Now turn the adjustment screw two complete turns clockwise to obtain an initial mixture setting.

25 Fit a new O-ring seal to the float chamber cover. Fit the cover with the previously made marks aligned and secure with the four retaining screws.

26 Refit the piston needle, spring and needle guide to the piston ensuring that the needle guide is flush with the underside of the piston and the triangular etch mark on the guide is between the two transfer holes in the piston.

Refit and tighten the locking screw (photo).

27 Temporarily refit the piston and dashpot to the carburettor body without the spring. Engage the piston in its guide and, with the suction chamber in its correct position relative to the retaining screws, mark the piston-to-suction chamber relationship. Remove the suction chamber and piston.

28 Fit the spring to the piston, align the previously made marks and slide the suction chamber over the piston and spring. Avoid turning the piston in the suction chamber, otherwise the spring will be wound up.

29 Push the piston rod up and refit the circlip to the piston rod.

30 Refit the piston and suction chamber, and secure with the three retaining screws tightened evenly. Fill the piston damper with engine oil up to the top of the piston and refit the damper.

31 Refit the fuel shut-off valve using a new gasket, if necessary, and secure the unit with the three screws.

25 Thermac switch - removal and refitting

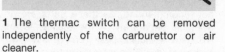

1 The thermac switch can be removed independently of the carburettor or air cleaner.

2 Prise the sensor and grommet from the plenum chamber. Remove the seal and disconnect both vacuum hoses.

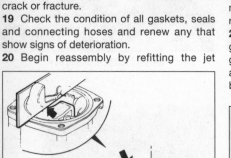

Fig. 3.17 SU carburettor float setting diagram (Sec 24)

A 1.0 to 1.5 mm (0.039 to 0.059 in)

24.26 Needle, spring and guide

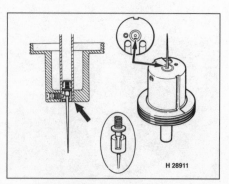

Fig. 3.18 SU carburettor needle arrangement (Sec 24)

3 Reassemble the new switch to the grommet and secure it with the spring clip.

4 When installed, check that the switch is firmly held in the grommet.

5 Apply suitable sealant to the grommet and fit the switch assembly into the plenum chamber so that the switch is in the horizontal plane. Reconnect both vacuum hoses.

26 Inertia switch (1.6 models) - removal and refitting

1 Open the cover of the fuse box and remove the bolt from the inertia (fuel cut-off) switch mounting bracket.

2 Withdraw the switch and disconnect the multi-plug.

3 To check the action of the inertia switch, depress the button and then strike the front of the switch against the hand which will cause the button to lock in the raised position.

4 Once the switch is fitted, depress the button to set it.

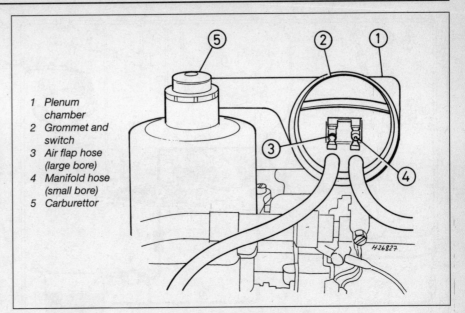

1 Plenum chamber
2 Grommet and switch
3 Air flap hose (large bore)
4 Manifold hose (small bore)
5 Carburettor

Fig. 3.19 Thermac switch (Sec 25)

Part B Models with fuel injection

27 Description and operation

1 The system consists of a fuel tank located ahead of the rear suspension, an electrically operated fuel pump, a temperature controlled air cleaner and a Lucas electronic fuel injection system.

2 The main components of the fuel injection system are shown in Fig. 3.20 and their function is described in the following paragraphs.

3 Directly associated with the system are the ignition electronic control unit, the injection coil and the speed sensor.

Fuel electronic control unit

4 This is located under the front left-hand seat and is the control centre for the fuel injection system.

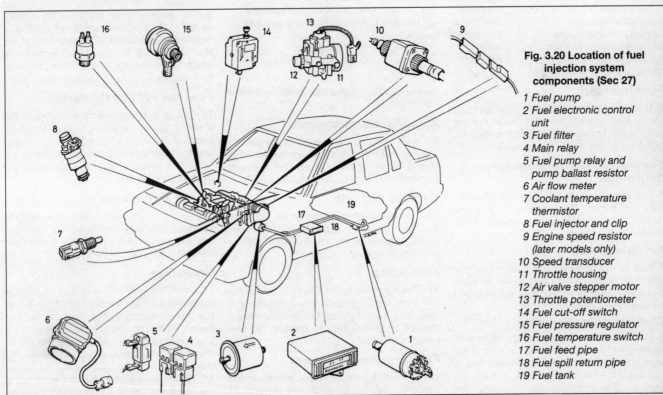

Fig. 3.20 Location of fuel injection system components (Sec 27)

1 Fuel pump
2 Fuel electronic control unit
3 Fuel filter
4 Main relay
5 Fuel pump relay and pump ballast resistor
6 Air flow meter
7 Coolant temperature thermistor
8 Fuel injector and clip
9 Engine speed resistor (later models only)
10 Speed transducer
11 Throttle housing
12 Air valve stepper motor
13 Throttle potentiometer
14 Fuel cut-off switch
15 Fuel pressure regulator
16 Fuel temperature switch
17 Fuel feed pipe
18 Fuel spill return pipe
19 Fuel tank

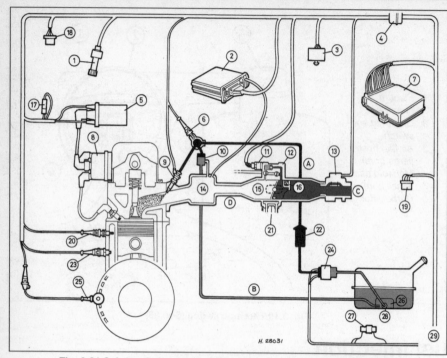

Fig. 3.21 Schematic layout of electronic fuel injection system (Sec 27)

1 Speed sensor
2 Ignition ECU
3 Inertia (fuel cut-off) switch
4 Engine harness multi-plug
5 Ignition coil
6 Fuel temperature switch
7 Fuel ECU
8 Distributor cap and spark plug leads
9 Injector
10 Fuel pressure regulator
11 Air valve stepper motor
12 Base idle speed and mixture adjustment screw

13 Air flow meter
14 Inlet manifold
15 Throttle potentiometer
16 Throttle speed screw
17 Engine speed resistor
18 Fuel pump relay
19 Main relay
20 Coolant temperature thermistor
21 Throttle housing – coolant and crankcase ventilation ports
22 Fuel filter

23 Knock sensor
24 Fuel pump
25 Crankshaft sensor
26 Fuel spill return swirl pot
27 Fuel pump ballast resistor
28 Fuel tank pick-up strainer
29 To main harness multi-plug
A Regulated fuel pressure
B Spill return low pressure fuel
C Inlet air flow
D Manifold depression

Fuel injectors

5 The fuel injectors are solenoid operated and are located between the pressurised fuel rail and the inlet manifold. The injector nozzles are designed to give good fuel atomisation.

Engine coolant temperature thermistor

6 This is located in the coolant inlet elbow on the cylinder head. The thermistor is a resistive device, its resistance varying with temperature changes.

Air flow meter

7 This is of hot wire type over which the intake air flows. A proportion of the air flows through a bypass in which a sensing and compensating element are located.

Throttle potentiometer

8 This is mounted at the rear of the throttle housing and is directly coupled to the throttle shaft. Movement of accelerator pedal and in consequence the throttle shaft, rotates the arm in the potentiometer to vary the

resistance which is then monitored by the fuel control unit.

Air valve stepper motor

9 This is screwed into the top of the throttle housing and has directional control windings so that the air valve can be opened or closed as directed by the fuel control unit.

Throttle housing

10 This is attached directly to the inlet manifold and incorporates the throttle speed screw, base idle speed screw and the mixture adjusting screw.

Fuel pump

11 This is located on the left-hand side of the fuel tank and is of self-priming centrifugal type. The pump supplies fuel under pressure through an in-line filter to the fuel rail and pressure regulator.

Fuel pressure regulator

12 This is a mechanical device which controls fuel rail pressure by means of

27.13 Fuel injection system relay

manifold vacuum pressure. The regulator is located on the fuel rail. Under normal driving conditions, the fuel rail pressure is maintained at 2.5 bar (36 lbf/in²) above manifold vacuum to ensure that the pressure difference across the injector nozzles remains constant.

Relays

13 These are located on the air cleaner housing mounting bracket (photo). The main relay is energised with the ignition on and provides a feed to the fuel ECU. The fuel pump relay is energised by the ECU briefly when the ignition is switched on, and continuously when the engine is running.

Fuel temperature switch

14 This is a bi-metallic switch which when the temperature in the fuel rail rises above 90°C (194°F), the switch closes and the engine coolant temperature thermistor signal is bypassed. This action is sensed by the fuel control unit which then increases the opening period of the injectors during hot starting to reduce the effects of fuel vaporisation. At hot start, it is normal for the coolant temperature gauge and warning lamp to indicate high temperature.

Fuel cut-off inertia switch

15 This is a safety switch mounted on the steering column bracket behind the facia panel. In the event of a collision, the switch shuts off the control unit and the fuel pump relay. The switch is reset by depressing the button inside the fuse box.

Speed transducer

16 This is mounted on the engine compartment rear bulkhead, its purpose being to provide the fuel system control unit with road speeds.

Operation

17 When the ignition is switched on, voltage is applied through the fuel cut-off switch to the fuel pump relay, the fuel and ignition system electronic control units. The fuel rail is pressurised and voltage is applied to the air flow meter, the fuel injectors and the ignition control unit.

18 When the ignition switch is turned to the start position, the fuel control unit receives

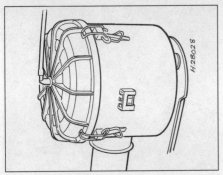

Fig. 3.22 Air cleaner (fuel injection system) showing vacuum pipe (Sec 29)

29.1 Air cleaner casing and element

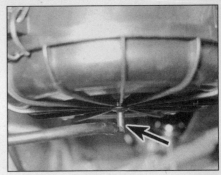

29.6 Air cleaner cover vacuum hose

data from the transducer, thermistor, potentiometer air flow meter and ignition pulses to determine fuel injector opening time and fuel enrichment.

19 Once the engine fires, the fuel control unit regulates the injector opening and consequently the volume of fuel injected, varying this as the engine temperature rises.

20 Constant engine idle speed is maintained by the control unit regulating the air valve position.

21 If while the engine is idling, engine load is increased through the alternator having to supply a greater output, because of electrical accessories being switch on, then the stepper motor will be energised and the air valve opened by the control unit to maintain a constant engine idle speed.

22 During normal driving, the control unit continually monitors road speed, air flow engine temperature, throttle opening and engine speed. All changes in these parameters are monitored to vary the injector opening times to suit all monitoring conditions. An electronic memory is used as a basis for engine speed/load fuel requirement computations.

23 During engine overrun conditions, the control unit cuts off the fuel, provided certain conditions apply regarding the engine coolant temperature, which should be above 36°C (96.8°F), the throttle in idle position and the engine speed in excess of 1400 rev/min.

24 As the engine speed falls below 110 rev/min and the accelerator pedal depressed, fuel is again supplied for smooth take up.

25 At full throttle conditions, the fuel electronic control unit provides more fuel for full load enrichment by holding the injectors open for a longer period.

26 The fuel electronic control unit signals the ignition control unit during idling to ensure that the ignition timing is held at 20° BTDC so that the idle speed is held steady.

28 Maintenance and inspection

1 At the intervals given in Routine Maintenance at the beginning of this Manual, carry out the following service operations to the fuel system components.

2 With the car over a pit, raised on a vehicle lift, or securely supported on axle stands, carefully inspect the fuel pipes, hoses and unions for chafing, leaks and corrosion. Renew any pipes that are severely pitted with corrosion or in any way damaged. Renew any hoses that show signs of cracking or other deterioration. Only use specially supplied cut to length fuel injection hoses as they have a special lining to resist the high temperature and pressure of the fuel.

3 Always position the hose clips 3.0 mm

(0.12 in) from the end of the hoses, never flush with the end.

4 Examine the fuel tank for leaks, particularly around the fuel gauge sender unit, and for signs of corrosion or damage.

5 Check condition of exhaust system, as described in Section 41.

6 From within the engine compartment, check the security of all fuel hose attachments and inspect the fuel hoses and vacuum hoses for kinks, chafing or deterioration.

7 Renew the air cleaner element and clean the air cleaner body and cover.

8 Check the operation of the accelerator linkage and lubricate the linkage, cable and pedal pivot with a few drops of engine oil.

9 Check the fuel injection system idle speed and mixture settings, as described in Section 36 where necessary.

10 Renew the fuel filter as described in Section 31.

29 Air cleaner - servicing, removal and refitting

1 To renew the air cleaner element, spring back the retaining clips and lift off the air cleaner cover (photo).

2 Withdraw the element then wipe clean the inside of the air cleaner housing and cover.

3 Fit a new element, locate the cover on the air cleaner housing and secure with the retaining clips.

4 To remove the air cleaner and bracket, first disconnect and remove the battery (Chapter 12).

5 Slacken the clip and detach the cold air intake hose from the air cleaner housing.

6 Disconnect the small vacuum hose from the centre of the air cleaner cover (photo).

7 Disconnect the air flow meter wiring plug, undo the bolts and remove the air flow meter from the air cleaner. Move the meter to one side, with the hose still attached, or disconnect the hose to the throttle housing and remove the air flow meter (photos).

8 Pull the two relays, with their sockets, from

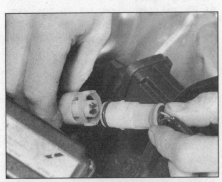

29.7A Disconnecting the air flow meter wiring plug

29.7B Removing the air flow meter

29.8 Main and fuel pump relays clipped to air cleaner bracket

29.11 Close up of bracket securing bolt

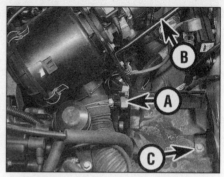

29.12 General view of air cleaner and bracket showing resistor (A), support tube (B) and bracket securing bolt (C)

the air cleaner bracket and place them to one side, still connected (photo).

9 Disconnect the two wires to the fuel pump ballast resistor, marking them for correct refitting.

10 Remove the bolts from the air cleaner bracket support tube and remove the tube.

11 Remove the bolt securing the air cleaner bracket to the battery tray and lift out the air cleaner and bracket (photo).

12 Refitting is a reversal of removal, ensuring that the relay caps are uppermost (photo).

30 Fuel system - depressurising

> **⚠ Warning: Take adequate fire precautions during this procedure**

1 The fuel system must be depressurised before any part of the fuel line between the fuel pump and fuel regulator is disconnected.

2 Disconnect the fuel pump relay and then disconnect the blue/red lead from the starter solenoid. This will prevent the fuel pump from operating. As a safety measure, if it is not wished for the engine to run, disconnect the HT lead from the ignition coil. Do not disconnect the LT lead .

3 Crank the engine for at least ten seconds or allow it to run until it stops.

4 Disconnect the battery and then uncouple

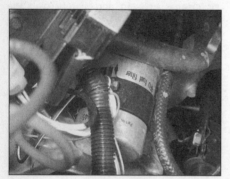

31.4 Fuel filter

the fuel line or component. Be prepared for some fuel to drain out.

5 On completion of work, reconnect the relay, HT lead and battery.

31 Fuel filter - renewal

> **⚠ Warning: Take adequate fire precautions during this procedure**

1 Depressurise the fuel system as described in the preceding Section.

2 Slacken the clips on the air intake elbow at the flow meter and on the fuel intake hose at the throttle housing.

3 Remove the air intake hose with elbow.

4 Slacken the fuel filter clamp bracket, ease the filter forward and out of its bracket. Release the filter from the fuel inlet hose (photo).

5 Refit the new filter by reversing the removal operations, but make sure that the arrow on the filter points towards the fuel outlet hose.

32 Fuel pump - removal and refitting

> **⚠ Warning: Take adequate fire precautions during this procedure**

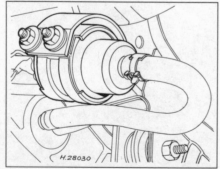

Fig. 3.23 Fuel pump (fuel injection system) (Sec 32)

H.28030

1 Depressurise the fuel system as described in Section 30 then disconnect the battery negative terminal.

2 Syphon, or hand pump all the fuel from the fuel tank.

3 Jack up the rear of the car and support it on axle stands.

4 Disconnect the wiring connectors at the fuel pump which is located to the rear of the fuel tank, just above the rear axle transverse member (photo).

5 Undo the two nuts and washers securing the pump retaining strap to the mounting bracket.

6 Ease the strap studs out of the mounting bracket, then manoeuvre the pump down between the rear axle member and the spare wheel well.

7 Position a suitable bowl beneath the pump and disconnect the inlet and outlet hoses from the pump nozzles. Plug the hoses after removal. **Note:** *a quantity of fuel will be released during this operation.*

8 Note the fitted relationship of the pump terminals to the strap studs and push the pump out of the strap support rubbers. Free the pump from the rubbers if adhesive has been used for retention.

9 To refit the pump apply adhesive to the strap rubbers and insert the pump into the strap. Position the pump in the strap as noted during removal so that the terminals will be vertical when the pump is installed.

10 Reconnect the inlet and outlet hoses to the pump nozzles.

11 Fit the plain washers to the strap mounting studs, manoeuvre the pump into position and secure with the plain washers and nuts.

12 Reconnect the pump wiring and lower the car to the ground.

13 Reconnect the fuel relay circuit, reconnect the battery and fill the fuel tank.

33 Fuel tank - removal, repair and refitting

The operations are as described in Section 8 of Part A.

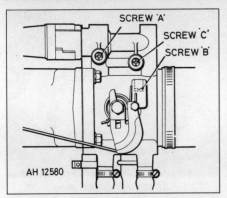

Fig. 3.24 Fuel injection system adjustment screws (Sec 36)

A Mixture screw
B Base idle screw
C Throttle by-pass screw (early models only)

34 Fuel level transmitter and gauge

Refer to Part A, Sections 9 and 10.

35 Throttle cable and accelerator pedal

Refer to Part A, Sections 11 and 13. Note that the cable is attached to the lever on the throttle housing.

36 Idle speed and mixture - adjustment

See Chapter 13, Section 5

Note: Idle speed is controlled by the fuel ECU and should not normally need adjusting. Idle mixture may need adjusting after long periods of service. The complete procedure described here would be used after major component renewal, and may require special equipment - see paragraph 6.

Some adjustment screws may be protected

37.2 Air flow meter

36.9 Adjusting the mixture screw

by tamperproof caps. Satisfy yourself that you are not breaking local or national anti-pollution laws before removing such caps; fit new caps on completion when required by law.

1 Bring the engine to normal operating temperature (cooling fan having operated at least once). Switch off all electrical equipment.
2 Connect an accurate tachometer (rev counter) to the engine in accordance with the maker's instructions.
3 Set the air valve in the closed position as follows:
(a) With the ignition on, disconnect the air valve stepper motor multi-plug. Switch the ignition off, wait five seconds and reconnect the multi-plug
(b) Switch the ignition on, wait five seconds and repeat paragraph (a)
(c) Switch the ignition on, wait five seconds and disconnect the multiplug
4 Turn the throttle by-pass screw fully clockwise. (This screw is not present on later models).
5 Start the engine and allow it to idle. The idle speed should be within the limits given with the air valve closed (see Specifications). Turn the base idle screw if necessary to bring the idle speed within limits.
6 If the base idle screw has been disturbed, the throttle potentiometer must now be adjusted by a Rover dealer or other competent specialist using dedicated test equipment.
7 Reconnect the air valve stepper motor multi-plug. Run the engine and check that the idle speed (now controlled by the ECU) is as specified.

37.5 Stepper motor plug (arrowed)

8 Connect an exhaust gas analyser in accordance with its maker's instructions.
9 Read the exhaust CO level at idle and compare it with that specified. If adjustment is necessary, turn the mixture screw clockwise to increase the CO level, anti-clockwise to reduce it (photo).
10 If the radiator cooling fan cuts in during adjustment, wait until it stops before proceeding.
11 Stop the engine, disconnect the test gear and (when applicable) fit new tamperproof caps.

37 Fuel injection system components - removal and refitting

Air flow meter

1 Disconnect the air flow meter wiring plug.
2 Release the retaining clip and detach the intake air hose from the air flow meter (photo).
3 Undo the two bolts securing the meter to the air cleaner bracket and withdraw the unit from the bracket and air cleaner body.
4 Refitting is the reverse sequence to removal. Make sure that the hose clip is fitted squarely.

Air valve stepper motor

5 Slide back the rubber cover and disconnect the stepper motor multi-plug (photo).
6 Using a 32 mm spanner, unscrew the stepper motor from the throttle housing.
7 To refit the stepper motor, fit a new sealing washer and apply a thread sealant to the stepper motor threads.
8 Screw the unit in finger tight then carefully tighten with the spanner.
9 Refit the multi-plug and the rubber cover.

Fuel temperature switch

10 Disconnect the wiring multi-plug and unscrew, then switch from the top of the fuel rail.
11 Refit the switch using the reverse sequence of removal.

Fuel pressure regulator

 Warning: Take adequate fire precautions during this procedure

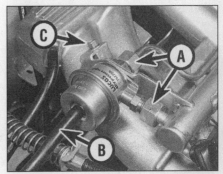

37.13 Fuel pressure regulator union nuts (A), vacuum hose (B) and retaining nut (C)

3

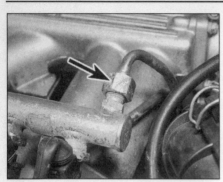

37.21A Fuel rail union nut (arrowed)

37.21B Fuel rail

37.22 Fuel injector plug

12 Depressurise the fuel system as described in Section 30, then disconnect the battery negative terminal.

13 Place absorbent rags beneath the regulator, unscrew the union nuts and remove the two fuel hoses (photo).

14 Disconnect the vacuum hose from the rear of the regulator.

15 Undo the retaining nut and washer then withdraw the unit from its support bracket.

16 Refitting is the reverse sequence of removal. After fitting, reconnect the fuel relay circuit as described in Section 30 and reconnect the battery.

Fuel rail

 Warning: Take adequate fire precautions during this procedure

17 Depressurise the fuel system as described in Section 30 then disconnect the battery negative terminal.

18 Place absorbent rag beneath the fuel rail.

19 Unscrew the fuel pressure regulator to fuel rail hose union at the regulator. Plug the hose and regulator after removal.

20 Slacken the fuel pressure regulator retaining nut, slide the regulator out of its support bracket and place it to one side.

21 Unscrew the fuel inlet hose union at the fuel rail, remove the hose and plug its end (photos).

22 Disconnect the wiring multi-plug at each fuel injector (photo).

23 Extract the clips securing the fuel injectors to the fuel rail.

24 Undo the two bolts securing the fuel rail to the manifold, holding the injectors to prevent displacement, and remove the fuel rail.

25 Before refitting the fuel rail, renew the O-ring seals on each fuel injector.

26 Refitting the fuel rail is the reverse sequence of removal. After fitting, reconnect the fuel relay circuit as described in Section 30 and reconnect the battery.

Fuel injectors

 Warning: Take adequate fire precautions during this procedure

27 Slacken the fuel pressure regulator retaining nut, slide the regulator out of its support bracket and lay it on the manifold with hoses still attached.

28 Undo the two bolts securing the fuel rail to the manifold. Lift up the fuel rail and at the same time ease the injectors out of their seatings in the manifold. Lay the injectors over the engine wiring harness.

29 Switch on the ignition, wait ten seconds, then switch off. The fuel pump will operate for approximately three seconds while the ignition is switched on and will pressurise the injectors.

30 Observe each injector and renew any that leak more than two drops of fuel per minute.

31 To check the injector spray pattern, disconnect all the injector multi-plugs except the one on the injector to be tested.

32 Place a glass jar under the connected injector so that the sprayed fuel can be contained but the pattern still observed.

33 Ensure that the ignition is switched off (to avoid damage to the ECU), then disconnect the ECU wiring multi-plug. The ECU is located behind the carpet above the passenger's footwell.

34 Earth pin No 16, followed by pin No 4. This will allow the fuel pump relay and the main relay to be energised, thus allowing the

fuel pump to provide full pressure and the injector to be energised.

35 Switch on the ignition, and carefully earth pin No 1. The chosen injector should now spray while pin No 1 is earthed. The spray pattern should be regular, and fuel should be delivered at a rate of 185cc/minute. If this is not the case, the injector should be renewed.

36 Repeat the above tests on the remaining injectors, reconnecting each individual injector after testing. On completion, renew any injectors which are faulty, as described below.

37 Depressurise the fuel system (Section 30), then disconnect the battery. Disconnect the wiring multi-plug at the fuel temperature switch, and the multi-plug at each fuel injector.

38 Lift the fuel rail up and at the same time ease the injectors out of their locations in the manifold. Extract the retaining clip(s) and withdraw the injector(s) from the fuel rail.

39 To refit the injector(s), wipe clean the injector and manifold seating areas and fit a new O-ring seal to the base of each injector. Fit a new O-ring seal to the top of any injector that was removed from the fuel rail.

40 Fit the injectors to the fuel rail and secure with the retaining clips.

41 Align the injectors with their seatings in the manifold and press them fully into position.

42 Refit the two fuel rail retaining bolts and tighten securely.

43 Reconnect the fuel temperature switch and fuel injector multi-plugs.

44 Slide the fuel pressure regulator back into its support bracket and tighten the retaining nut.

45 Reconnect the fuel pump relay circuit as described in Section 30. Before reconnecting the battery, check that the ECU multi-plug is correctly refitted.

Throttle housing

46 Disconnect the battery negative terminal.

47 Disconnect the wiring multi-plug at the end of the throttle potentiometer lead.

48 Slide back the rubber cover and disconnect the wiring multi-plug at the air valve stepper motor.

Fig. 3.25 Fuel injector (Sec 37)

1 Fuel injector   5 Injector retaining clip
2 O-ring seal   4 Fuel rail
3 O-ring seal

49 Slacken the retaining clip and detach the intake air hose from the throttle housing.

50 Slacken the retaining screw and release the accelerator cable from the connector on the throttle housing linkage.

51 On models with automatic transmission, disconnect the kickdown cable.

52 Unscrew the cooling system expansion tank filler cap to release all pressure in the cooling system. Remove the cap slowly if the system is hot.

53 Disconnect the air and vacuum hoses at the rear of the throttle housing, noting their location.

54 Undo the bolts securing the throttle housing to the manifold and ease the unit off the flange.

55 Disconnect the coolant and crankcase breather hoses from beneath the housing and remove the housing from the engine. Plug the coolant hose.

56 The air valve stepper motor may be removed from the throttle housing by simply unscrewing it using a 32 mm spanner, it is advisable to leave the throttle potentiometer undisturbed so as not to lose its set fitted position. If the potentiometer is disturbed,

recalibration by a BL dealer will be necessary.

57 Refitting the throttle housing is the reverse sequence of removal, bearing in mind the following points:

(a) *Ensure that the throttle housing and manifold mating faces are perfectly clean and if necessary use a new gasket*

(b) *Reconnect the accelerator cable*

(c) *Top-up the cooling system if necessary to the level indicated on the expansion tank.*

Fuel cut-off inertia switch

58 Unbolt the switch mounting bracket from below and to the right of the heater unit.

59 Disconnect the wiring plug from the switch.

60 Unscrew the two through-bolts and disconnect the switch from its bracket.

61 Refitting is a reversal of removal.

Electronic control unit

62 Disconnect the battery.

63 Remove the left-hand front seat.

64 Disconnect the multi-plug from the control unit and unbolt the control unit mounting bracket.

65 Refitting is a reversal of removal.

37.66 Speed transducer

Speed transducer

66 Disconnect the multi-plug from the speed transducer (photo).

67 Unscrew the speedometer cable from the speed transducer.

68 Unscrew the nut which holds the speed transducer mounting bracket to the engine compartment rear bulkhead and lift away the speed transducer and bracket.

69 Refitting is a reversal of removal.

3

Part C Exhaust systems and manifolds

38 Manifolds (1.3 models) - removal and refitting

Inlet manifold

1 The inlet manifold is coolant-heated and is of light alloy construction.

2 To remove the manifold, drain the cooling system and then disconnect all hoses from the manifold.

3 Disconnect all leads, hoses and control cables from the carburettor and remove it.

4 Unbolt the manifold support bracket (photo).

5 Unscrew the manifold fixing nuts and withdraw the manifold. Discard the gasket (photo).

Exhaust manifold

6 The exhaust manifold is of cast iron construction and incorporates a hot air collecting shroud.

7 To remove the manifold, disconnect the battery, raise the front of the car and support it securely.

8 Remove the centre undershield.

9 Disconnect the exhaust downpipe from the manifold. Retrieve the sealing ring (photo).

10 Disconnect the weathershield from the

38.4 Wiring harness support clip at inlet manifold

38.5 Unscrewing inlet manifold nuts

38.9 Exhaust manifold to downpipe flange support bracket (arrowed)

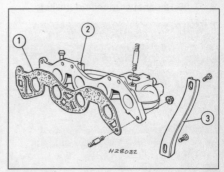

Fig. 3.26 Inlet manifold (1.3 models) (Sec 38)

1 Gasket   2 Manifold   3 Support bracket

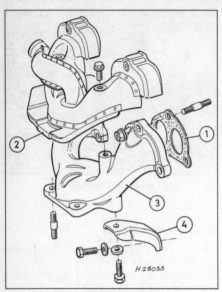

Fig. 3.27 Exhaust manifold (1.3 models) (Sec 38)

1 Gasket
2 Hot air collecting shroud
3 Manifold
4 Support bracket

front panel and disconnect the hot air duct from the manifold shroud.
11 Remove the hot air shroud and the manifold support bracket (photos) .
12 Unscrew the fixing nuts and lift the manifold from the cylinder head. Discard the gasket (photo).
13 Refitting both manifolds is a reversal of removal. Use new gaskets fitted to clean

38.12 Exhaust manifold gaskets

38.13 Inlet manifold gasket

38.11A Exhaust manifold hot air collector

38.11B Exhaust manifold with hot air collector removed

mating surfaces and tighten all nuts and bolts to the specified torque (photo).
14 If the inlet manifold was removed, refill the cooling system (Chapter 2).
15 Reconnect the battery.

39 Manifolds (1.6 carburettor models) - removal and refitting

1 The inlet manifold incorporates an electric heater which operates as soon as the ignition switch is turned on. Its purpose is to reduce cold start enrichment. The manifold is also coolant-heated and as the temperature of the coolant rises, a temperature sensor reduces and then switches off the electric heater.
2 To reduce the manifolds, first disconnect the battery.

3 Remove the air cleaner (Section 3).
4 Remove the carburettor (Section 23).
5 Drain the cooling system.
6 Disconnect all hoses and leads from the inlet manifold.
7 Raise the front of the car and support it securely. Disconnect the exhaust downpipe from the manifold.
8 Unbolt the inlet manifold support struts.
9 Unbolt and remove the heat shield from the inlet manifold and the hot air shroud from the exhaust manifold.
10 Unscrew all fixing nuts and bolts and lift the manifolds from the cylinder head. Discard the gasket.
11 Refitting is a reversal of removal. Use a new gasket on clean mating surfaces and tighten all nuts and bolts to the specified torque.
12 Refill the cooling system.
13 Reconnect the battery.

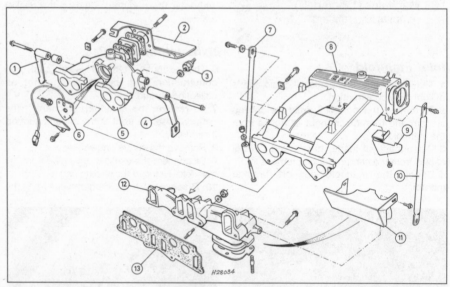

Fig. 3.28 Manifolds - 1.6 models with carburettor (left) and with fuel injection (right) (Secs 39 and 40)

1 Support strut (RH - carburettor models)
2 Heat shield
3 Induction temperature sensor
4 Support strut (LH - carburettor models)
5 Inlet manifold (carburettor models)
6 Induction heater
7 Support strut (RH - fuel injection models)
8 Inlet manifold (fuel injection models)
9 Throttle cable bracket
10 Support strut (LH - fuel injection models)
11 Hot air collecting shroud
12 Exhaust manifold
13 Gasket

41.3A Spring-loaded exhaust joint

41.3B Exhaust system support at transmission (1.3 shown)

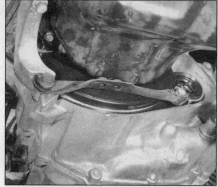

41.3C Exhaust support bracket at transmission (1.3 models)

40 Manifolds (1.6 fuel injection models) - removal and refitting

1 Depressurise the fuel system as described in Section 30.
2 Disconnect the battery.
3 Disconnect the vacuum hoses from the inlet chamber and the multi-plug from the air valve stepper motor.
4 Disconnect the wiring plugs from the fuel injectors and fuel temperature switch.
5 Disconnect the spill return hose from the fuel regulator valve - be prepared for some loss of fuel.
6 Release the fuel rail from the manifold and place the fuel rail to one side.
7 Release the throttle cable from its support bracket.
8 Disconnect the throttle housing from the flange on the inlet manifold.
9 Extract the two screws which hold the heater rail to the inlet manifold.
10 Slacken all manifold fixing nuts and bolts which are accessible from above. Remember the nut under the thermostat housing.

11 Slacken the manifold support strut bolts.
12 If the inlet and exhaust manifolds are to be removed, then disconnect the exhaust downpipe from the manifold.
13 Unscrew the remaining manifold and support strut nuts and bolts from underneath the car.
14 Withdraw the manifolds and discard the gaskets.
15 Refitting is a reversal of removal. Use new gaskets on clean mating surfaces. Tighten all nuts and bolts to the specified torque.

41 Exhaust system - inspection, removal and refitting

1 The exhaust system should be examined for leaks, damage and security at regular intervals (see Routine Maintenance). To do this, apply the handbrake and in a well-ventilated area, allow the engine to idle. Lie down on each side of the car in turn, and check the full length of the exhaust system for leaks while an assistant temporarily places a wad of cloth over the end of the tailpipe. If a leak is evident, stop the engine and use a proprietary repair kit to seal. If the leak is excessive, or damage is evident, renew the section. Check the rubber mountings for deterioration, and renew them, if necessary.
2 On 1.3 models, a single downpipe is used while on 1.6 versions, a dual downpipe is used.
3 All systems are of three section type using a flexible joint with bolts and coil springs, or ball couplings with tension springs according to vehicle model, to absorb the flexing of the engine on its mountings (photos).
4 If only one section of the system requires renewal, it is recommended that the complete exhaust is withdrawn from under the car to make separation easier. Do this by disconnecting the downpipe from the manifold and releasing the flexible mountings (photos).
5 When reassembling the system, do not tighten the clamps until the exhaust has been attached to the car. Once the pipe and silencer have been correctly aligned and they are not likely to knock against any adjacent suspension or body components, fully tighten the clamps.

3

41.4A Exhaust system fixed joint

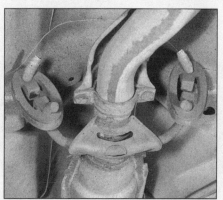

41.4B Exhaust system centre mounting

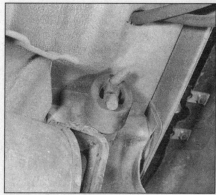

41.4C Exhaust silencer flexible mounting

Fault finding - fuel system (carburettor models)

Unsatisfactory engine performance, bad starting and excessive fuel consumption are not necessarily the fault of the fuel system or carburettor. In fact they more commonly occur as a result of ignition and timing faults. Before acting on the following, it is necessary to check the ignition system first. Even though a fault may lie in the fuel system, it will be difficult to trace unless the ignition system is correct. The faults below, therefore, assume that, where applicable, this has been attended to first. If during the fault diagnosis procedure it is suspected that the carburettor electronic mixture control or any of its related systems may be at fault, it is recommended that the help of a reputable BL dealer is sought. Accurate testing of the system and its components entails the use of a systematic checking procedure using specialist equipment and this is considered beyond the scope of the average home mechanic.

Difficult starting when cold

☐ Faulty electronic mixture control system or related component
☐ Carburettor piston sticking (SU)
☐ Fuel tank empty or pump defective
☐ Incorrect float chamber fuel level
☐ Manual choke maladjusted (Keihin)
☐ Weak mixture

Difficult starting when hot

☐ Faulty electronic mixture control system or related component
☐ Air cleaner choked
☐ Carburettor piston sticking (SU)
☐ Float chamber flooding or incorrect fuel level
☐ Fuel tank empty or pump defective
☐ Carburettor idle mixture adjustment incorrect
☐ Accelerator pedal pumped before starting

Fuel starvation

☐ Fuel level flow
☐ Leak on suction side of pump
☐ Fuel pump faulty
☐ Float chamber fuel level incorrect
☐ Fuel tank breather restricted
☐ Fuel tank inlet or carburettor inlet filter blocked

Smell of petrol when engine is idling

☐ Leaking fuel line unions between pump and carburettor
☐ Overflow of fuel from float chamber due to wrong level setting,
☐ ineffective needle valve or punctured float

Smell of petrol when engine is stopped

☐ Leaking fuel lines or unions
☐ Leaking fuel tank

Excessive fuel consumption

☐ Leakage from tank, pipes, pump or carburettor
☐ Air cleaner choked
☐ Carburettor idle mixture adjustment incorrect
☐ Carburettor float chamber flooding
☐ Faulty fuel shut-off solenoid or control system
☐ Carburettor worn
☐ Excessive engine wear or other internal fault
☐ Tyres underinflated
☐ Brakes binding
☐ Worn jets (Keihin)
☐ Choke maladjusted (Keihin)

Poor performance, hesitation or erratic running

☐ Carburettor idle mixture adjustment incorrect
☐ Faulty carburettor vacuum switch (SU)
☐ Carburettor piston damper oil level low (SU)
☐ Leaking manifold gasket
☐ Fuel starvation
☐ Carburettor worn
☐ Excessive engine wear or other internal fault
☐ Faulty accelerator pump (Keihin)
☐ Blocked jets (Keihin)
☐ Slack in throttle cable

Engine runs on

☐ Fuel cut-off valve stuck open

Fault finding - fuel system (Fuel injection models)

Owing to the complexity of the electronic circuitry and the nature of the computer controlled operation, special test equipment has been developed for fault diagnosis on the fuel injection system. Therefore any suspected faults on the system or its related components should be referred to a suitably equipped BL dealer.

Chapter 4 Ignition system

For modifications, and information applicable to later models, see Supplement at end of manual

Contents

Degrees of difficulty

Easy, suitable for novice with little experience	**Fairly easy,** suitable for beginner with some experience	**Fairly difficult,** suitable for competent DIY mechanic	**Difficult,** suitable for experienced DIY mechanic	**Very difficult,** suitable for expert DIY or professional

Specifications

Part A 1.3 models

System type .... Electronic (breakerless)

Distributor

Firing order .... 1 - 3 - 4 - 2
Rotor rotation .... Clockwise

Ignition timing (at idle speed, vacuum pipe connected) ...... 15 to 19° BTDC

Advance

Centrifugal advance (crankshaft degrees BTDC, vacuum
disconnected) ....
28 to 32° at 5500 rev/min
22 to 25° at 4000 rev/min
18 to 21° at 3000 rev/min
8 to 12° at 2000 rev/min
0 to 4° at 1200 rev/min
No advance below 800 rev/min

Vacuum advance:
  Starts .... 55 to 85 mm Hg (2.2 to 3.3 in Hg)
  Finishes .... 220 to 280 mm Hg (8.7 to 11.0 in Hg)
Maximum advance .... 9 to 11°

Spark plugs

Type/gap .... Champion RN9YCC or RN9YC/1.0 mm (0.040 in)

Ignition coil

Primary winding resistance .... 1.24 to 1.46 ohms at 20°C (68°F)
Secondary winding resistance .... 8000 to 12 000 ohms at 20°C (68°F)

Part B 1.6 models

System type .... Programmed electronic
Firing order .... 1 - 3 - 4 - 2
Rotor rotation .... Anti-clockwise

4

Ignition timing

Carburettor engine at 1400 rev/min:
    Vacuum disconnected from ECU .... 13° BTDC
    Vacuum connected to ECU .... 40° BTDC
Fuel injection engine at 750 rev/min:
    Vacuum disconnected from ECU .... 20° BTDC
    Vacuum connected to ECU .... 20° BTDC

Spark plugs

Type/gap:
    Carburettor and fuel injection engines .... Champion RC9YCC or RC9YC/0.8 mm (0.032 in)

HT leads .... Champion LS-05, boxed set

Ignition coil

Primary resistance at 20°C (68°F) .... 0.71 to 0.81 ohms

Part C All models

Torque wrench settings

	Nm	lbf ft
Spark plugs	18	13
Distributor mounting bolts	24	18

Part A 1.3 models

1 General description

The ignition system on 1.3 models is of electronic, breakerless type and incorporates a distributor driven from the rear of the camshaft, an igniter module mounted on the distributor body and a coil.

The distributor contains a reluctor mounted on its shaft and a magnet and stator fixed to the baseplate.

Ignition advance is controlled in the conventional way mechanically by centrifugal weights and a diaphragm unit for vacuum advance.

Instead of the conventional method of interrupting the low tension circuit to generate high tension voltage in the coil by means of a mechanical contact breaker, when the electronic ignition is switched on the switching of the transistors in the igniter module prevents current flow in the coil primary windings.

Once the crankshaft rotates, the reluctor moves through the magnetic field created by the stator and when the reluctor teeth are in alignment with the stator projections, a small AC voltage is created. The module amplifies this voltage and applies it to switch the transistors and so provide an earth path for the primary circuit.

As the reluctor teeth move out of alignment with the stator projections the AC voltage changes, the transistors in the module are switched again to interrupt the primary circuit earth path. This causes a high voltage to be induced in the coil secondary winding.

A time control circuit in the module controls the charging time for the coil according to engine speed. This reduces consumption at low engine speeds and also prevents secondary voltage drop at high engine speeds.

2 Maintenance

1 Compared with a mechanical breaker type distributor, maintenance operations are simple and include the following.
2 Remove the battery and take off the distributor cap (two screws) and pull off the rotor (photo).
3 Wipe the cap clean and inspect it for hair cracks, erosion of the terminals and a worn centre carbon brush. If any of these faults are found, renew the cap.
4 The contact end of the rotor may be cleaned up carefully using very fine 'wet and dry' paper.
5 It is unlikely that the air gaps between the reluctor and stator will be unequal but if there is any doubt, check them with a feeler gauge and reset them by releasing the stator screws

2.2 Removing distributor cap

and moving the position of the stator, until all four air gaps are equal.
6 Check the distributor cap seal and renew if necessary.

3 Ignition timing

1 The valve clearances and spark plug gaps should be correctly set and the carburettor in perfect tune.
2 Have the engine at normal operating temperature. Do not disconnect the distributor vacuum hose.
3 Connect a stroboscope in accordance with the manufacturer's instructions. With the engine idling, point the light from the stroboscope at the timing marks on the front of the engine.
4 The red mark on the crankshaft pulley should be aligned with the timing mark on the

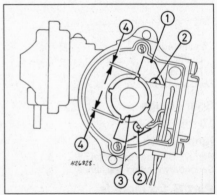

Fig. 4.1 Distributor air gaps (Sec 2)

1 Stator	3 Reluctor
2 Stator fixing screws	4 Air gaps

3.4 Crankshaft pulley timing marks

4.6 Distributor offset dog

4.7A Fitting distributor. Note O-ring seal

oil pump cover. If necessary, increase the contrast of the red (BTDC) pulley mark with a dab of white paint (photo).

5 If the marks are not in alignment, release the distributor mounting screws and rotate the distributor in either direction until they are.

6 Tighten the mounting screws, switch off the engine and remove the stroboscope.

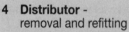
4 Distributor –
removal and refitting

1 To provide clearance, remove the battery and take off the distributor cap and place it to one side.

2 Disconnect the hose from the distributor vacuum advance unit.

3 Disconnect the primary (low tension) leads by pulling off the coil rubber cap and unscrewing the terminal nuts.

4 Scribe a line across the joint between the distributor mounting flange and the drive housing (holder).

5 Unscrew and remove the distributor mounting bolts and withdraw the distributor.

6 When refitting the distributor, note that the drive dog is offset so that the rotor cannot be set incorrectly (180° out) (photo).

7 Push the distributor into its drive housing, align the scribed marks and insert and tighten the fixing bolts (photos).

8 Reconnect the vacuum hose, low tension lead and fit the distributor cap.

4.7B Tightening distributor mounting bolt

5 Distributor – overhaul

1 With the distributor removed from the engine, clean away external dirt.

2 Remove and discard the O-ring from the distributor mounting shoulder.

3 Take off the rotor.

4 Remove the reluctor from the distributor shaft. Do this by prising it upwards using two screwdrivers held at opposite points.

5 Retrieve the roll pin.

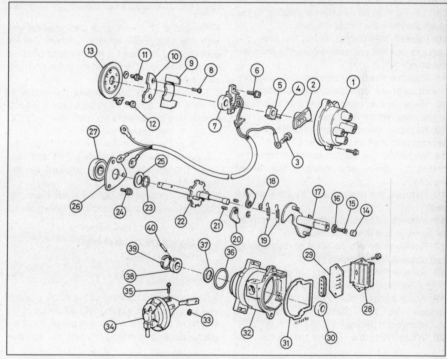

Fig. 4.2 Exploded view of the distributor (Sec 5)

1 Distributor cap	14 Rubber cap	27 Bearing
2 Rotor	15 Distributor shaft screw	28 Module cover
3 Module cover screw	16 Washer	29 Module (igniter)
4 Reluctor roll pin	17 Distributor upper shaft	30 Oil seal
5 Reluctor	18 C-clip	31 Distributor cap seal
6 Pick-up coil fixing screw	19 Counterweight governor springs	32 Distributor body
7 Pick-up coil unit	20 Counterweights	33 C-clip
8 Magnet screw	21 Pivot pins	34 Vacuum advance unit
9 Stator	22 Distributor shaft	35 Screw
10 Magnet	23 Circlip	36 O-ring
11 Vacuum unit link arm pivot stud	24 Screw	37 Thrust washer
12 Baseplate screw	25 Thrust washer	38 Drive dog
13 Baseplate	26 Thrust plate	39 Pin retainer
		40 Pin

4

5.6 Distributor module cover

5.7A Removing distributor igniter

5.7B Distributor igniter removed

6 Extract the screws which hold the module cover, remove the cover (photo).

7 Pull the igniter away from the distributor body. Use two screwdrivers as levers if necessary (photos).

8 Extract the screws which hold the pick-up coil and remove the coil.

9 Knock out the drive dog pin, remove the dog having marked its offset in relation to the shaft. Retrieve the thrust washer.

10 Extract the C-clip which secures the vacuum unit link rod and release the rod from the stud.

11 Remove the fixing screws and withdraw the vacuum unit from the distributor body.

12 Remove the vacuum unit link rod stud, stator, magnet set and baseplate.

13 Remove the advance counterweights, springs and shaft upper section.

14 Withdraw the distributor shaft from the distributor body and retrieve the thrust washer.

15 Remove the thrust plate, bearing and oil seal.

16 Inspect all components for wear, cracks or damage and renew as necessary.

17 Reassembly is a reversal of dismantling, but observe the following points.

18 Renew the shaft circlip, oil seal and O-ring. Also remove the drive dog pin.

19 Apply a smear of molybdenum disulphide grease to the distributor shaft and counterweight pivots.

20 When fitting the reluctor, make sure that

the gap in the roll pin faces away from the distributor shaft.

21 Adjust the air gap so that they are equal.

6 Ignition coil

1 The coil is of special type designed for use with the electronic ignition system. Never substitute a coil from a mechanical breaker system. The coil is mounted on the right-hand wing valance.

2 To check a coil, disconnect the coil high tension lead from the distributor (pull off rubber cap complete with lead) and earth it. Using a voltmeter, check that there is a voltage of between 1 and 3 volts between the coil positive (+) and negative (-) terminals when the engine is being cranked on the starter (photo).

3 Always connect the coil LT leads correctly, black/yellow to positive and blue to negative.

7 Spark plugs and high tension leads

1 The correct functioning of the spark plugs is vital for the correct running and efficiency of the engine. It is essential that the plugs fitted are appropriate for the engine, and the suitable

type is specified at the beginning of this chapter. If this type is used and the engine is in good condition, the spark plugs should not need attention between scheduled replacement intervals. Spark plug cleaning is rarely necessary and should not be attempted unless specialised equipment is available, as damage can easily be caused to the firing ends.

2 To remove the plugs, open the bonnet, and pull the HT leads from them. Grip the rubber end fitting, not the lead, otherwise the connection to the end fitting may fracture.

3 Brush out any accumulated dirt or grit from the spark plug recesses in the cylinder head, otherwise it may drop into the combustion chamber when the plug is removed.

4 Unscrew the spark plugs with a deep socket or a box spanner. Do not allow the tool to tilt, otherwise the ceramic insulator may be cracked or broken.

5 Examination of the spark plugs will give a good indication of the condition of the engine.

6 If the insulator nose of the spark plug is clean and white, with no deposits, this is indicative of a weak mixture, or too hot a plug (a hot plug transfers heat away from the electrode slowly, a cold plug transfers heat away quickly).

7 If the tip and insulator nose are covered with hard black-looking deposits, then this is indicative that the mixture is too rich. Should the plug be black and oily, then it is likely that the engine is fairly worn, as well as the mixture being too rich.

8 If the insulator nose is covered with light tan

6.1 Ignition coil (1.3 models)

6.2 Removing coil cover and HT lead

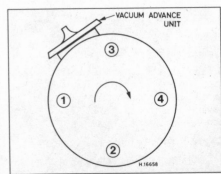

Fig. 4.3 HT lead sequence at distributor cap (1.3 models) (Sec 7)

It's often difficult to insert spark plugs into their holes without cross-threading them. To avoid this possibility, fit a short piece of rubber hose over the end of the spark plug. The flexible hose acts as a universal joint, to help align the plug with the plug hole. Should the plug begin to cross-thread, the hose will slip on the spark plug, preventing thread damage.

to greyish brown deposits, then the mixture is correct and it is likely that the engine is in good condition.

9 The spark plug gap is of considerable importance, as, if it is too large or too small, the size of the spark and its efficiency will be seriously impaired. For the best results the spark plug gap should be set in accordance with the Specifications at the beginning of this Chapter.

10 To set it, measure the gap with a feeler gauge and then bend open, or close, the outer electrode until the correct gap is achieved. The centre electrode should never be bent as this may crack the insulation and cause plug failure if nothing worse.

11 Special spark plug electrode gap adjusting tools are available from most motor accessory stores.

12 Screw each plug in by hand. This will ensure that there is no chance of cross-threading.

13 Tighten to the specified torque. If a torque wrench is not available just lightly tighten each plug. It is better to undertighten than strip the threads from the light alloy cylinder head.

7.14 Spark plug leads

14 When reconnecting the spark plug leads, make sure that they are refitted in their correct order, 1 - 3 - 4 - 2, No 1 cylinder being at the timing belt end of the engine (photo).

15 The spark plug leads require no routine attention other than being kept clean by wiping them regularly.

16 In order to minimise corrosion in the distributor cap lead sockets smear the HT cable end fittings with a light coating of petroleum jelly.

Part B 1.6 models

8 General description

1 These models are fitted with a programmed ignition system in which timing is controlled electronically instead of by centrifugal weights and a vacuum unit, as is the case in a conventional distributor system.

2 The normal method of high tension voltage distribution is retained using a rotor and distributor cap, but not the distributor body. The rotor is driven from the rear end of the camshaft.

3 Information in respect of engine speed and crankshaft position is transmitted to the electronic control unit by the crankshaft sensor. This ensures that there is no variation in timing due to wear in mechanical components.

4 The purpose of the main components of the system is described in the following paragraphs.

Reluctor disc

5 The disc is mounted on the flywheel and takes the form of a toothed rotor. The rotor has 34 teeth spaced at 10° intervals but having two spaces 180° apart which correspond to two TDC positions.

Crankshaft sensor

6 This is an inductive device located on the transmission adaptor plate. It runs between the reluctor disc teeth (photo).

7 When the crankshaft is turning, the sensor

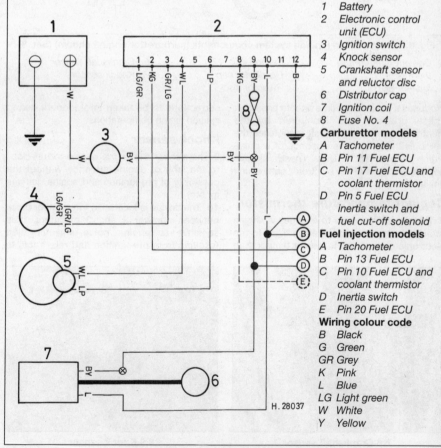

1   Battery
2   Electronic control unit (ECU)
3   Ignition switch
4   Knock sensor
5   Crankshaft sensor and reluctor disc
6   Distributor cap
7   Ignition coil
8   Fuse No. 4
Carburettor models
A   Tachometer
B   Pin 11 Fuel ECU
C   Pin 17 Fuel ECU and coolant thermistor
D   Pin 5 Fuel ECU inertia switch and fuel cut-off solenoid
Fuel injection models
A   Tachometer
B   Pin 13 Fuel ECU
C   Pin 10 Fuel ECU and coolant thermistor
D   Inertia switch
E   Pin 20 Fuel ECU
Wiring colour code
B   Black
G   Green
GR Grey
K   Pink
L   Blue
LG Light green
W   White
Y   Yellow

H. 28037

Fig. 4.4 Ignition circuit (1.6 models) (Sec 8)

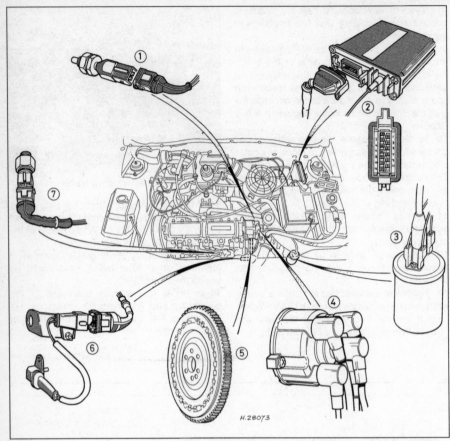

Fig. 4.5 Programmed ignition system components (carburettor engine shown) (Sec 8)

1 *Coolant temperature thermistor*	3 *Ignition coil*	6 *Crankshaft sensor*
	4 *Distributor cap*	7 *Knock sensor*
2 *Ignition ECU*	5 *Reluctor disc*	

produces a pulse every time a tooth passes it. These problems are monitored by the electronic control unit which recognises the 10° pulsations and the absence of a pulse which represents TDC. These signals provide the basis of the electronic control unit timing.

Coolant temperature thermistor

8 This device responds to changes in engine coolant temperature and relays them to the electronic control unit to permit temperature

corrections to be taken into account during ignition timing computations.

Knock sensor

9 This sensor allows the engine to run close to the limit of engine advance without the possibility of pre-ignition and engine damage (photo).
10 The device is located in the cylinder block between number 2 and 3 cylinders. It is sensitive to engine noise and vibration resulting from pre-ignition and relays this to

the electronic control unit which in turn adjusts the ignition advance.

Ignition coil

11 This is similar in appearance, but totally different in characteristics, from ignition coils used in other systems. It is located in front of the battery.

Pressure transducer

12 This is located in the electronic control unit and is connected to the inlet manifold by a vacuum pipe.
13 Its purpose is to monitor engine load and signal the electronic control unit which then determines the optimum switching times of the coil.

Electronic control unit

14 This is basically a printed circuit board upon which the electronic components are mounted (photo).

Distributor cap and rotor

15 The rotor is mounted on a vibration damped stub shaft driven directly from the camshaft.
16 The distributor cap is secured to the camshaft carrier by two screws.

9 Maintenance and inspection

1 The only components of the system which require periodic maintenance are the distributor cap, HT leads and spark plugs. The spark plugs and HT leads should be treated in the same way as for 1.3 litre models, as described in Section 7. Attend to the distributor cap and rotor arm as described in Section 2.
2 On this system, dwell angle and ignition timing are a function of the electronic control unit and there is no provision for adjustment. It is possible to check the ignition advance using a stroboscopic timing light, but this should only be necessary as part of a fault finding procedure. Further details will be found in Section 3.

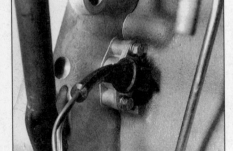

8.6 Crankshaft sensor

8.9 Knock sensor

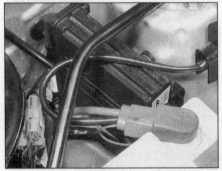

8.14 Electronic control unit (ECU)

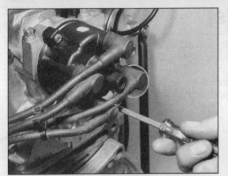
10.1 Extracting a distributor cap screw

10.2A Rotor arm with socket headed fixing screw

10.2B Distributor shield

10 Distributor cap and rotor arm - removal and refitting

1 Undo the two screws and lift the cap off the camshaft carriers. Thoroughly clean the cap inside and out with a dry lint-free rag. Examine the four HT lead segments inside the cap. If the segments appear badly burned or pitted, renew the cap. Make sure that the carbon brush in the centre of the cap is free to move and stands proud of its holders. If renewal of the cap is necessary, mark the position of the HT leads then pull them off. Transfer the leads to a new cap, fitting them in the same position (photo).
2 To remove the rotor arm, undo the retaining screw using a suitable Allen key and withdraw the rotor arm from the end of the camshaft. If necessary remove the rotor arm shield (photos).
3 Refitting the shield, rotor arm and distributor cap is the reverse sequence to removal. It is advisable to clean the rotor arm

retaining screw threads in the camshaft using an M6 tap to remove all traces of old thread-locking compound. If this is not done, it is possible for the screw to seize in position rendering subsequent removal impossible.

11 Ignition coil - description and testing

1 The coil is located under the cold air intake duct for the air cleaner. It should be cleaned occasionally to prevent high tension (HT) voltage loss (photo).
2 To ensure correct HT polarity at the spark plugs, the LT coil leads must always be connected correctly, ie, white lead to the coil positive terminal and white/black lead to the coil negative terminal. Incorrect connections can cause bad starting, misfiring and short spark plug life.
3 Accurate checking of the coil output requires special equipment and for the home mechanic the easiest test is by substitution of a new unit.

11.1 Ignition coil (1.6 models)

4 If a new coil is to be fitted, ensure that it is of the correct type, specifically for use on the programmed electronic ignition system. Failure to do so could cause irreparable damage to the electronic control unit.
5 To remove the coil, disconnect the HT and LT wiring, undo the two retaining bolts and lift away the coil. Refitting is the reverse sequence to removal.

4

Fault finding - ignition system (1.3 models)

Engine fails to start
☐ Faulty or disconnected leads
☐ Faulty spark plug
☐ Air gap incorrect
☐ Fault in ignition coil
☐ Fault in pick-up or control unit

Engine starts and runs but misfires
☐ Incorrect timing
☐ Fouled spark plug
☐ Incorrectly connected HT leads
☐ Crack in distributor cap or rotor
☐ Poor battery, engine and earth connections

Engine overheats, lacks power
☐ Seized distributor weights
☐ Perforated vacuum pipe
☐ Incorrect ignition timing

Engine 'pinks'
☐ Timing too advanced
☐ Advance mechanism stuck in advanced position
☐ Broken distributor weight spring
☐ Low fuel octane
☐ Upper cylinder oil used in fuel
☐ Excessive oil vapour from crankcase ventilation system or worn piston rings

Fault finding - ignition system (1.6 models)

Problems associated with the programmed electronic ignition system can usually be grouped into one of two areas. Those caused by the more conventional HT side of the system such as spark plugs. HT leads, rotor arm and distributor cap, and those caused by the LT circuitry including the electronic control unit and its related components.

Apart from checking the wiring and terminal connections, testing the system components should be left to your dealer or automotive electrician, as special equipment will be required If you are in possession of a voltmeter and ohmmeter then the following tests will be possible.

Programmed ignition system test procedure

Engine fails to start

Test

1 Connect a voltmeter across pins 9(+) and 12(-) of the electronic control unit (ECU) wiring connector. Does the voltmeter indicate battery voltage 10 seconds after switching on the ignition?

Remedy
Yes: Proceed to test 2
No: Check the wiring between the ignition switch and pin 9, and between pin 12 and earth. Rectify as required

2 Connect a voltmeter across pins 10(+) and 12(-) of the ECU wiring connector. Does the voltmeter indicate battery voltage 10 seconds after switching on the ignition?

Yes: Proceed to test 3
No: Check the wiring between the ignition switch and coil (+) terminal and between pin 10 and the coil (-) terminal. Rectify as required

3 Connect an ohmmeter across the coil terminals. If the coil primary winding resistance between 0.7 and 0.81 ohms?

Yes: Proceed to test 4
No: Renew the coil

4 Connect a voltmeter between the battery (+) terminal and the coil (-) terminal. Does the reading on the voltmeter increase when the engine is cranking?

Yes: Engine should start. If not check ignition HT components. fuel system and engine internal components
No: Proceed to test 5

5 Switch ignition off and connect an ohmmeter across terminals 4 and 6 of the ECU. Does the ohmmeter register 1.5 k ohms approximately?

Yes: Probable ECU fault
No: Check crankshaft sensor wiring and connections. If satisfactory, sensor is suspect

Engine misfires and performance is unsatisfactory

Test

1 Highlight ignition timing marks (notch on crankshaft pulley, corresponding notch on water pump bracket) with white chalk, connect a stroboscopic timing light, disconnect ECU vacuum pipe at manifold and start engine. Does the pulley mark advance as engine speed is increased?

Remedy
Yes: Proceed to test 2
No: Probable ECU fault

2 With the engine operating as in test 1 above, apply suction to the end of the disconnected ECU vacuum pipe. Does the pulley mark advance as suction is applied?

Yes: Ignition system is satisfactory, fault lies elsewhere
No: Check for leaks in vacuum pipe and connections. If satisfactory, ECU is faulty.

Chapter 5 Clutch

For modifications, and information applicable to later models, see Supplement at end of manual

Contents

5

Degrees of difficulty

Easy, suitable for novice with little experience	**Fairly easy,** suitable for beginner with some experience	**Fairly difficult,** suitable for competent DIY mechanic	**Difficult,** suitable for experienced DIY mechanic	**Very difficult,** suitable for expert DIY or professional

Specifications

General

Type	Single dry plate, diaphragm spring, cable actuation

1.3 models

Driven plate diameter	195.0 mm (7.5 in)
Release arm free play	4.0 to 5.0 mm (0.157 to 0.196 in)
Pedal free play:	
Up to VIN 800 014/1985 model year	16.0 to 21.0 mm (0.63 to 0.83 in)
From VIN 800 015/1985 model year	12.0 to 18.0 mm (0.47 to 0.70 in)

1.6 models

Driven plate diameter	200.0 mm (7.87 in)
Pedal free play	12.0 to 28.0 mm (0.47 to 1.10 in)

Torque wrench settings	Nm	lbf ft
Clutch bellhousing to engine bolts:		
1.3	68	50
1.6	90	66
Clutch cover to flywheel bolts:		
1.3	26	19
1.6	23	17

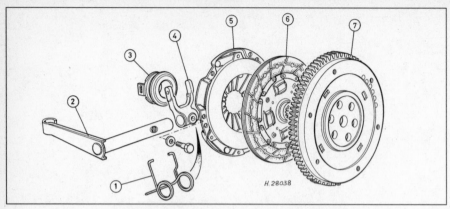

Fig. 5.1 Clutch components (1.3 models) (Sec 1)

1 Release arm spring
2 Release arm and shaft
3 Release bearing
4 Release fork
5 Clutch cover/pressure plate
6 Driven plate
7 Flywheel

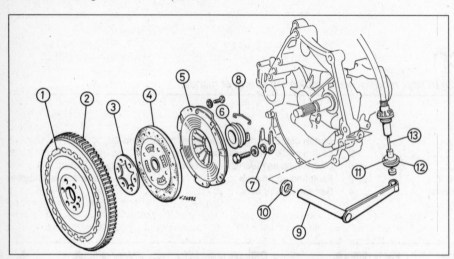

Fig. 5.2 Clutch components (1.6 models) (Sec 1)

1 Reluctor ring
2 Flywheel
3 Lockplate
4 Driven plate
5 Pressure plate
6 Release bearing
7 Release fork
8 Retaining spring
9 Release shaft
10 Shaft seal
11 Cable seat
12 Rubber pad
13 Clutch cable

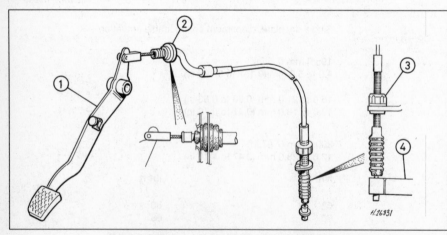

Fig. 5.3 Clutch cable (manually adjustable) (Sec 3)

1 Pedal   2 Cable   3 Adjuster nut   4 Release arm

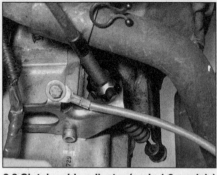

2.2 Clutch cable adjuster (early 1.3 models)

1 General description

The clutch is of simple dry plate type with a diaphragm spring pressure plate.

The driven plate used on 1.3 models incorporates rubber torsional dampers while they are of coil spring type on 1.6 models. The clutch release bearing is of sealed ball type.

Clutch actuation is by means of a cable. The clutch cable is self-adjusting on all 1.6 models, but only from VIN 800014 on 1.3 versions.

2 Clutch cable (1.3 up to VIN 800014) - adjustment

1 The clutch pedal free play on the 1.3 model up to 1985 model year should be maintained at between 16.0 and 21.0m (0.63 to 0.83 in). The free play is the amount of movement felt when the pedal is depressed with the fingers from the fully released position to the point where diaphragm spring pressure can be felt.
2 Adjust by turning the cable adjusting nut at the support bracket within the engine compartment (photo).

3 Clutch cable (manually adjustable type) - renewal

1 Slacken the cable adjuster nut right off.
2 Disconnect the inner cable from the release arm on the clutch bellhousing.
3 Detach the outer cable from the gearbox and servo brackets.
4 Working under the facia panel, release the cable from the clutch pedal arm.
5 Withdraw the clutch cable assembly from the bulkhead into the engine compartment.
6 Refitting is a reversal of removal. Adjust pedal free movement as described in the preceding Section.

4 Clutch cable (automatically adjustable type) - renewal

1 Working within the engine compartment, disconnect the clutch outer cable from its support clips.
2 Pull out the C-clip from the self-adjuster coil spring.
3 Disconnect the end of cable from the release arm.
4 Withdraw the cable through the gearbox support bracket, the rubber retainer will have to be disengaged from the guide sleeve.
5 Working within the car, unhook the cable from the clutch pedal and then withdraw the cable through the bulkhead into the engine compartment.
6 Refitting the new cable is a reversal of removal of the old one, but observe the following.
7 When passing the cable through the bulkhead, smear the inside of the cable abutment tube with rubber grease or petroleum jelly. Press the rubber bush into the tube so that the steel washer is fully up against the tube.
8 Once the cable is connected to both pedal and release lever, pull on the outer cable, compress the coil spring and fit the C-clip.
9 Now set the initial automatic adjustment. To do this, hold the adjuster mechanism in the bulkhead tube at the same time pulling the outer cable until resistance can be felt.

5 Clutch pedal - removal and refitting

1 Working inside the car, remove the facia lower access panel (Chapter 11).
2 Disconnect the clutch cable from the pedal as previously described.
3 Disconnect the pedal return spring.
4 Unscrew the nut from the pivot bolt which serves the brake and clutch pedals and withdraw it until the clutch pedal can be removed.
5 The pedal bushes can be renewed if worn.
6 Grease the bushes and pivot bolt when refitting.
7 Adjust the clutch cable as described in earlier Sections.

6 Clutch - removal

1 Disconnect the battery.
2 Remove the gearbox (Chapter 6).
3 Unscrew each of the clutch cover bolts progressively until the diaphragm spring pressure is relieved. Lock the flywheel with a tool inserted in the starter ring gear teeth to prevent it rotating.

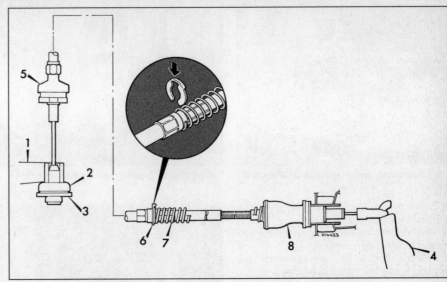

Fig. 5.4 Clutch cable (automatically adjustable) (Sec 4)

1 Release arm
2 Cable seat
3 Rubber pad
4 Clutch pedal
5 Support at gearbox
6 C-clip
7 Self-adjuster coil spring
8 Support at bulkhead

4 Remove the bolts and take the cover/pressure plate from the locating dowels on the flywheel. Catch the driven plate as it drops out.

7 Clutch - inspection

1 Slipping of the clutch will probably have been the reason for overhaul and the driven plate will show that the linings have worn down to the rivets.
2 The clutch cover should also be renewed, as clutch overhaul is normally carried out so infrequently it is not worthwhile putting the old one back. This will certainly be the case if the diaphragm spring fingers are stepped due to wear by contact with the release bearing.
3 Renew the driven plate and the cover/pressure plate assembly with complete units.
4 If there is any evidence of oil leaking within the bellhousing, this will probably be due to a worn crankshaft rear oil seal or the gearbox input shaft oil seal. Renew the faulty seal and clean away all the oil residue.
5 Examine the face of the flywheel. If it is grooved or deeply scored or is covered in tiny cracks, caused by overheating, it may be possible to have it surface ground. If it is not possible to refinish the flywheel, it will have to be renewed.
6 Lastly, renew the clutch release bearing as a matter of routine. Removal and refitting of the bearing is described in the next Section.

8 Clutch release mechanism - removal and refitting

The engine and gearbox must be separated for access to the clutch release mechanism.

1.3 models

1 Remove the release fork lock bolt from inside the clutch bellhousing (photo).

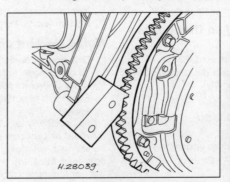

Fig. 5.5 Typical flywheel locking tool (Sec 6)

8.1 Unscrewing clutch release fork lockbolt

8.3 Removing clutch release bearing and fork

8.4 Release bearing spring arrangement

9.2 Offering clutch to flywheel

2 Withdraw the release shaft complete with arm from the bellhousing.

3 Take out the release fork complete with bearing and spring (photo) .

4 Release the spring and separate the bearing/holder from the fork (photo) .

5 The clutch release bearing is a grease-sealed unit, never immerse it in solvent of any kind.

6 Refit the new bearing by reversing the removal operations. Apply a little molybdenum disulphide grease to the release shaft bushes and to the bearing and guide sleeve sliding surfaces.

1.6 models

7 Prise the retaining spring legs apart and withdraw the release bearing and its carrier.

8 Fit the new bearing and make sure that the legs of the retaining spring are located behind the release fork.

9 Clutch - refitting

1 Clean the friction surfaces of the flywheel and pressure plate, but do not remove the protective coating from the clutch cover.

9.6 Centralising the clutch driven plate

2 Offer the driven plate to the flywheel so that the side with the greater projecting hub is away from the flywheel and towards the gearbox (photo). The driven plate may be marked 'FLYWHEEL SIDE'.

3 Offer the clutch cover onto the flywheel dowels so that it sandwiches the driven plate between it and the flywheel.

4 Screw in the clutch cover bolts finger tight.

5 The driven plate must now be centralised so that when the gearbox is offered to the engine, the input shaft splines will pass smoothly through the splines in the driven plate hub.

9.7 Tightening a clutch cover bolt

6 Centralisation can be carried out using a clutch alignment tool, an old input shaft or simply a round bar. Insert the tool into the driven plate hub and move the plate up or down or sideways until the splined hub is absolutely concentric with the ends of the circle of diaphragm spring fingers (photo).

7 Tighten the clutch cover bolts evenly to the specified torque, again locking the flywheel against rotation. Withdraw the centralising tool (photo) .

8 Refit the gearbox (Chapter 6).

9 Reconnect the battery.

Fault finding - clutch

Judder when taking up drive

☐ Loose engine or gearbox mountings
☐ Badly worn friction linings or contaminated with oil
☐ Worn splines on gearbox input shaft or driven plate hub

*Clutch spin (failure to disengage) so that gears cannot be meshed

☐ Incorrect release bearing to pressure plate clearance
☐ Rust on splines (may occur after vehicle standing idle for long periods)
☐ Damaged or misaligned pressure plate assembly
☐ Cable stretched or broken

Noise evident as clutch pedal released

☐ Distorted driven plate
☐ Broken or weak driven plate cushion coil springs or dampers
☐ Incorrect pedal adjustment
☐ Weak or broken clutch pedal return spring
☐ Distorted or worn input shaft
☐ Release bearing loose on retainer hub

Clutch slip (increase in engine speed does not result in increase in vehicle road speed - particularly on gradients)

☐ Incorrect release bearing to pressure plate finger clearance
☐ Friction linings worn out or oil contaminated

Noise evident on depressing clutch pedal

☐ Dry, worn or damaged release bearing
☐ Incorrect pedal adjustment
☐ Weak or broken pedal return spring
☐ Excessive play between driven plate hub splines and input shaft splines

This condition may also be due to the driven plate being rusted to the flywheel or pressure plate. It is possible to free it by applying the handbrake, engaging top gear, depressing the clutch pedal and operating the starter motor. If really badly corroded, then the engine will not turn over, but in the majority of cases the driven plate will free. Once the engine starts, rev it up and slip the clutch several times to clear the rust deposits.

Chapter 6 Manual transmission

For modifications, and information applicable to later models, see Supplement at end of manual

Contents

Degrees of difficulty

Easy, suitable for novice with little experience	Fairly easy, suitable for beginner with some experience	Fairly difficult, suitable for competent DIY mechanic 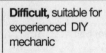	Difficult, suitable for experienced DIY mechanic	Very difficult, suitable for expert DIY or professional

Specifications

Part A 1.3 models

Type .... Five forward speeds and reverse. Synchromesh on all forward speeds. Differential/final drive integral with transmission. Unit mounted on right-hand side of car transversely in line with engine.

Ratios

1st	2.916:1
2nd	1.764:1
3rd	1.181:1
4th	0.846:1
5th	0.714:1
Reverse	2.916:1
Final drive	4.428:1

Gear endfloats and gearbox clearances

1st speed gear	0.03 to 0.18 mm (0.001 to 0.007 in) Adjustment by selective thrust washer
Washer thickness	1.89 to 1.92 mm (0.074 to 0.076 in) 1.92 to 1.95 mm (0.076 to 0.077 in) 1.95 to 1.98 mm (0.077 to 0.078 in)
2nd, 3rd, 4th speed gears	0.05 to 0.18 mm (0.002 to 0.007 in) Adjustment by selective spacer collars
Collar thickness	28.01 to 28.04 mm (1.103 to 1.104 in) 28.04 to 28.07 mm (1.104 to 1.105 in) 28.07 to 28.10 mm (1.105 to 1.106 in) 28.10 to 28.13 mm (1.106 to 1.107 in)
5th gear endfloat	0.05 to 0.4 mm (0.002 to 0.016 in)
Reverse idler shaft running clearance	0.4 mm (0.016 in)
Selector fork clearance in synchro groove 1st/2nd, 3rd/4th and 5th ..	1.0 mm (0.040 in)
Reverse gear to fork (max)	0.7 mm (0.028 in)
Reverse shaft fork:	
End gap	6.9 to 7.0 mm (0.27 to 0.28 in)
Groove width	7.05 to 7.25 mm (0.278 to 0.285 in)
Fork to shaft clearance (max)	0.5 mm (0.020 in)
Finger thickness (minimum)	6.0 mm (0.236 in)
Shaft arm to dog clearance (maximum)	0.15 mm (0.006 in)
Final drive crownwheel to pinion backlash	0.073 to 0.25 mm (0.0029 to 0.010 in)
Differential pinion gear backlash	0.05 to 0.15 mm (0.002 to 0.006 in) Adjustment by selective thrust washers
Washer thickness	0.7 mm (0.028 in) 0.8 mm (0.031 in) 0.9 mm (0.035 in) 1.0 mm (0.039 in)

6

Gear endfloats and gearbox clearances (continued)

Differential side clearance .... 0.10 to 0.15 mm (0.004 to 0.006 in)
Adjustment by selective circlip

Circlip thickness .... 2.45 mm (0.096 in)
2.55 mm (0.100 in)
2.65 mm (0.104 in)
2.75 mm (0.108 in)
2.85 mm (0.112 in)
2.95 mm (0.116 in)

Oil capacity .... 2.3 litre (4.0 pint)

Oil type/specification .... Multigrade engine oil, viscosity SAE 10W/30 or 10W/40, to API SF

Torque wrench settings

	Nm	lbf ft
Countershaft nut	110	81
Crownwheel bolts	103	76
Oil drain plug	40	30
Oil filler/level plug	45	33
Gear selector remote control rod pivot bolt	22	16
Reverse gear fork nut	24	18
Selector arm holder bolts	12	9
Detent plugs	22	16
Selector fork lock bolts	17	13
Torque rod to body bolts	22	16
Torque rod to transmission	9	7
Transmission to engine torque bracket bolts	45	33
5th speed gear housing bolts	12	9
Transmission casing to flywheel housing bolts	28	21
Flywheel housing to engine bolts	68	50
Rear mounting bracket bolts	65	48
Right-hand mounting to body bolts	39	29
Rear mounting bracket nuts	22	16
Left-hand mounting bracket nuts	39	29
Suspension arm balljoint nut	44	32
Driveshaft nut	185	137

Part B 1.6 models

Type .... Five forward speeds and reverse. Synchromesh on all forward speeds. Differential/final drive integral with transmission. Unit mounted on left-hand side of car transversely in line with engine

Ratios

	Carburettor models	Fuel injection models
1st	2.92:1	3.25:1
2nd	1.75:1	1.89:1
3rd	1.15:1	1.33:1
4th	0.87:1	1.04:1
5th	0.66:1	0.85:1
Reverse	3.00:1	3.00:1
Final drive	4.1:1	3.87:1

Gear endfloats and gearbox clearances

Mainshaft endfloat .... 0.14 to 0.21 mm (0.006 to 0.008 in)
Adjustment by selective circlips

Circlip thickness .... 0.50 mm (0.020 in)
0.55 mm (0.022 in)
0.60 mm (0.024 in)
0.65 mm (0.026 in)
0.70 mm (0.028 in)
0.75 mm (0.030 in)
0.80 mm (0.032 in)
0.85 mm (0.034 in)
0.90 mm (0.036 in)
0.95 mm (0.038 in)
1.00 mm (0.040 in)
1.05 mm (0.042 in)
1.10 mm (0.044 in)
1.15 mm (0.046 in)

Gear endfloats and gearbox clearances (continued)

Countershaft gear endfloat	0.1 to 0.35 mm (0.004 to 0.014 in)
	Adjustment by selective collars and shims
Collar availability	28.99 mm (1.142 in)
	29.04 mm (1.144 in)
Shim thicknesses	1.96 mm (0.077 in)
	1.99 mm (0.078 in)
	2.02 mm (0.080 in)
	2.05 mm (0.081 in)
	2.08 mm (0.082 in)
Baulk ring to gear cone clearance (minimum)	0.40 mm (0.016 in)
Reverse idler gear to shaft clearance (maximum)	0.14 mm (0.006 in)
Fork to synchro sleeve groove clearance (maximum)	1.0 mm (0.040 in)
Reverse gear to fork clearance (maximum)	0.7 mm (0.028 in)
Final drive pinion to crownwheel backlash	0.07 to 0.14 mm (0.003 to 0.005 in)
Planet gear backlash	0.05 to 0.15 mm (0.002 to 0.006 in)
	Adjustment by selective thrust washers
Washer thickness	0.70 mm (0.028 in)
	0.75 mm (0.030 in)
	0.80 mm (0.031 in)
	0.85 mm (0.033 in)
	0.90 mm (0.035 in)
	0.95 mm (0.037 in)
	1.00 mm (0.039 in)
	1.05 mm (0.041 in)
Differential side clearance	0.15 mm (0.006 in)
	Adjustment by selective circlip
Circlip thickness	2.45 mm (0.096 in)
	2.55 mm (0.100 in)
	2.65 mm (0.104 in)
	2.75 mm (0.108 in)
	2.85 mm (0.112 in)
	2.95 mm (0.116 in)

Oil capacity

2.2 litres (3.75 pints)

Oil type/specification

Multigrade engine oil, viscosity SAE 10W/30 or 10W/40, to API SF

Torque wrench settings

	Nm	lbf ft
Gearchange shaft detent plug	22	16
Gearchange holder screw:		
M8	28	21
M6	14	10
Reverse fork bracket screws	14	10
Crown wheel bolts	110	81
Countershaft nut	110	81
Transmission casing to flywheel housing bolts	27	20
Breather pipe bracket bolt	27	20
Reverse idler shaft bolt	67	49
Reverse lamp switch	25	18
Drain plug	40	30
Oil level/filler plug	45	33
Flywheel bellhousing to engine adaptor plate	90	66
Remote control bracket	25	18
Gear lever to selector rod bolt	25	18
Casing end plug:		
Large (countershaft access plug)	70	52
Small	28	21
Suspension arm balljoint nut	44	32
Left and right-hand mountings:		
Engine bolts	45	33
Bracket nuts	40	30
Through bolt	120	89
Rear mounting:		
Bracket to transmission bolts	90	66
Support plate to bracket bolts	75	55
Mounting to bracket bolts	60	44
Mounting to crossmember	60	44

6

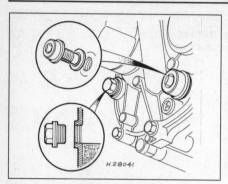

Fig. 6.1 Oil level/filler and drain plugs - 1.3 models (Sec 2)

2.1A Transmission oil filler/level plug - 1.6 models

2.1B Transmission filler/level plug - 1.6 models

1 General description

1.3 models

The transmission is fitted transversely on the right-hand side in line with the engine at the front of the car.

The transmission casing incorporates the gear trains and the final drive/differential.

The 1st. 2nd, 3rd, 4th and reverse speed gears are integral with the mainshaft and cannot be detached from the shaft.

The 5th speed synchro unit is splined to the mainshaft while the 5th speed gear is free on the shaft.

2.2 Topping up the transmission - 1.3 models

The countershaft incorporates a final drive pinion and carries the 5th speed gear, 1st/2nd and 3rd/4th synchro units. The 1st, 2nd, 3rd and 4th speed gears are free on the shaft. The 1st/2nd synchro sleeve incorporates the reverse gear teeth.

Except for reverse gear, all gears are in constant mesh. The transmission operates by transmitting engine torque through the mainshaft and selected gear to the countershaft pinion then to the final drive (crownwheel), driveshafts and roadwheels.

1.6 models

The gearbox is of Honda manufacture and is equipped with five forward and one reverse gear. Synchromesh gear engagement is used on all forward gears.

The mainshaft and countershaft carry the constant mesh gear cluster assemblies and are supported on ball and roller bearings. The short input end of the mainshaft eliminates the need for additional support from a crankshaft spigot bearing. The synchromesh gear engagement is by spring rings which act against baulk rings under the movement of the synchroniser sleeves. Gear selection is by means of a floor mounted transmitter to the selector forks via the gear change holder and interlock assembly.

The final drive (differential) unit is integral with the main gearbox and is located between the bellhousing and gearcase. The gearbox

and final drive components both share the same lubricating oil.

2 Maintenance

1 Have the car standing on a level surface then at the intervals specified in Routine Maintenance wipe the oil filler/level plug clean and remove it using a ring spanner (photos).
2 If the oil level is correct, oil will just run out of the level plug. If it does not, top up with specified oil until it does (photo).
3 Refit the plug.
4 Draining and refilling the transmission is still specified by the manufacturers and in the interest of long life it is recommended that the oil is drained hot every 24 000 miles (40 000 km) or at two yearly intervals and the transmission then filled with fresh oil of the specified type.
5 The drain plug can be unscrewed with a 3/8 in square bar (photos).

3 Gearchange lever - removal and refitting

1 Working under the car, remove the pivot bolt and disconnect the gear lever from the selector remote control rod (photo).

2.5A Unscrewing transmission drain plug - 1.3 models

2.5B Transmission drain plug - 1.6 models

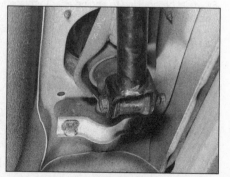

3.1 Gearchange lever connection to remote control rod

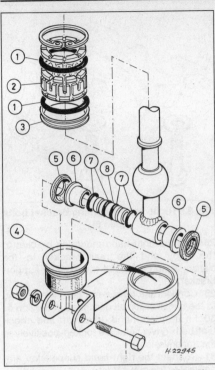

Fig. 6.2 Gear lever components (Sec 3)

1 O-rings	5 Sealing washer
2 Ball seat	6 Bushes
3 Stopper ring	7 O-rings
4 Dust cover	8 Spacer collar

2 Remove the gear lever washers, bushes and the spacer collar and the O-rings.
3 Remove the gear lever knob and the centre console (Chapter 11) if fitted.
4 Remove the rubber gaiter, extract the circlip and withdraw the gear lever.
5 Remove the gear lever ball seat, stopper ring, O-rings and dust cover.
6 Renew any worn or deformed components.
7 Refitting is a reversal of removal. Apply grease to the spacer collar and tighten the pivot bolt to the specified torque.

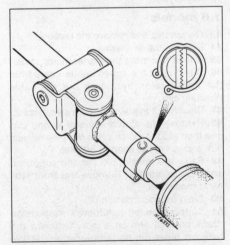

Fig. 6.3 Selector shaft connecting roll pin and safety clip (Sec 4)

4.1A Transmission torque rod

4.1B Removing transmission torque rod

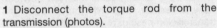

4 Gear selector shaft oil seal - renewal

1 Disconnect the torque rod from the transmission (photos).
2 Slide the selector shaft safety clip aside and drive out the roll pin which secures the remote control rod to the selector shaft (photo).
3 Disconnect the remote control rod from the selector shaft. This joint can rust. Soak it in penetrating fluid.
4 Pull back the gaiter from the selector shaft at the transmission casing and prise out the shaft oil seal (photo).
5 Grease the lips of the new seal and drive it into position.
6 When refitting the gaiter, make sure that the drain hole is at the bottom.
7 Reconnect the remote control rod, drive in the roll pin and fit the clip. Smear the joint with grease to prevent corrosion (photo).
8 Reconnect the torque rod.

5 Differential oil seals - renewal

1.3 models

1 These oil seals may be renewed without having to remove the transmission from the car.

4.2 Selector shaft roll pin safety clip

2 Disconnect the battery.
3 Drain the oil from the transmission.
4 If the oil seal on the left-hand side is to be renewed, then the left-hand driveshaft must be removed as described in Chapter 8.
5 If the oil seal on the right-hand driveshaft is to be renewed, then the driveshaft need only be disconnected from the transmission while remaining connected to the hub carrier.
6 The disconnection operations for the right-hand driveshaft are covered in Chapter 1, Section 19.
7 Prise the oil seal from the transmission.
8 Apply grease to the lips of the new seal and drive it squarely into position.
9 Reconnect or refit the driveshaft according to side. Use a new driveshaft circlip.
10 Refill the transmission and connect the battery.

6

4.4 Selector shaft gaiter and oil seal

4.7 Driving in selector shaft roll pin

1.6 models

11 Leakage of oil from these seals may be rectified by renewing the seals without removing the transmission from the car.

12 Raise the front of the car and remove the roadwheel from the side on which the oil seal is to be renewed. Support the body members securely on stands.

13 Drain the transmission oil, retaining it for further use if required.

14 Place a jack under the lower suspension (track control) arm. Unscrew the balljoint taper pin nut and using a suitable splitter tool disconnect the balljoint from the hub carrier.

15 Using the same tool, disconnect the tie-rod end balljoint from the steering arm.

16 Disconnect the driveshaft from the transmission by inserting a lever between the driveshaft inboard joint and the transmission casing, and prising against the resistance of the driveshaft securing clip.

17 Prise out the oil seal, apply grease to the lips of the new one and drive it squarely into position.

18 Reconnect the driveshaft using a new securing clip, making sure that it engages positively in the differential side gear.

19 Reconnect the balljoints and tighten the nuts to the specified torque.

20 Fit the roadwheel.

21 Refill the transmission with oil.

6 Transmission - removal and refitting

1.3 models

1 Disconnect and remove the battery.

2 Disconnect the transmission casing earth cable.

3 Disconnect the reverse lamp switch leads.

4 Disconnect the speedometer drive cable from the transmission. Do this by pulling up the rubber cover and extracting the clip. *Do not unbolt the retaining plate or the speedo pinion will drop into the gearbox.*

5 Unbolt and move the starter motor aside.

6 Disconnect the clutch cable from the release lever at the transmission (Chapter 5).

7 Raise the front of the car and support it securely on axle stands.

8 Remove the front right-hand roadwheel.

9 Drain the transmission oil.

10 Remove the right-hand and centre splash guard panels.

11 Disconnect the gear selector and torque rods from the transmission (see Section 4).

12 Unscrew and remove the two lower bolts (Fig. 6.4) which hold the rear mounting bracket to the transmission casing. Release but do not remove, the bracket upper bolt, as this is supporting the engine.

13 Support the right-hand lower suspension (track control) arm on a jack, unscrew the taper pin nut and then using a suitable splitter

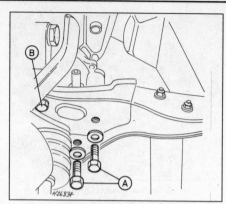

Fig. 6.4 Rear mounting bracket bolts (Sec 6)

A Lower bolts   B Upper bolt

tool, disconnect the balljoint from the hub carrier. Have the car well supported.

14 Using a suitable lever inserted between the driveshaft inboard joints and the transmission casing, release both driveshafts from the side gear securing clips.

15 Unscrew the right-hand driveshaft nut. This is very tight and the hub will have to be held against rotation either by having an assistant apply the brakes hard or by placing a long lever between two wheel studs. If the latter method is used, screw on the nut first to protect the threads.

16 Remove the right-hand driveshaft.

17 Support the engine using a hoist or by placing a block of wood and jack under the sump pan.

18 Release the right-hand front mounting bracket from the body.

19 Unscrew the bolts which hold the exhaust support bracket to the transmission.

20 Support the weight of the transmission on a trolley jack and remove the transmission to engine flange connecting bolts.

21 Unscrew and remove the cover plate bolts from the face of the flywheel housing.

22 Withdraw the transmission and have an assistant catch the inboard end of the left-hand driveshaft and lower it to the floor. Fit new driveshaft spring clips.

23 If the clutch has been disturbed, make sure that the driven plate has been centralised as described in Chapter 5.

24 Check that the engine to flywheel housing locating dowels are in position in the flange.

25 Apply a smear of grease to the splines of the input (clutch) shaft splines.

26 Offer the transmission to the engine. The input shaft splines should pass through those of the driven plate hub. If difficulty is experienced, have an assistant turn the crankshaft pulley bolt slightly to align the splines and grooves. As the transmission is being connected to the engine; have an assistant insert the left-hand driveshaft into the transmission.

27 Once the transmission is located on the dowels screw in and tighten the connecting bolts to the specified torque.

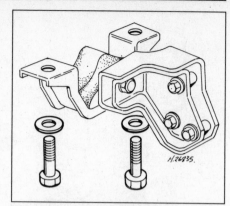

Fig. 6.5 Right-hand mounting bracket bolts (Sec 6)

28 Bolt the right-hand mounting bracket to the body and the rear bracket to the transmission casing. Fit the exhaust support bracket.

29 Connect the torque rod and selector rod to the transmission as described in Section 4.

30 Fit the right-hand driveshaft and check that both driveshafts are locked positively in the transmission.

31 Connect the right-hand suspension arm balljoint to the hub carrier.

32 Fit the splash guards.

33 Tighten a new driveshaft nut to the specified torque again holding the hub against rotation, using one of the methods described earlier in this Section.

34 Stake the nut into the shaft groove.

35 Fit the roadwheel and lower the car to the floor. Tighten the wheel nuts.

36 Fit the starter motor.

37 Connect the speedometer drive cable.

38 Connect and adjust the clutch cable, as described in Chapter 5.

39 Connect the reverse lamp switch leads.

40 Refit and reconnect the battery.

41 Reconnect the transmission casing earth cable.

42 Fill the transmission with oil of the specified type.

1.6 models

43 Disconnect and remove the battery.

44 Remove the air cleaner.

45 Unbolt and move the starter motor aside.

46 Disconnect the speedometer cable from the transmission by pulling out the cable retaining clip.

47 Disconnect the reverse lamp switch leads.

48 Remove the clutch adjuster spring clip and then slip the clutch cable from the release arm and out of the support bracket.

49 Raise the front of the car and support it securely on stands. Remove the front left-hand roadwheel.

50 Drain the transmission oil.

51 Support the left-hand lower suspension (track control) arm on a jack. Unscrew the balljoint taper pin nut and using a suitable splitter tool, disconnect the balljoint from the hub carrier.

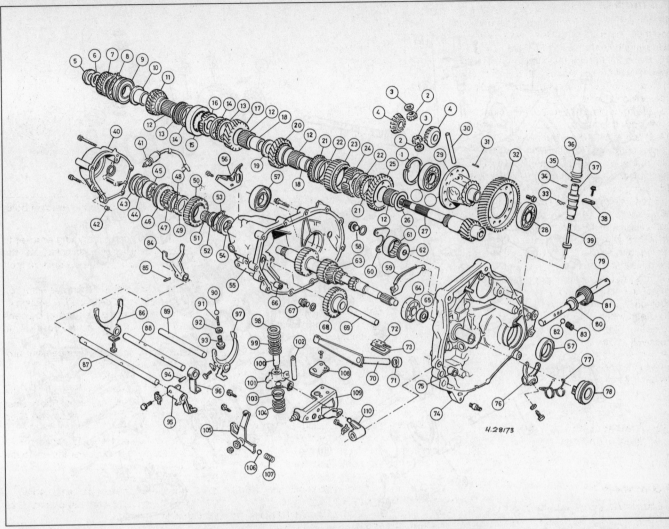

Fig. 6.6 Exploded view of the 1.3 model transmission (Sec 7)

1 Circlip
2 Differential pinion gear
3 Thrust washer
4 Differential side gear
5 Countershaft nut
6 Dished washer
7 5th speed countershaft gear
8 Circlip
9 Bearing
10 Flanged spacer collar
11 4th speed gear
12 Bearings
13 3rd/4th synchro baulk ring
14 Synchro spring
15 3rd/4th synchro sleeve
16 3rd/4th synchro hub
17 3rd speed gear
18 Spacer collar
19 Spacer washer
20 2nd speed gear
21 1st/2nd synchro baulk ring
22 Synchro spring
23 1st/2nd synchro sleeve
24 1st/2nd synchro hub
25 1st speed gear
26 Thrust washer
27 Countershaft
28 Bearing
29 Differential case
30 Pinion shaft
31 Roll pin
32 Crownwheel
33 Speedo pinion retaining clip
34 Speedo cable retaining clip
35 O-ring
36 Dust cover
37 Pinion housing
38 Retaining plate
39 Speedo gear pinion
40 5th gear housing
41 Reverse lamp switch
43 Dished spring washer
44 Circlip
45 Mainshaft bearing
46 5th speed gear synchro sleeve
47 5th speed synchro hub
48 Synchro spring
49 Baulk ring
50 Mainshaft 5th speed gear
51 Needle roller bearing
52 Thrust washer
53 Circlip
54 Mainshaft bearing
55 Transmission casing
56 Clutch cable bracket
57 Differential oil seal
58 Filler/level plug
59 Breather baffle plate
60 Bearing retainer plate
61 Countershaft bearing
62 Oil guide plate
63 Mainshaft
64 Mainshaft bearing
65 Oil seal
66 Locating dowel
67 Drain plug
68 Reverse idler gear
69 Reverse idler shaft
70 Clutch release arm and shaft
71 Dust seal
72 Magnet holder
73 Magnet
74 Flywheel housing
75 Locating dowel
75 Locating dowel
76 Clutch release fork
77 Spring
78 Clutch release bearing
79 Selector shaft
80 Selector shaft oil seal
81 Selector shaft gaiter
82 Detent ball
83 Detent spring
84 5th speed gear selector fork
85 Roll pin
86 3rd/4th selector fork
87 5th/reverse selector shaft
88 3rd/4th selector shaft
89 1st/2nd selector shaft
90 Detent ball
91 Detent spring
92 Washer
93 Detent plug
94 Roll pin
95 Reverse selector dog
96 3rd/4th selector dog
97 1st/2nd selector fork
98 Spring retainer
99 Spring
100 Selector arm shaft
101 Selector arm
102 Interlock shaft
103 Spring retainer
104 Spring
105 Reverse gear selector arm
106 Detent ball
107 Detent spring
108 Retainer plate
109 Selector arm holder
110 Selector shaft arm

6

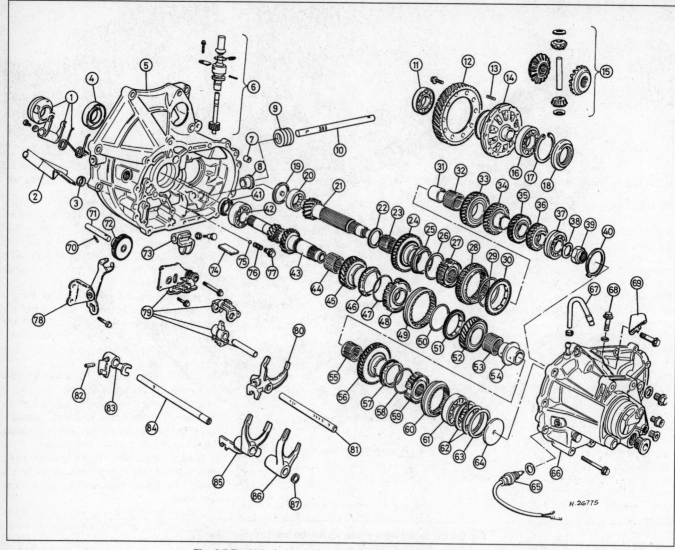

Fig. 6.7 Exploded view of the 1.6 model transmission (Sec 7)

1 Clutch release bearing, fork and retaining spring wire
2 Clutch operating lever
3 Clutch operating lever oil seal
4 Differential oil seal
5 Bellhousing (flywheel housing)
6 Speedometer pinion assembly
7 Locating dowel
8 Gearchange shaft oil seal
9 Rubber boot
10 Gearchange shaft
11 Final drive case bearing
12 Final drive crownwheel
13 Roll pin
14 Final drive case
15 Differential sun and planet gear components
16 Final drive case bearing
17 Differential endfloat circlip shim
18 Differential oil seal
19 Oil guide plate
20 Countershaft roller bearing

21 Countershaft
22 Thrust washer
23 Needle roller bearing
24 1st gear
25 Baulk ring
26 Spring ring
27 1st/2nd synchro hub
28 1st/2nd synchro sleeve
29 Spring ring
30 Baulk ring
31 Distance collar
32 Needle roller bearing
33 2nd gear
34 3rd gear
35 4th gear
36 5th gear
37 Countershaft ball bearing
38 Tongued washer
39 Retaining nut
40 Circlip
41 Mainshaft oil seal
42 Mainshaft ball bearing
43 Mainshaft

44 Needle roller bearing
45 3rd gear
46 Baulk ring
47 Spring ring
48 3rd/4th synchro hub
49 3rd/4th synchro sleeve
50 Spring ring
51 Baulk ring
52 4th gear
53 Needle roller bearing
54 Distance collar
55 Needle roller bearing
56 5th gear
57 Baulk ring
58 Spring ring
59 5th gear synchro hub
60 5th gear synchro sleeve
61 Mainshaft ball bearing
62 Selective circlips
63 Belleville washer
64 Oil guide plate
65 Reversing lamp switch
66 Transmission casing

67 Gearbox breather
68 Reverse idler shaft retaining bolt
69 Gearbox breather bracket
70 Roll pin
71 Reverse idler shaft
72 Reverse idler gear
73 Gearchange arm
74 Magnet
75 Detent ball
76 Detent spring
77 Detent plug
78 Reverse gear fork and bracket
79 Gearchange holder and interlock assembly
80 1st/2nd gear selector fork
81 1st/2nd gear selector shaft
82 Roll pin
83 5th/reverse gear selector
84 5th/reverse gear selector shaft
85 3rd/4th gear selector fork
86 5th gear selector fork
87 Circlip

6.53A Steady bar dished washer - 1.6 models

6.53B Steady bar flat washer - 1.6 models

6.54 Gearchange rod roll pin - 1.6 models

52 Insert a lever between the left-hand driveshaft joint and the transmission casing and prise the shaft out of the transmission.
53 Unscrew the bolt with washer which holds the steady bar to the transmission. Remove the bar and inner washer. Note that the lip on the inner washer is towards the flexible bush (photos).
54 Push the safety clip on the remote control selector rod aside and drive out the selector rod to shaft roll pin (photo).
55 Unscrew and remove the engine rear mounting bolts from the transmission and retrieve the spacer washers.
56 Support the engine under the sump pan using a jack and a block of wood as an insulator.
57 Unscrew the left-hand mounting through-bolt and detach the mounting bracket from the transmission.
58 Remove the battery tray.
59 Remove the clutch cable support bracket. Note that the earth straps will be disconnected as the battery tray and clutch cable bracket bolts are removed.
60 Attach a hoist to the transmission and take its weight.
61 Unscrew the transmission to engine adaptor plate bolts and withdraw the transmission from the engine about 25.4 mm

(1.0 in). At this point, have an assistant prise the driveshaft inboard joint free from the transmission using a lever as previously described.
62 Withdraw the transmission completely from the engine and have the assistant catch the driveshaft as it drops out of the transmission.
63 Lower the transmission to the floor and withdraw it from under the car.
64 Refitting is a reversal of removal, but observe the following points.
65 Use new driveshaft retaining clips.
66 Tighten all nuts and bolts to the specified torque.
67 Set the clutch cable automatic adjuster as described in Chapter 5.
68 Fill the transmission with oil.

7 Transmission overhaul - general

Overhauling a manual transmission unit is a difficult and involved job for the DIY home mechanic. In addition to dismantling and reassembling many small parts, clearances must be precisely measured and, if necessary, changed by selecting shims and spacers. Internal transmission components are also often difficult to obtain, and in many instances, are extremely expensive. Because of this, if the transmission develops a fault or becomes noisy, the best course of action is to have the unit overhauled by a specialist repairer, or to obtain an exchange reconditioned unit.

Nevertheless, it is not impossible for the more experienced mechanic to overhaul the transmission, provided the special tools are available, and that the job is done in a deliberate step-by-step manner so that nothing is overlooked.

The tools necessary for an overhaul may include internal and external circlip pliers, bearing pullers, a slide hammer, a set of pin punches, a dial test indicator, and possibly a hydraulic press. In addition, a large, sturdy workbench and a vice will be required.

During dismantling of the transmission, make careful notes of how each component is fitted, to make reassembly easier and accurate.

Before dismantling the transmission, it will help if you have some idea which area is malfunctioning. Certain problems can be closely related to specific areas in the gearbox, which can make component examination and replacement easier.

6

Fault finding - manual transmission

Note: *Before diagnosing faults from the table below, check that the gearbox oil level is correct and that the correct grade of oil is in use.*

A noisy gearbox, or one on which synchro action is weak, may continue to function for a long time in such a state. It is up to the owner to decide the degree of noise or malfunction which justifies an overhaul

Gearbox noisy in neutral

☐ Mainshaft bearings worn

Gearbox noisy only when moving (in all gears)

☐ Countershaft bearings worn
☐ Differential bearings worn
☐ Differential final drive gear or countershaft pinion chipped or worn

Gearbox noisy in only one gear

☐ Worn, damaged or chipped gear teeth
☐ Worn needle roller bearings

Gearbox jumps out of gear

☐ Worn synchro hubs or synchro sleeves
☐ Weak or broken selector shaft detent spring
☐ Weak or broken gearchange shaft detent spring
☐ Worn shaft detent grooves
☐ Worn selector forks

Ineffective synchromesh

☐ Worn baulk rings or synchro hubs

Difficulty in engaging gears

☐ Clutch fault
☐ Ineffective synchromesh
☐ Worn gear lever bushes and linkage

Notes

Chapter 7 Automatic transmission

For modifications, and information applicable to later models, see Supplement at end of manual

Contents

Degrees of difficulty

Easy, suitable for novice with little experience	**Fairly easy,** suitable for beginner with some experience	**Fairly difficult,** suitable for competent DIY mechanic	**Difficult,** suitable for experienced DIY mechanic	**Very difficult,** suitable for expert DIY or professional

Specifications

Part A: Three-speed (1.3 models)

Type . . . . Three forward speeds and reverse, torque converter and constant mesh geartrain

Gear ratios
1st . . . . 2.421 : 1
2nd . . . . 1.500 : 1
3rd . . . . 0.911 : 1
Reverse . . . . 1.954 : 1
Final drive . . . . 3.933 : 1

Fluid capacity
From dry . . . . 5.0 litres (8.75 pints)
Service fluid change . . . . 2.4 litres (4.25 pints)

Fluid type
For topping up . . . . Dexron IID type ATF
Complete refill . . . . Hondamatic fluid

Torque wrench settings	Nm	lbf ft
Drain plug	40	30
Cooler hose banjo bolts	29	21
Driveplate to crankshaft bolts	75	55
Driveplate to torque converter bolts	12	9
Torque converter housing to engine connecting bolts	45	33
Track control (lower suspension) arm balljoint nuts	44	32
Tie-rod end balljoint nuts	44	32
Mounting bracket to transmission	65	48
Mounting bracket to body	39	29

7

Part B: Four-speed (1.6 models)

Type	Four forward speeds and reverse, torque converter

Gear ratios

1st	2.41 : 1
2nd	1.37 : 1
3rd	1.00 : 1
4th	0.74 : 1
Reverse	2.83 : 1
Final drive	3.28 : 1

Fluid capacity

From dry	5.75 litres (10.0 pints)
Service fluid change	2.0 litres (3.5 pints)

Fluid type

....	Dexron IID type ATF

Torque wrench settings

	Nm	lbf ft
Torque converter to adaptor plate:		
M10 bolts	45	33
M12 bolts	90	60
Driveplate to crankshaft screws	110	81
Driveplate to torque converter screws	32	24
Starter inhibitor switch	40	30
Fluid cooler centre screw	50	37
Sump pan screws	10	7
Drain plug	15	11
Transmission mounting bracket to casing bolts	45	33
Mounting to body bolts	40	30
Through-bolt	120	89
Track control (lower suspension) arm balljoint nuts	44	32
Tie-rod end balljoint nuts	44	32

Part A: Three-speed (1.3 models)

1 General description

The transmission is of Honda manufacture and has a mechanical constant mesh geartrain driven through a torque converter.

Three forward speeds and reverse are provided, selection being made by a floor-mounted selector lever.

The transmission incorporates the final drive and is mounted transversely with the engine, at the front of the car.

A transmission fluid cooler is incorporated in the cooling system radiator.

2 Maintenance

1 Keep the fluid level correctly maintained as described in the following Section.
2 Keep the transmission casing clean by periodically removing grease and dirt.
3 Regularly check the condition of the fluid cooler hoses.
4 Maintain the adjustments described in the following Sections of this Chapter.

3 Transmission fluid - level checking and renewal

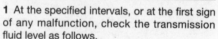

1 At the specified intervals, or at the first sign of any malfunction, check the transmission fluid level as follows.
2 Park the vehicle on a level surface, fully apply the handbrake and select 'P'. Start the engine and allow it to idle for a few minutes.
3 Open the bonnet and locate the dipstick (under the battery). Stop the engine. The level check must be completed within one minute of stopping the engine.
4 Unscrew the dipstick and withdraw it. Wipe it on a clean non-fluffy rag, re-insert it fully *without screwing it in*, withdraw it again and read the fluid level. The level should be between the MIN and MAX marks.
5 Top up if necessary to the midway point between the two marks with fluid of specified type, through the dipstick hole.
6 Refit the dipstick and screw it home.
7 At the intervals recommended in Routine Maintenance, the transmission fluid should be drained hot after coming in from a run.

 Warning: Take precautions against scalding. The fluid may be very hot.

8 Remove the dipstick and then the drain plug and catch the fluid in a suitably large container of 3.0 litres (5.3 pints). The torque converter will not drain.
9 Refit the drain plug.
10 Fill slowly through the dipstick hole using recommended fluid and check the level as previously described.

4 Kickdown cable - adjustment

1 Check that the throttle cable has some slackness at the carburettor. Under light finger pressure, the cable should deflect between 10.0 and 12.0 mm (0.39 and 0.47 in).
2 Check that the throttle lever is up against its stop (full throttle) when the accelerator pedal is fully depressed.
3 The engine should be at normal operating temperature with the idling speed correctly set (see Chapter 3). Switch off the engine.
4 Release the kickdown inner cable from the lever on the transmission and then release the outer cable (conduit) from its support bracket.
5 Measure the distance between the kickdown lever and the throttle cable bracket. This should be 83.5 mm (3.287 in). If it is

incorrect, release the bracket bolts and move the bracket.

6 Depress the accelerator pedal using a 1.3 kg (2.9 lb) weight.

7 Set the kickdown cable conduit locknut (B) so that dimension (A) (Fig. 7.1) is 84.0 mm (3.306 in).

8 Connect the inner cable to the lever on the transmission and engage the conduit with its bracket. Tighten the locknut (C) without disturbing the set position of locknut (B).

9 Remove the weight from the accelerator pedal.

5 Selector cable - adjustment

1 Start the engine, apply the footbrake and engage reverse gear, then stop the engine.
2 Remove the centre console (Chapter 11), then select D.
3 Release the locknut (2) (Fig. 7.2). Remove the retaining pin (1).
4 Turn the adjuster (3) until its hole is in alignment with the one in the selector cable.
5 Tighten the locknut and refit the pin.
6 Check that the starter only operates in N and P and then road test the car to check the selection of all speeds.
7 Refit the centre console.

6 Selector cable - removal and refitting

1 Remove the engine compartment under shield.
2 Disconnect the exhaust downpipe from the manifold and then separate and remove the downpipe from the rest of the exhaust system.
3 Remove the exhaust retaining brackets from the transmission.
4 Unbolt and remove the semi-circular cover plate from the torque converter housing.
5 Select N, remove the selector cable clevis pin and disconnect the cable from the transmission.
6 Remove the centre console (see Chapter 11) and disconnect the cable from the selector lever.
7 Refitting is a reversal of removal. Adjust as described in Section 5.

7 Speed selector control lever - removal, overhaul and refitting

1 Remove the centre console as described in Chapter 11.
2 Disconnect the starter inhibitor/reverse lamp switch connector plug, also the selector index illumination lead.
3 Extract the screws which retain the index plate.

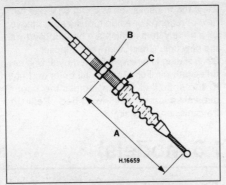

Fig. 7.1 Three-speed transmission kickdown cable (Sec 4)

A = 84.0 mm (3.306 in)
B and C Locknuts

4 Select R and remove the selector cable retaining pin.
5 Unscrew the selector lever retaining nuts and remove the lever assembly.
6 To dismantle the assembly, extract the securing screws and withdraw the handle from the lever. Remove the push-button and spring.
7 Select N and remove the starter inhibitor/reverse lamp switch.
8 Remove the index panel and twist the lamp through 90° to remove it.
9 Release the spring and remove the detent lever. Withdraw the pivot bolt and withdraw the selector lever.
10 Reassembly and refitting are reversals of removal and dismantling. Smear the pivots and rubbing surfaces with grease and check operation after installation.

8 Automatic transmission - removal and refitting

In the event of a fault occurring on the transmission, it is first necessary to determine whether it is of a mechanical or hydraulic nature and to do this the transmission must be in the car. Special test equipment is necessary for this purpose, together with a systematic test procedure, and the work should be entrusted to a suitably equipped BL dealer or automatic transmission specialist.

Do not remove the transmission from the car for repair or overhaul until professional fault diagnosis has been carried out.

1 Disconnect and remove the battery and remove its tray.
2 Disconnect the speedometer cable from the transmission by pulling up the rubber cover and extracting the retaining clip.
3 Disconnect the transmission earth cable.
4 Disconnect the leads from the starter motor. Then unbolt and remove the starter motor.
5 Disconnect the transmission fluid cooler hoses and plug them.
6 Drain the transmission fluid.

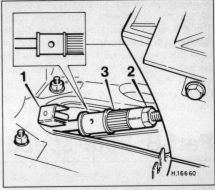

Fig. 7.2 Three-speed transmission selector cable (Sec 5)

1 Retaining pin   2 Locknut   3 Adjuster

7 Raise the front of the car and support it securely, then remove the front roadwheels.
8 Remove the engine compartment undershield.
9 Support the lower suspension arms on jacks and unscrew the nuts from their balljoints.
10 Using a suitable splitter tool, disconnect the balljoints from the hub carriers. Make sure that the car is well supported when the balljoint is released as the torque at the suspension arm is considerable.
11 Disconnect both steering rod balljoints using the same tool as for the hub carrier balljoint.
12 Prise both driveshafts from the transmission and lower them to the floor. Do this by inserting a lever between the transmission casing and the driveshaft inboard joint and prising against the tension of the shaft locking clip. The front suspension struts can now be pulled outwards within the limit of flexibility of their upper mountings and the driveshafts disconnected from transmission. The left-hand brakepipe bracket may have to be released to prevent strain on the pipe.
13 Unbolt and remove the exhaust downpipe from the manifold and the rest of the exhaust system.
14 Unbolt and remove the torque converter cover plate.
15 Disconnect the selector cable and the kickdown cable from the transmission .
16 Working through the aperture left by removal of the torque converter cover plate, unscrew the bolts which hold the driveplate to the torque converter. The crankshaft will have to be turned by means of its pulley bolt to bring the bolts into view.
17 Support the weight of the engine either on a hoist or by locating a jack and block of wood as an insulator under the sump pan.
18 Disconnect and remove the rear and right-hand transmission mountings.
19 Using a second hoist or workshop jack, take the weight of the transmission and then unscrew the engine to transmission connecting bolts.

7

20 Withdraw the transmission until it comes off its positioning dowels. Then lower it to the floor and remove it from under the car. During the removal operations, have an assistant keep the torque converter pushed fully into the bellhousing and retain it afterwards using a plate bolted to the bellhousing flange. Failure to do this may damage the fluid seal and will cause loss of fluid.

21 If the transmission is being changed for a new or reconditioned unit, make sure that you take off any items which are not supplied with the new unit. Check with your supplier.
22 Refitting is a reversal of removal. Use new driveshaft circlips. Tighten all bolts and nuts to the specified torque, adjust the control cables as previously described. Refill the transmission with fluid.

9 Differential fluid seals - renewal

The operations are as described in Chapter 6, Section 5, but use petroleum jelly to fill the seal lips.

Part B: Four-speed (1.6 models)

10 General description

The transmission is of ZF four-speed type and incorporates a torque converter.

The transmission is mounted in line with the engine on the left-hand side at the front of the car.

A kickdown facility is provided.

The final drive/differential is incorporated within the transmission casing.

The transmission fluid is cooled by an externally mounted cooler, through which engine coolant flows.

11 Maintenance

Refer to Section 2, Part A.

12 Transmission fluid - level checking and renewal

1 The fluid level should be checked when the car is standing on level ground with the transmission fluid hot, after at least 10 miles running. Check that the handbrake is fully applied.

2 With the engine idling in P (Park), withdraw the transmission dipstick and wipe it clean. Re-insert it and withdraw it again immediately. The fluid level should be between the MIN and MAX marks on the HOT side of the dipstick. 0.3 litre (0.5 pint) will raise the level from MIN to MAX.

3 Top up as necessary, but do not overfill.

4 At the intervals specified in Routine Maintenance, remove the drain plugs and the dipstick and drain the fluid. The torque converter cannot be drained.

⚠️ *Warning: Take precautions against scalding. The transmission fluid may be very hot.*

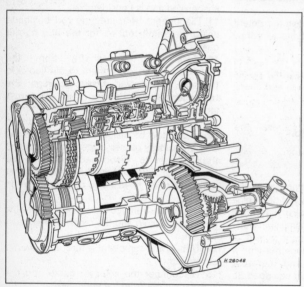

Fig. 7.3 Cutaway view of the four-speed transmission (Sec 10)

Fig. 7.4 Sectional view of four-speed automatic transmission (Sec 10)

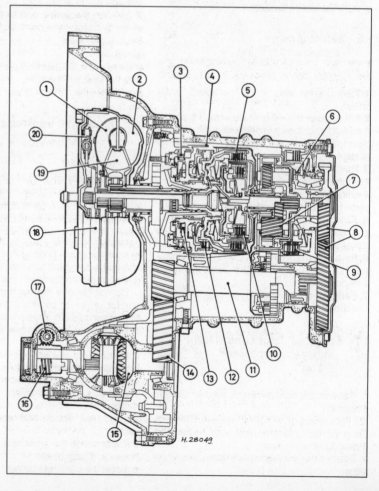

1 Turbine
2 Impeller
3 Brake
5 Clutch
6 1st speed one-way clutch
7 Planetary gear set
8 Spur gears
9 Brake
10 Clutch
11 Countershaft
12 Clutch
13 2nd speed one-way clutch
14 Brake band
14 Crownwheel
15 Differential pinion gears
16 Speedo drive gear
17 Speedo drive pinion
18 Torque converter
19 Stator
20 Torsional damper

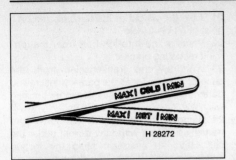

Fig. 7.5 Dipstick markings (Sec 12)

5 Refit the drain plugs and fill through the dipstick guide tube to the MAX mark on the cold side of the dipstick.
6 Start the engine and run it at idle speed. Move the speed selector lever slowly through all positions. With the engine still idling, withdraw the dipstick, wipe it clean, re-insert it and then withdraw it for the second time. The level should be between MIN and MAX on the COLD side of the dipstick.
7 Top up as necessary. 0.3 litre (0.5 pint) will raise the fluid level from the MIN to the MAX level marks.

13 Kickdown cable - adjustment

1 Slacken the locknuts at the kickdown and the throttle cable brackets in the engine compartment.
2 Adjust the nuts on the kickdown cable to give it some slackness.
3 Adjust the throttle cable nuts until all slack is removed from the cable, but it is not under tension.
4 Tighten the throttle cable locknuts.
5 Hold the throttle in the fully open position and pull the kickdown outer cable (conduit) until it is felt to pass the kickdown detent. Tighten the locknuts at the bracket.
6 Release the throttle and check that the gap between the crimped sleeve on the inner cable and the end of the outer cable threaded adjuster is between 0.2 and 0.5 mm (0.01 and 0.02 in). If it is not as specified then the crimped sleeve will have to be repositioned.

14 Selector cable - adjustment

1 Move the selector lever to P (Park).
2 Slacken the selector cable trunnion nut at the lever on the transmission and then rotate the lever fully anti-clockwise. Retighten the trunnion nut.
3 Check that the starter operates only when the selector lever is in N or P.

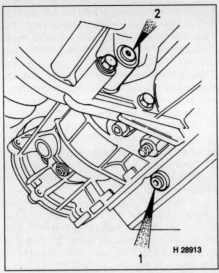

Fig. 7.6 Fluid drain plugs (Sec 12)

1 Gear case   2 Final drive

15 Selector cable - removal and refitting

1 Before removing the cable, make a sketch of its routing.
2 Remove the centre console (Chapter 11).
3 Extract the selector lever knob fixing screws and take off the knob, plunger and spring.
4 Extract the screws and remove the speed position indicator plate.
5 Unscrew the detent bracket bolts and move the bracket aside.
6 Extract the spring clip and withdraw the clevis pin.
7 Unscrew the cable locknut, take off the split washer and withdraw the cable from under the car.
8 Release the cable from the trunnion at the transmission and from its support bracket.
9 Refitting is a reversal of removal, but renew the nylon bush in the trunnion eye if it is worn. Wear in this bush could affect the operation of the starter inhibitor switch.
10 Adjust the cable as described in the preceding Section.

16 Selector lever - removal and refitting

1 Remove the centre console (Chapter 11).
2 Place the car over an inspection pit or raise the front end and support it securely on stands.
3 Carry out the operations described in Section 15, paragraphs 3 to 6.
4 Pull the selector lever into the car so that the lever pivot bolt can be unscrewed and the lever removed from the housing.

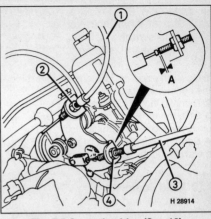

Fig. 7.7 Control cables (Sec 13)

1 Throttle cable	A Crimped sleeve
2 Locknuts	clearance on
3 Kickdown cable	kickdown cable
4 Locknuts	0.2 to 0.5 mm
	(0.01 to 0.02 in)

5 Extract the circlip and remove the lever plunger, spacers and dowel.
6 Unscrew the nut which retains the detent stud lever. Remove the lever and spring.
7 Refitting is a reversal of removal.

17 Brake band - adjustment

1 Place the car over an inspection pit, on ramps or raise the front end and support it securely.
2 Set the selector lever in N.
3 Slacken the brake band adjuster screw locknut and tighten the screw to 10.0 Nm (7.0 lbf ft). Unscrew the adjuster screw exactly two complete turns and tighten the locknut to 80.0 Nm (59.0 lbf ft).

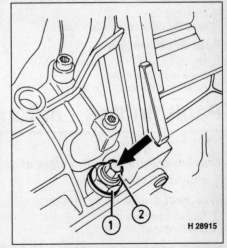

Fig. 7.8 Brake band adjuster screw (2) and locknut (1) (Sec 17)

18 Starter inhibitor/reverse lamp switch - removal and refitting

1 Open the bonnet, disconnect and remove the battery and its tray.
2 Remove the air cleaner.
3 Disconnect the electrical leads and unscrew and remove the switch.
4 Refitting is a reversal of removal. Tighten the switch to the specified torque.

19 Fluid cooler - removal and refitting

1 Disconnect the battery.
2 Drain the cooling system (Chapter 2).
3 Disconnect the coolant hoses from the fluid cooler.
4 Unscrew the fluid cooler centre mounting bolt and remove the cooler.
5 Discard all seals and renew them.
6 Refitting is a reversal of removal. Tighten the centre bolt to the specified torque.
7 Refill the cooling system.
8 Check the transmission fluid level and top up.

20 Automatic transmission - removal and refitting

1 Disconnect and remove the battery.
2 Drain the cooling system.
3 Drain the transmission fluid.
4 Raise the front end of the car, support it securely and remove the front roadwheels.

5 Remove the air cleaner and the battery tray.
6 Disconnect the selector cable from the transmission. Also disconnect the earth cable.
7 Disconnect the coolant hoses from the fluid cooler.
8 Disconnect the kickdown cable and the leads from the starter inhibitor/reverse lamp switch.
9 Unbolt and remove the starter motor.
10 Release the fuel filter mounting bracket from the transmission and move the filter assembly to one side (when applicable).
11 Disconnect both driveshafts from the transmission as described in Section 8, paragraphs 8 to 12.
12 Working through the starter motor aperture, unscrew the bolts which hold the driveplate to the torque converter. The crankshaft will have to be turned by means of its pulley bolt to bring each of the three bolts into view.
13 Support the engine under the sump pan using a jack with a wooden block as an insulator.
14 Unscrew the bolts which hold the rear mounting to the transmission.
15 Unscrew the transmission to adaptor plate bolts noting that the bolts on either side of the sump plate can only be partially unscrewed at this stage.
16 Disconnect the speedometer drive cable from the transmission. Do this by pulling up the rubber cover and extracting the clip.
17 Release the hose from the side of the engine breather.
18 Release the transmission fluid filler tube bracket from the adaptor plate.
19 Disconnect the crankshaft sensor plug.
20 Unscrew any remaining transmission to adaptor plate bolts.

21 Take the weight of the transmission on a hoist or a trolley jack.
22 Remove the through-bolt from the left-hand mounting bracket.
23 Withdraw the transmission from the adaptor plate as far as the partially unscrewed bottom bolts on the torque converter housing will allow.
24 Remove the bottom bolts, lower the transmission and withdraw it from under the car. Have an assistant keep the torque converter pushed fully into the bellhousing during removal and retain it afterwards using a plate bolted to the bellhousing flange. Failure to do this may damage the oil seal and will cause loss of fluid.
25 If the transmission is being changed for a new or reconditioned unit, make sure that you take off any items which are not supplied with the new unit. Check with your supplier.
26 Refitting is a reversal of removal. Use new driveshaft circlips. Tighten all nuts and bolts to the specified torque. Check the adjustment of the selector and kickdown cables.
27 Check that the driveshafts are positively locked into the transmission with their circlips engaged.
28 Refill the transmission with specified fluid.
29 Refill the cooling system.

21 Differential fluid seals - renewal

The procedure is essentially the same as that described in Chapter 6, but the lips of the new seals should be packed with petroleum jelly.

Fault finding - automatic transmission (three-speed type)

This is meant to be a guide only. For more comprehensive fault diagnosis, the car should be road tested by your dealer.

No movement when a speed position selected
☐ Low fluid level
☐ Selector cable out of adjustment

Poor acceleration
☐ High fluid level
☐ Slack in throttle cable
☐ Selector cable out of adjustment

Engine vibrates at idle
☐ Faulty fluid pump

Incorrect upshift or downshift, harsh shift or jumps between high and low speeds in D
☐ Faulty internal shift valve

Car creeps in N
☐ Faulty internal clutch

Fault finding - automatic transmission (four-speed type)

This is meant to be a guide only. For more comprehensive fault diagnosis, the car should be road tested by your dealer.

Transmission noisy and slips after a long journey
☐ Blocked internal fluid strainer

Incorrect shifts up or down
☐ Faulty valve block
☐ Low fluid level

With D selected car moves off in 2nd speed
☐ Brake band requires adjustment

No drive in R
☐ Adjustment required to selector cable

Engine will not start in N or P
☐ Fault in starter inhibitor switch
☐ Selector cable requires adjustment

Kickdown point incorrect
☐ Kickdown cable requires adjustment

Chapter 8
Driveshafts, hubs, roadwheels and tyres

For modifications, and information applicable to later models, see Supplement at end of manual

Contents

Degrees of difficulty

| Easy, suitable for novice with little experience | | Fairly easy, suitable for beginner with some experience | | Fairly difficult, suitable for competent DIY mechanic | | Difficult, suitable for experienced DIY mechanic | | Very difficult, suitable for expert DIY or professional | |

Specifications

Type .... Open driveshaft with CV and tripode joints, sealed hub bearings, pressed steel or cast alloy roadwheels radial ply tyres

Driveshaft joint lubricant
Inboard (tripode) joint:
  Type .... Mobil 525 grease
  Quantity .... 185 cc (5.2 fl oz)
Outboard (CV) joint:
  Type .... Mobil 171-AM3 grease
  Quantity .... 90 cc (2.5 fl oz)

Roadwheels
Type:
  All models except Vitesse .... Pressed steel
  Vitesse .... Cast alloy
Size:
  1.3 models .... 4 1/2J x 13
  1.6 models (except Vitesse) .... 5J x 13
  Vitesse .... 5J x 14

Tyres
Size (depending upon model) .... 155 SR13, 165/70, SR 13,165 SR 13,165 R 1382S, 175/65R 1482T

Pressures, cold, in bar (lbf/in²)*:	Front	Rear
All 213 models	1.7 (24)	1.7 (24)
216 models with 165/13 tyres	2.0 (28)	1.8 (26)
216 models with 175/65 14 tyres	2.0 (28)	2.0 (28)

These are the maker's recommended pressures at the time of writing.
Pressures given in operator's handbook may vary slightly. If in doubt consult a Rover dealer or tyre specialist

Torque wrench settings	Nm	lbf ft
Driveshaft to hub nut	185	137
Front suspension arm balljoint nut	44	32
Tie-rod end balljoint nut	44	32
Roadwheel nuts	81	60
Rear hub nut	185	137
Front brake caliper bolts	78	57

8

1 General description

The driveshafts are of unequal length, the right-hand one being solid while the left-hand one is of tubular construction.

The inboard joints are of tripode roller type while the outboard ones are of constant velocity type.

The outboard joint is renewable, but the inboard one is not and must be renewed complete with shaft.

The driveshafts are held in the differential by circlips.

The front hubs are supported on sealed type bearings which can be renewed independently of the hub carrier.

The rear hub bearings are integral with the hub and in the event of wear must be renewed as an assembly.

The roadwheels may be of pressed steel or cast alloy construction according to model while the tyres are of radial ply type.

2 Maintenance

1 This is largely visual and should be carried out at the intervals specified in Routine Maintenance.
2 Raise the front roadwheels and turn them slowly while examining the boots on the joints for splits or signs of leaking lubricant. Extend the boots with the fingers to ensure that there are no splits at the base of the pleats.
3 If the boot is found to be damaged then the joint must be dismantled as described in Section 4. All the old lubricant must be removed and the boot discarded. Fresh lubricant should be applied and a new boot fitted.
4 Also at the specified intervals, raise each roadwheel in turn (handbrake off), grip the top and bottom of the tyre and attempt to rock the wheel. Provided the hub nut has been correctly tightened, any movement will be due

3.1 Releasing driveshaft/hub nut

to worn bearings. Noise when cornering will be due to the same reason.
5 Keep the tyres inflated to the specified pressure and examine them regularly for wear or damage.

3 Driveshaft - removal and refitting

1 Remove the centre cap from the roadwheel. Relieve the staking on the driveshaft/hub nut and remove the nut (photo). (If the roadwheel has no centre cap, the nut will have to be undone after removing the wheel, with an assistant applying the brakes.) Slacken the wheel nuts, raise and support the front of the vehicle and remove the wheel.
2 Support the front suspension lower suspension arm, unscrew the balljoint nut and then using a splitter tool, disconnect the balljoint from the hub carrier. Be prepared for reaction from the torsion bar on the suspension arm as the balljoint is released (photo).
3 On models equipped with automatic transmission, if the left-hand driveshaft is being removed, remove the brake pipe bracket bolt and disconnect the left-hand steering tie-rod end balljoint.
4 Insert a lever between the driveshaft inboard joint and the transmission casing and release the driveshaft (photo).
5 Pull the hub carrier outwards within the limit

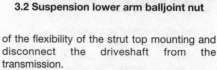

3.2 Suspension lower arm balljoint nut

of the flexibility of the strut top mounting and disconnect the driveshaft from the transmission.
6 Push the driveshaft out of the hub carrier using a plastic-faced hammer (photo).
7 Refitting is a reversal of removal, use a new circlip and make sure that it engages in the differential side gear as the driveshaft is pushed into the transmission. Tighten all nuts and bolts to the specified torque. Use a new driveshaft/hub nut and stake it.

4 Driveshaft boot - renewal

1 To renew a split or damaged boot, first remove the driveshaft as previously described.
2 Remove the clips from the outboard joint boot and peel it back to expose the joint (photo).
3 Hold the driveshaft vertically so that the outboard joint is at the bottom end.
4 Using a soft-faced mallet strike the edge of the lower (CV) joint to drive it from the shaft (photo).
5 Slide off the boot.
6 If it is the inboard joint boot which must be renewed, cut the clips and slide the boot from the shaft.
7 Clean away all original lubricant and repack the joints with the specified type and quantity of grease. Fit the new or original boot, if

3.4 Driveshaft released from transmission

3.6 Driveshaft released from hub carrier

4.2 Driveshaft outboard joint

4.4 Removing outboard (CV) joint

undamaged, and secure with new clips. Heavy quality ratchet type cable ties are suitable for this purpose.

8 Use a new circlip when refitting the outboard joint to the driveshaft. Compress the circlip with pliers to assist its entry into the joint.

5 Driveshaft outboard (CV) joint - renewal

1 This joint may be renewed by removing and refitting it as described in the preceding Section.
2 New joint and shaft circlips should be fitted whenever the driveshaft or joint is removed and refitted.

6 Front hub bearing - renewal

1 Refer to Section 3, paragraph 1.
2 Unscrew the brake caliper mounting bolts and tie the caliper up out of the way without straining the hydraulic hose.
3 Extract the fixing screws and remove the brake disc from the hub. If necessary, two 8.0 mm diameter bolts may be screwed into the tapped holes provided to push the disc from the hub.

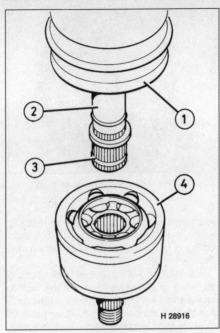

Fig. 8.1 Driveshaft outboard (CV) joint (Sec 5)

1 Boot	3 Circlip
2 Driveshaft	4 CV joint

4 Disconnect the suspension arm and tie-rod end balljoints as described in Section 3.
5 Unscrew the pinch-bolt from the clamp at the base of the suspension strut and separate the hub carrier from the strut.
6 Pull the hub carrier from the driveshaft. If it is tight, use a three-legged puller so that its centre screw will push the driveshaft out of the hub.
7 Press the hub from the hub carrier. The bearing inner track may come out on the hub. Remove the track with an extractor. If a press is not available, drive the hub out with a piece of tubing (photos).
8 Extract the hub bearing circlip using circlip pliers and remove the bearing from the hub.
9 Fit the new bearing by reversing the removal operations.
10 Reassemble the other components, tighten all nuts and bolts to the specified torque.

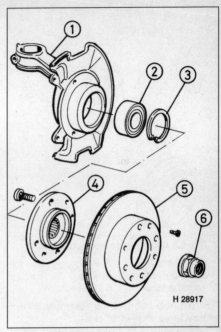

Fig. 8.2 Front hub components (Sec 6)

1 Hub carrier	4 Hub (drive flange)
2 Bearing	5 Brake disc
3 Circlip	6 Nut

11 Use a new hub nut and stake its collar into the groove in the driveshaft (photo).

7 Rear hub bearing - renewal

1 As previously described, the rear hub and bearing are serviced as an assembly.
2 The bearing is a sealed unit and requires no lubrication.
3 Raise the rear of the car, support it securely and remove the roadwheel.
4 Remove the brake drum as described in Chapter 9, Section 6.
5 Remove the hub cap. Relieve the staking on the hub and unscrew the nut. Take off the thrust washer.
6 Using a suitable puller draw the hub from the stub axle.

8

6.7A Removing front hub from carrier

6.7B Removing bearing inner track from hub

6.11 Staking driveshaft/hub nut

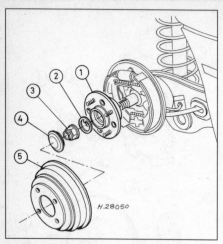

Fig. 8.3 Rear hub components (Sec 7)

1 Hub/bearing   3 Nut
   assembly   4 Cap
2 Thrust washer   5 Brake drum

7 Fit the new hub/bearing assembly, a new thrust washer and nut (photos) .

8 Tighten the nut to the specified torque and then stake its collar into the groove in the stub axle (photo).

Caution: The washer must be fitted on the stub axle shaft with the rounded edge facing the hub.

9 Refit the brake drum, the hub cap and the roadwheel (photo).

8 Wheels and tyres

Wheels and tyres should give no real problems in use provided that a close eye is kept on them with regard to excessive wear or damage. To this end, the following points should be noted.

Ensure that tyre pressures are checked regularly and maintained correctly. Checking should be carried out with the tyres cold and not immediately after the vehicle has been in use. If the pressures are checked with the tyres hot, an apparently high reading will be obtained owing to heat expansion. Under no

7.7A Rear hub/bearing assembly

circumstances should an attempt be made to reduce the pressures to the quoted cold reading in this instance, or effective inderinflation will result.

Underinflation will cause overheating of the tyre owing to excessive flexing of the casing, and the tread will not sit correctly on the road surface. This will cause a consequent loss of adhesion and excessive wear, not to mention the danger of sudden tyre failure due to heat build-up.

Overinflation will cause rapid wear of the centre part of the tyre tread coupled with reduced adhesion, harsher ride, and the danger of shock damage occurring in the tyre casing.

Regularly check the tyres for damage in the form of cuts or bulges, especially in the sidewalls. Remove any nails or stones embedded in the tread before they penetrate the tyre to cause deflation. If removal of a nail does reveal that the tyre has been punctured, refit the nail so that its point of penetration is marked. Then immediately change the wheel and have the tyre repaired by a tyre dealer. Do not drive on a tyre in such a condition. In many cases a puncture can be simply repaired by the use of an inner tube of the correct size and type. If in any doubt as to the possible consequences of any damage found, consult your local tyre dealer for advice.

Periodically remove the wheels and clean any dirt or mud from the inside and outside surfaces. Examine the wheel rims for signs of

7.7B Fitting rear hub

rusting, corrosion or other damage. Light alloy wheels are easily damaged by 'kerbing' whilst parking, and similarly steel wheels may become dented or buckled. Renewal of the wheel is very often the only course of remedial action possible.

The balance of each wheel and tyre assembly should be maintained to avoid excessive wear, not only to the tyres but also to the steering and suspension components. Wheel imbalance is normally signified by vibration through the vehicle's bodyshell, although in many cases it is particularly noticeable through the steering wheel. Conversely, it should be noted that wear or damage in suspension or steering components may cause excessive tyre wear. Out-of-round or out-of-true tyres, damaged wheels and wheel bearing wear/maladjustment also fall into this category. Balancing will not usually cure vibration caused by such wear.

Wheel balancing may be carried out with the wheel either on or off the vehicle. If balanced on the vehicle, ensure that the wheel-to-hub relationship is marked in some way prior to subsequent wheel removal so that it may be refitted in its original position.

General tyre wear is influenced to a large degree by driving style - harsh braking and acceleration or fast cornering will all produce more rapid tyre wear. Interchanging of tyres may result in more even wear, but this should only be carried out where there is no mix of tyre types on the vehicle. However, it is worth

7.7C Rear hub thrust washer

7.8 Staking rear hub nut

7.9 Fitting rear hub cap

Tyre tread wear patterns

Shoulder Wear

Underinflation (wear on both sides)
Under-inflation will cause overheating of the tyre, because the tyre will flex too much, and the tread will not sit correctly on the road surface. This will cause a loss of grip and excessive wear, not to mention the danger of sudden tyre failure due to heat build-up.
Check and adjust pressures
Incorrect wheel camber (wear on one side)
Repair or renew suspension parts
Hard cornering
Reduce speed!

Centre Wear

Overinflation
Over-inflation will cause rapid wear of the centre part of the tyre tread, coupled with reduced grip, harsher ride, and the danger of shock damage occurring in the tyre casing.
Check and adjust pressures

If you sometimes have to inflate your car's tyres to the higher pressures specified for maximum load or sustained high speed, don't forget to reduce the pressures to normal afterwards.

Uneven Wear

Front tyres may wear unevenly as a result of wheel misalignment. Most tyre dealers and garages can check and adjust the wheel alignment (or "tracking") for a modest charge.
Incorrect camber or castor
Repair or renew suspension parts
Malfunctioning suspension
Repair or renew suspension parts
Unbalanced wheel
Balance tyres
Incorrect toe setting
Adjust front wheel alignment
Note: *The feathered edge of the tread which typifies toe wear is best checked by feel.*

bearing in mind that if this is completely effective, the added expense of replacing a complete set of tyres simultaneously is incurred, which may prove financially restrictive for many owners.
Front tyres may wear unevenly as a result of wheel misalignment.
The front wheels should always be correctly aligned according to the settings specified by the vehicle manufacturer.

Legal restrictions apply to the mixing of tyre types on a vehicle. Basically this means that a vehicle must not have tyres of differing construction on the same axle. Although it is not recommended to mix tyre types between front axle and rear axle, the only legally permissible combination is crossply at the front and radial at the rear. When mixing radial ply tyres, textile braced radials must always go on the front axle, with steel braced radials at the rear. An obvious

disadvantage of such mixing is the necessity to carry two spare tyres to avoid contravening the law in the event of a puncture.
In the UK, the Motor Vehicles Construction and Use Regulations apply to many aspects of tyre fitting and usage. It is suggested that a copy of these regulations is obtained from your local police if in doubt as to the current legal requirements with regard to tyre condition, minimum tread depth, etc.

Fault finding - driveshafts, hubs, roadwheels and tyres

8

Vibration
- [ ] Driveshaft bent
- [ ] Worn universal joints
- [ ] Out-of-balance roadwheels

Noise or roar especially when cornering
- [ ] Worn hub bearings
- [ ] Incorrectly tightened hub flange or driveshaft nuts

'Clonk' on taking up drive or on overrun
- [ ] Worn universal joints
- [ ] Worn splines on shaft, hub carrier or differential side gears
- [ ] Loose driveshaft nut
- [ ] Loose roadwheel bolts

Notes

Chapter 9 Braking system

For modifications, and information applicable to later models, see Supplement at end of manual

Contents

Degrees of difficulty

Easy, suitable for novice with little experience	**Fairly easy,** suitable for beginner with some experience	**Fairly difficult,** suitable for competent DIY mechanic 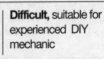	**Difficult,** suitable for experienced DIY mechanic	**Very difficult,** suitable for expert DIY or professional 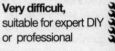

Specifications

System type	Four wheel hydraulic dual circuit with vacuum servo assistance. Front discs, rear drums. Handbrake mechanical on rear wheels

Disc brakes

Disc diameter and type:	
1.3 models	190.0 mm (7.1 in) solid
1.6 models	231.0 mm (9.0 in) ventilated
Thickness:	
1.3 models	12.0 mm (0.47 in)
1.6 models	17.0 mm (0.67 in)
Regrind limit (minimum thickness):	
1.3 models	10.0 mm (0.39 in)
1.6 models	15.0 mm (0.59 in)
Run-out (maximum)	0.10 mm (0.004 in)
Minimum disc pad friction material thickness	3.0 mm (0.12 in)

Drum brakes

Internal diameter	180.0 mm (7.09 in)
Regrind limit (maximum internal diameter)	181.0 mm (7.126 in)
Minimum shoe lining thickness	2.0 mm (0.08 in)

Pedal height from floor	174.0 mm (6.8 in)

Pedal free play	1.0 to 5.0 mm (0.04 to 0.20 in)

Brake fluid type/specification	Hydraulic fluid to FMVSS 116 DOT 4

Torque wrench settings

	Nm	lbf ft
Hose banjo bolt caliper	35	26
Caliper guide pin bolts	18	13
Caliper mounting bolts	78	57
Brake pipe flare nuts	15	11
Bleed screws	9	7
Master cylinder stop bolt (1.3)	9	7
Rear brake backplate bolts	45	33
Rear hub nut	185	137
Roadwheel nuts	80	59

9

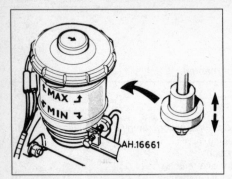

Fig. 9.1 Master cylinder fluid reservoir – typical for 1.3 models (Sec 21

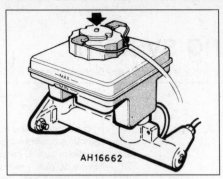

Fig. 9.2 Master cylinder fluid reservoir – typical for 1.6 models (Sec 21)

2.1 Topping up the brake fluid

1 General description

The braking system is of dual-circuit hydraulic type.

The hydraulic circuit is split diagonally, front right-hand and rear left-hand brakes and front left-hand and rear right-hand brakes.

Vacuum servo assistance is provided.

The front disc calipers are of single piston sliding type and the rear drum brakes incorporate self-adjusting shoes.

A pressure regulating valve is incorporated in the hydraulic circuit to restrict pressure to the rear brakes during heavy braking and so prevent the rear wheels locking.

A low level warning sensor is fitted in the master cylinder fluid reservoir.

The handbrake is operated by cable to the rear wheels.

2 Maintenance and inspection

1 At the weekly service check, inspect the brake hydraulic fluid level in the translucent reservoir on the master cylinder. The level should be at, or just below the MAX MARK. If not, remove the cap and top up (photo) .

2 The addition of fluid should only be necessary very infrequently, just a small quantity to compensate for the displaced fluid as the friction linings wear.

3 Where large quantities of fluid are needed, look for a leak in the pipelines or hydraulic cylinders. A leak can often be overlooked at the rear of the master cylinder pushrod inside the car. This is caused by failure of the master cylinder seals.

4 Regularly inspect the condition of the hoses and pipes as described in Section 13.

5 At the specified intervals, check the disc pads and brake linings for wear as described in the following Sections.

3 Disc pads - inspection and renewal

1 Raise the front end of the car and support it securely. Remove the front roadwheels.

2 Check the thickness of the disc pad friction material through the inspection hole in the caliper (photo).

3 If the pads have worn down to their specified minimum thickness, then they must be renewed. Unscrew the caliper lower guide pin bolt, release the upper bolt and pivot the caliper upwards (photo).

4 If the pads have worn unevenly then it is

permissible to interchange them. In this case check that the caliper can slide freely on the guide pins.

5 Remove the pads, spring clips and note the shim on the back of the outboard pad (photo).

6 Clean away dust and dirt from the caliper, taking care not to inhale it as it is injurious to health.

7 The piston must now be pushed fully back into its cylinder in order to accommodate the new thicker pads. This will cause the fluid level to rise in the master cylinder reservoir. Anticipate this by syphoning out some of the fluid using a poultry baster or clean battery hydrometer.

8 Lightly smear the backs of the pads with silicone grease and clean both sides of the anti-squeal shim.

9 Fit the pads, shim and springs.

10 Pivot the caliper downwards and tighten the guide pin bolts to the specified torque.

11 Repeat the operations on the opposite wheel as new pads must be fitted as axle sets.

12 Refit the roadwheels, lower the car and apply the brake pedal several times to position the pads against the discs. Tighten the wheel nuts.

13 Check the fluid level in the reservoir and top up if necessary.

14 Avoid harsh braking if possible for the first few hundred miles to allow the new pads to bed in.

3.2 Disc pad inspection hole. Note ventilated disc (1.6 models)

3.3 Pivoting caliper upwards

3.5 Removing a disc pad

4 Caliper - removal, overhaul and refitting

1 Raise the front of the car, support it securely and remove the roadwheel.
2 Disconnect the brake hose from the caliper by unscrewing the banjo union bolt. Prevent loss of fluid by pinching the hose with a special clamp available from most motor stores or self-locking grips, provided their jaws have been taped to prevent damage. Alternatively, place a rubber disc on each side of the union and retain them with self-locking grips.
3 Unscrew the guide pin bolts and remove the caliper.
4 Remove the disc pads, shim and springs.
5 Clean away dust and dirt, taking care not to inhale it as it is injurious to health.
6 Remove the dust excluding boot.
7 Remove the piston. Do this by applying air pressure to the fluid union hole. Only a low air pressure is required such as is generated from a hand or foot-operated tyre pump.
8 Examine the surfaces of the piston and cylinder bore. If they are scored or there is any sign of rust or corrosion then a new caliper must be obtained. If the components are in good condition then extract the piston seal from its groove in the cylinder. Take great care not to scratch the bore surfaces when doing this. Discard the seal.
9 Obtain a repair kit which will contain all the necessary seals and other renewable items.
10 Clean the piston and cylinder in clean hydraulic fluid or methylated spirit - nothing else, and observe absolute cleanliness during the reassembly operations.
11 Fit the new piston seal, manipulating it into the cylinder groove using the fingers.
12 Smear the cylinder bore with clean hydraulic fluid and push the piston squarely into it. Do not push the piston fully home until the dust excluding boot has been engaged in its groove.
13 Refit the disc pads, springs and anti-squeal shim as described in Section 3.
14 Fit the caliper over the disc and screw in

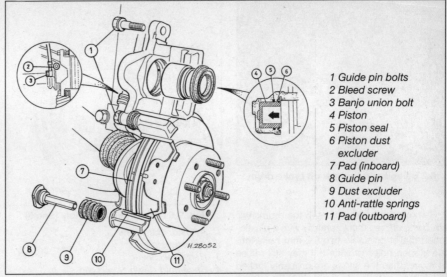

Fig. 9.3 Front disc caliper (Sec 4)

1 Guide pin bolts
2 Bleed screw
3 Banjo union bolt
4 Piston
5 Piston seal
6 Piston dust excluder
7 Pad (inboard)
8 Guide pin
9 Dust excluder
10 Anti-rattle springs
11 Pad (outboard)

the guide pin bolts. Tighten them to the specified torque.
15 Use new sealing washers and reconnect the hydraulic hose to the caliper.
16 Refit the roadwheel and lower the car. Tighten the wheel nuts.
17 Bleed the brakes as described in Section 14.

5 Brake disc - inspection, renovation or renewal

1 Raise the front of the car and remove the roadwheel.
2 Examine the disc for grooving or deep scoring, iight scoring is normal (photo).
3 If severe scoring has occurred it may be possible to have the disc reground, provided the finished thickness is not less than the specified minimum (see Specifications).
4 If as a result of reference to the Fault Diagnosis Section, the disc is suspected of being distorted, the run-out should be checked against the tolerance specified using a dial gauge or feeler blades inserted between

the disc and a fixed point while the disc is being rotated.
5 It may be possible to correct disc run-out by moving the disc through 90° in relation to its location on the hub. If not, then the disc must be renewed.
6 To remove the disc, first unbolt the caliper and tie it up out of the way. Extract the two disc fixing screws (photo).
7 Remove the disc from the hub, pushing it off if necessary using two 8.0 mm bolts screwed into the tapped holes provided.
8 Before fitting a new disc clean away any protective grease using a suitable solvent.
9 Fit the disc. Fit the caliper with pads and apply the brake pedal two or three times to locate the pads against the disc (see Section 4).
10 Refit the roadwheel and lower the car.

6 Rear brake shoes - inspection and renewal

1 At the intervals specified in Routine Maintenance, raise the rear of the car and remove the roadwheels. Release the handbrake.

9

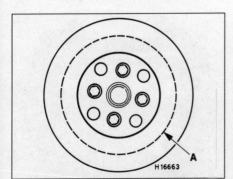

Fig. 9.4 Point for checking disc run-out (Sec 5)

5.2 Ventilated type disc (1.6 models)

5.6 Disc retaining screws

6.2 Using bolts to draw off brake drum

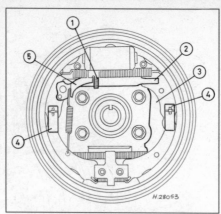

Fig. 9.5 Rear brake assembly (Sec 6)

1 Adjuster star wheel
2 Adjuster strut
3 Handbrake lever
4 Shoe hold-down spring clip
5 Self-adjuster lever

6.3 Rear brake – right-hand side

2 Remove the brake drums. If the drums will not come off, tap them carefully with a plastic-faced mallet or screw two 8.0 mm bolts into the tapped holes provided. If they still refuse to move, then the shoes are probably locked in wear grooves inside the drums. To release them, extract the rubber plug from the backplate just forward of the wheel cylinder attachment point, insert a screwdriver and turn the star wheel adjuster on the self-adjuster strut. Pivot the point on the screwdriver downwards (photo).

3 With the drums removed, brush away dust, taking care not to inhale it as it is dangerous to health. Inspect the shoe linings. If they are worn down to their minimum thickness then the shoes must be renewed as an axle set (photo).

4 Do not attempt to re-line the shoes

yourself, but fit new or factory relined ones. Shoes can be renewed without removing the hub, but the job will be easier if it is removed (see Chapter 8).

5 To remove the shoes, release the shoe hold-down spring pins by gripping them with a pair of pliers and then turn them through 90° (photo) .

6 Pull the upper ends of the shoes outwards off the wheel cylinder tappets, pull the shoes slightly forward and gently release them taking care that the shoes do not damage the wheel cylinder rubber boots.

7 Prise the lower ends of the shoes apart and remove them from the anchor block.

8 Pull the shoes outwards against the tension of their return springs and remove them from around the hub drive flange.

9 Disconnect the handbrake cable from the shoe lever and withdraw the complete shoe assembly together with return springs, and adjuster mechanism (photos).

10 Lay the assembly on the bench noting the relative position of the leading and trailing shoes and the holes in the shoe webs in which the springs engage. Make a sketch if necessary (photo).

11 Transfer the handbrake lever from the old

trailing shoe to the new one. This will require removal of the circlip and washer. When refitting, make sure that the head of the retaining pin will be towards the hub drive flange when the shoe is on the backplate.

12 Reassemble the shoes and return springs. Fit the adjuster strut having fully retracted it after having cleaned and lightly greased its threads. Engage the spring with the self-adjuster lever.

13 Apply a smear of high melting-point grease to the shoe rubbing high spots on the backplate and to the slots in the wheel cylinder tappets and anchor block. Be careful not to get grease onto the brake shoe linings.

14 Offer the shoe assembly to the backplate. Connect the handbrake cable to the shoe lever, then engage the shoe ends with the wheel cylinder and anchor block. Fit the hold-down clips and pins.

15 Centralise the shoes on the backplate, then rotate the star wheel adjuster until the brake drum will just slide over the shoes.

16 If the hub was removed, refit it as described in Chapter 8.

17 Refit the brake drum and the roadwheel.

18 Repeat the operations on the other rear wheel.

19 Lower the car and tighten the wheel nuts.

20 Apply the footbrake several times to operate the self-adjusting mechanism.

21 If the new shoes have been fitted, avoid harsh braking if possible for the first few hundred miles to allow the new shoes to bed in.

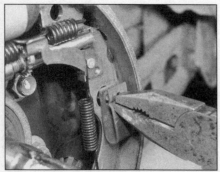

6.5 Releasing brake shoe hold down pin

6.9A Disconnecting handbrake cable from shoe

6.9B Brake backplate (right-hand side) with shoes removed

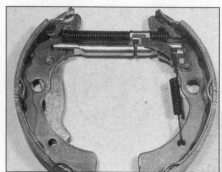

6.10 Brake shoes (right-hand side) ready for fitting

7.4 Wheel cylinder components

9.3 Master cylinder

9.4 Removing master cylinder from servo

7 Rear wheel cylinder - removal, overhaul and refitting

1 Remove the brake shoes as described in the preceding Section.
2 Disconnect the brake pipe from the rear wheel cylinder and cap the pipe to prevent loss of fluid. A bleed nipple dust cap is useful for this purpose.
3 Unscrew the nuts and remove the wheel cylinder from the brake backplate.
4 Clean away external dirt, remove the dust excluding boots and take out the pistons and spring. The pistons may be ejected by shaking the cylinder or by applying low air pressure to the fluid entry port on the cylinder body (photo).
5 Inspect the surfaces of the cylinder bore and pistons. If there is any sign of scoring, rust or corrosion then the cylinder must be renewed complete.
6 If the components are in good condition, clean away external dirt, discard the seals and obtain a repair kit which will contain all the necessary seals and other renewable components.
7 Observe strict cleanliness during reassembly and manipulate the new seals into position using the fingers only, using clean hydraulic fluid as a lubricant. Make sure the seals are fitted the right way round (sealing lips facing the spring ends of the pistons).

8 Dip the pistons in clean hydraulic fluid and insert them into the cylinder with the spring between them. Fit the dust excluding boots.
9 Fit the cylinder to the backplate, tighten the retaining nuts and reconnect the brake pipe.
10 Refit the shoes and drum.
11 Refit the roadwheel, lower the car to the floor,
12 Bleed the hydraulic system as described in Section 14.

8 Brake drum - inspection, renovation or renewal

1 Whenever the brake drum is removed, take the opportunity to clean out all dust and dirt and inspect it for scoring, grooving or cracks.
2 If any of these problems is evident or as a result of reference to the Fault Finding Section the drum is suspected of being out of round, it may be possible to refinish it provided the finished internal diameter does not exceed the maximum specified.
3 If it does, then a new drum must be fitted.

9 Master cylinder - removal and refitting

1 Drain the master cylinder fluid reservoir. Do this either by syphoning or by opening the

caliper bleed screws and pumping the brake pedal. Discard the ejected fluid.
2 Disconnect the fluid level sensor wiring plug and remove the reservoir cap.
3 Disconnect the brake pipes from the master cylinder and cap their open ends (photo).
4 Unscrew the retaining nuts and remove the master cylinder from the vacuum servo unit (photo).
5 Clean away external dirt.
6 Refitting is a reversal of removal. On 1.3 models the servo pushrod clearance should be checked if a new or overhauled unit is being fitted. With the servo pushrod flush with the face of the servo shell, the depth of the master cylinder pushrod recess should be 45.5 mm (1.79 in) when measured with a depth gauge. The distance between the end-face of the master cylinder pushrod and the face of the master cylinder mounting flange should be 43.7 mm (1.72 in). If the actual measurements taken are shorter than those specified, reduce the length of the servo pushrod by the difference. If the measurements taken are longer than those specified, extend the length of the servo pushrod. To alter the length of the servo pushrod, release the locknut (not the pedal clevis fork locknut) and turn the adjuster nut. These nuts are very inaccessible under the facia and it may be easier to remove the servo completely as described in Section 17 (photos).
7 When correctly carried out, the adjustment

9

9.6A Checking servo pushrod is flush with face of servo shell

9.6B Checking depth of master cylinder pushrod recess

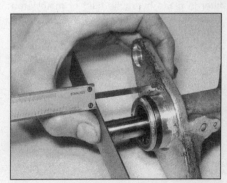

9.6C Checking flange to pushrod end face dimension on master cylinder

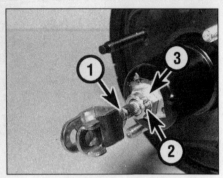

9.6D Vacuum servo pushrod

1 Clevis fork locknut	3 Pushrod
2 Pushrod adjuster	locknut

will provide a clearance at the contact point of the servo and master cylinder pushrods of between 0 and 0.4 mm (0.016 in) when the servo and master cylinder are bolted together.
8 Check and adjust the pedal height as described in Section 20.
9 Bleed the complete hydraulic system as described in Section 14.

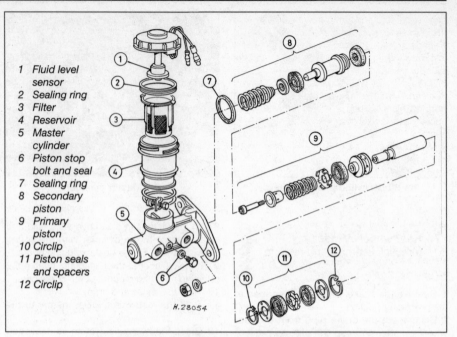

1	Fluid level sensor
2	Sealing ring
3	Filter
4	Reservoir
5	Master cylinder
6	Piston stop bolt and seal
7	Sealing ring
8	Secondary piston
9	Primary piston
10	Circlip
11	Piston seals and spacers
12	Circlip

H.28054

Fig. 9.6 Master cylinder – typical (1.3 models) (Sec 10)

10 Master cylinder (1.3 models) - overhaul

1 With the master cylinder removed from the car, clean away external dirt.
2 Refer to Fig. 9.6 and extract the primary piston end circlip.
3 Shake the primary piston from the cylinder.
4 Insert a rod and depress the secondary piston and then unscrew and remove the stop bolt.
5 Shake out the secondary piston assembly. If it is difficult to remove, apply low air pressure to the secondary fluid entry port.
6 Examine the surface of the cylinder bore. If it is corroded or scored, renew the master cylinder complete.
7 If the components are in good order, discard the primary piston and all other seals. Clean everything, including the reservoir and filter in clean hydraulic fluid or methylated spirit - nothing else.
8 Obtain a repair kit which will contain a new primary piston assembly complete with seals and all other renewable components.
9 Manipulate the new seals into position using the fingers only, dip the components in clean hydraulic fluid before assembly. Make sure that the seals are fitted the right way round.
10 Insert the secondary piston using a twisting motion to prevent trapping of the seal lips. Depress the piston using a rod and screw in the stop bolt.
11 Fit the primary piston and the circlip.
12 Fit the new mounting flange seal.

11 Master cylinder (1.6 models) - overhaul

1 With the master cylinder removed from the car and cleaned externally, remove the fluid reservoir. Do this by rocking it from side to side and at the same time pulling it away from the cylinder body.

2 Refer to Fig. 9.7 and remove the sealing washers and the baffle plates.
3 Using a rod, compress the piston springs so that the secondary piston stop pin can be removed from the reservoir fluid inlet port.
4 Depress the primary piston slightly and extract the circlip.
5 Shake out the primary piston assembly.
6 Remove the secondary piston by tapping the end of the cylinder on a piece of

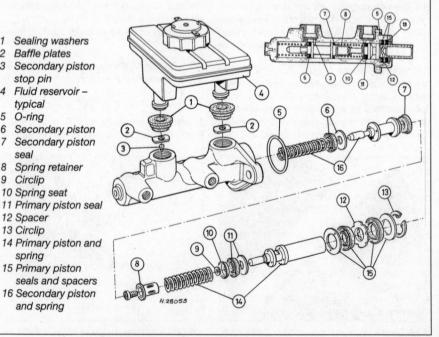

1	Sealing washers
2	Baffle plates
3	Secondary piston stop pin
4	Fluid reservoir – typical
5	O-ring
6	Secondary piston
7	Secondary piston seal
8	Spring retainer
9	Circlip
10	Spring seat
11	Primary piston seal
12	Spacer
13	Circlip
14	Primary piston and spring
15	Primary piston seals and spacers
16	Secondary piston and spring

H.28055

Fig. 9.7 Master cylinder (1.6 models) (Sec 11)

hardwood or by applying low air pressure to the secondary fluid outlet port,

7 Inspect the surface of the cylinder bore. If it is scored or corroded, renew the master cylinder complete.

8 If the cylinder is in good condition, clean it in clean hydraulic fluid or methylated spirit - nothing else. Obtain a repair kit which will contain all the new seals and other renewable items.

9 Manipulate the new seals into place with the fingers, using clean hydraulic fluid as a lubricant. Make sure that the seals are fitted the right way round. Dip the secondary piston into clean hydraulic fluid and fit it into the cylinder using a twisting motion to avoid trapping the seal lips.

10 Depress the secondary piston with a rod and fit the stop pin.

11 Fit the primary piston in a similar way.

12 Secure it with the circlip.

13 Fit the reservoir with baffle plates and seals.

12 Pressure regulating valve - removal and refitting

1 The valve cannot be overhauled or repaired and in the event of a fault, it must be renewed.

2 Disconnect the brake pipes from the valve and quickly cap them to prevent loss of fluid. Catch fluid leaking from the valve to prevent damage to the engine compartment paintwork.

3 Refitting is a reversal of removal, make sure that the valve is mounted vertically.

4 Bleed the hydraulic system as described in Section 14.

13 Hydraulic pipes and hoses - inspection, removal and refitting

1 At intervals given in Routine Maintenance carefully examine all brake pipes, hoses, hose connections and pipe unions.

2 First check for signs of leakage at the pipe unions. Then examine the flexible hoses for signs of cracking, chafing and fraying.

3 The brake pipes must be examined carefully and methodically. They must be cleaned off and checked for signs of dents, corrosion or other damage. Corrosion should be scraped off and, if the depth of pitting is significant, the pipes renewed. This is particularly likely in those areas underneath the vehicle body where the pipes are exposed and unprotected.

4 If any section of pipe or hose is to be removed, first unscrew the master cylinder reservoir filler cap and place a piece of polythene over the filter neck. Secure the polythene with an elastic band ensuring that

an airtight seal is obtained. This will minimise brake fluid loss when the pipe or hose is removed.

5 Brake pipe removal is usually quite straight-forward. The union nuts at each end are undone, the pipe and union pulled out and the centre section of the pipe removed from the body clips. Where the unions nuts are exposed to the full force of the weather they can sometimes be quite tight. As only an open-ended spanner can be used, burring of the flats on the nuts is not uncommon when attempting to undo them. For this reason a self-locking wrench is often the only way to separate a stubborn union.

6 To remove a flexible hose, wipe the unions and brackets free of dirt and undo the union nut from the brake pipe end(s).

7 Next extract the hose retaining clip, or unscrew the nut, and lift the end of the hose out of its bracket. If a front hose is being removed, it can now be unscrewed from the brake caliper.

8 Brake pipes can be obtained individually, or in sets, from most accessory shops or garages with the end flares and union nuts in place. The pipe is then bent to shape, using the old pipe as a guide, and is ready for fitting to the car.

9 Refitting the pipes and hoses is a reverse of the removal procedure. Make sure that the hoses are not kinked when in position and also make sure that the brake pipes are securely supported in their clips. After refitting, remove the polythene from the reservoir and bleed the brake hydraulic system, as described in Section 14.

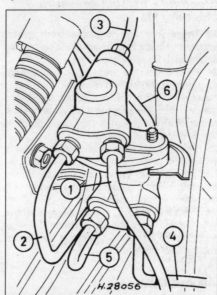

Fig. 9.8 Pressure regulating valve (Sec 12)

1 From master cylinder
2 To right-hand front brake
3 To left-hand rear brake
4 From master cylinder
5 To left-hand front brake
6 To right-hand rear brake

14 Hydraulic system - bleeding

1 The correct functioning of the brake hydraulic system is only possible after removal of all air from the components and circuit; this is achieved by bleeding the system. Note that only clean unused brake fluid, which has remained unshaken for at least 24 hours, must be used.

2 If there is any possibility of incorrect fluid being used in the system, the brake lines and components must be completely flushed with uncontaminated fluid and new seals fitted to the components.

3 *Never re-use* brake fluid which has been bled from the system.

4 During the procedure, do not allow the level of brake fluid to drop more than halfway down the reservoir.

5 Before starting work, check that all pipes and hoses are secure, unions tight and bleed screws closed. Take great care not to allow brake fluid to come into contact with the car paintwork, otherwise the finish will be seriously damaged. Wash off any spilled fluid immediately with cold water.

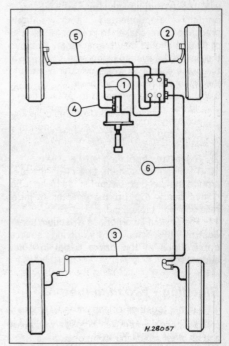

Fig. 9.9 Brake hydraulic circuits (Sec 14)

Primary circuit
1 Master cylinder to pressure regulating valve
2 Pressure regulating valve to RH front brake
3 Pressure regulating valve to LH rear brake

Secondary circuit
4 Master cylinder to pressure regulating valve
5 Pressure regulating valve to LH front brake
6 Pressure regulating valve to RH rear brake

9

14.14 Unscrewing caliper bleed screw fitted with bleed tube

6 There is a number of one-man, do-it-yourself, brake bleeding kits currently available from motor accessory shops. Always follow the instructions supplied with the kit. It is recommended that one of these kits is used wherever possible, as they greatly simplify the bleeding operation and also reduce the risk of expelled air and fluid being drawn back into the system.

7 If brake fluid has been lost from the master cylinder due to a leak in the system, ensure that the cause is traced and rectified before proceeding further.

8 If the hydraulic system has only been partially disconnected and suitable precautions were taken to prevent further loss of fluid, it should only be necessary to bleed the part of the system being worked on (i.e. at the brake caliper or wheel cylinder nearest to the disconnected pipe or hose).

9 if the complete system is to be bled then it should be done in the following sequence:
Secondary circuit:
Left-hand front then right-hand rear
Primary circuit:
Right-hand front then left-hand rear

10 To bleed the system, first clean the area around the bleed screw and fit the bleed tube. If necessary top up the master cylinder reservoir with brake fluid.

11 The system incorporates a vacuum servo, destroy the vacuum by giving several applications of the brake pedal in quick succession.

Bleeding - two man method

12 Gather together a clean jar and a length of rubber or plastic tubing which will be a tight fit on the brake bleed screws.

13 Engage the help of an assistant.

14 Push one end of the bleed tube onto the first bleed screw and immerse the other end in the jar which should contain enough hydraulic fluid to cover the end of the tube (photo).

15 Open the bleed screw one half a turn and have your assistant depress the brake pedal fully then slowly release it. Tighten the bleed screw at the end of each pedal downstroke to obviate any chance of air or fluid being drawn back into the system.

16 Repeat this operation until clean brake

fluid, free from air bubbles, can be seen coming through into the jar.

17 Tighten the bleed screw at the end of a pedal downstroke and remove the bleed tube. Bleed the remaining screws in a similar way.

Bleeding - using one-way valve kit

18 It is recommended that one of these kits is used wherever possible as it will greatly simplify the bleeding operation and also reduce the risk of air or fluid being drawn back into the system, quite apart from being able to do the work without the help of an assistant.

19 To use the kit, connect the tube to the bleed screw and open the screw one half turn.

20 Depress the brake pedal fully then slowly release it. The one-way valve in the kit will prevent expelled air from returning at the end of each pedal downstroke. Repeat this operation several times to be sure of ejecting all air from the system. Some kits include a translucent container which can be positioned so that the air bubbles can actually be seen being ejected from the system.

21 Tighten the bleed screw, remove the tube and repeat the operations on the remaining brakes.

22 On completion, depress the brake pedal. If it still feels spongy, repeat the bleeding operations, as air must still be trapped in the system.

Bleeding - using a pressure bleeding kit

23 These kits are available from motor accessory shops and are usually operated by air pressure from the spare tyre.

24 By connecting a pressurised container to the master cylinder fluid reservoir, bleeding is then carried out simply by opening each bleed screw in turn and allowing the fluid to run out, rather like turning on a tap, until no air is visible in the expelled fluid.

25 By using this method, the large reserve of brake fluid provides a safeguard against air being drawn into the master cylinder during bleeding which may occur if the fluid level in the reservoir is not maintained.

26 Pressure bleeding is particularly effective when bleeding 'difficult' systems or when bleeding the complete system at the time of routine fluid renewal.

All methods

27 When bleeding is completed, check and top up the fluid level in the master cylinder reservoir.

28 Check the feel of the brake pedal. If it feels at all spongy, air must still be present in the system and the need for further bleeding is indicated. Failure to bleed satisfactorily after a reasonable repetition of the bleeding

operations may be due to worn master cylinder seals.

29 Discard brake fluid which has been expelled. It is almost certain to be contaminated with moisture, air and dirt, making it unsuitable for further use. Clean fluid should always be stored in an airtight container as it is hygroscopic (absorbs moisture readily) which lowers its boiling point and could affect braking performance under severe conditions.

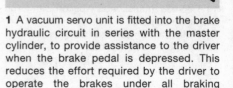

15 Vacuum servo unit - description

1 A vacuum servo unit is fitted into the brake hydraulic circuit in series with the master cylinder, to provide assistance to the driver when the brake pedal is depressed. This reduces the effort required by the driver to operate the brakes under all braking conditions.

2 The unit operates by vacuum obtained from the inlet manifold and comprises basically a booster diaphragm, control valve, and a non-return valve.

3 The servo unit and hydraulic master cylinder are connected together so that the servo unit piston rod acts as the master cylinder pushrod. The driver's braking effort is transmitted through another pushrod to the servo unit piston and its built-in control system. The servo unit piston does not fit tightly into the cylinder, but has a strong diaphragm to keep its edges in constant contact with the cylinder wall, so ensuring an airtight seal between the two parts. The forward chamber is held under vacuum conditions created in the inlet manifold of the engine and, during periods when the brake pedal is not in use, the controls open a passage to the rear chamber so placing it under vacuum conditions as well. When the brake pedal is depressed, the vacuum passage to the rear chamber is cut off and the chamber opened to atmospheric pressure. The consequent rush of air pushes the servo piston forward in the vacuum chamber and operates the main pushrod to the master cylinder.

4 In the event of failure of the servo unit, the hydraulic circuit remains unaffected except that increased pedal pressure will be required.

5 If a servo unit is suspected of being faulty, carry out the following test.

6 With the engine switched off, depress the brake pedal several times, finally press hard and hold for 15 seconds. If the pedal sinks then there is a leak in the hydraulic system and the servo is not necessarily faulty.

7 Hold the brake pedal depressed and start the engine. The pedal should sink slightly. If it does not, check the non-return valve and manifold adaptor; if these are satisfactory, then the servo is faulty.

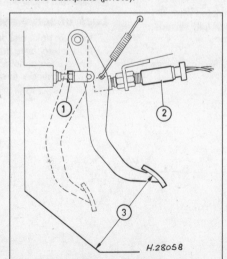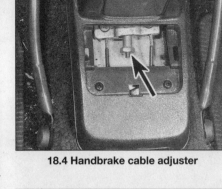

18.4 Handbrake cable adjuster

19.4 Compressing handbrake cable spigot in brake backplate

16 Vacuum servo unit - maintenance

1 The following operations should be considered the limit of work carried out to the servo unit. A unit in need of repair should be changed for a new or factory reconditioned unit.
2 Keep the hoses in good condition and with their clips tight.
3 At the intervals specified in Routine Maintenance disconnect the non-return valve from the vacuum hose and blow through it. Air should pass in one direction only, otherwise renew it.

17 Vacuum servo unit - removal and refitting

1 Disconnect the hydraulic pipes from the master cylinder. Cap the ends of the pipes.
2 Disconnect the servo vacuum hose.
3 Remove the steering joint cover and disconnect the pushrod from the brake pedal.
4 Unscrew the fixing nuts and withdraw the servo from the engine compartment rear bulkhead. Retrieve the seal.
5 Unscrew the nuts and remove the master cylinder from the front face of the servo unit.
6 Refitting is a reversal of removal. On 1.3 models, check the pushrod clearance (Section 9) and the pedal height (Section 20).
7 Bleed the hydraulic system as described in Section 14.

18 Handbrake - adjustment

1 The handbrake is normally kept in constant adjustment by the action of the shoe automatic adjusters. However, if the handbrake lever has to be pulled through more than eight notches (clicks) of the ratchet quadrant to fully apply the brake, this will be due to cable stretch and must be rectified in the following way.
2 Raise the rear of the car so that the rear wheels are clear of the floor.

3 Pull the handbrake lever over one notch only.
4 Remove the cover from the rear of the centre console and turn the cable adjuster nut until the rear wheels drag very slightly when the roadwheels are turned (photo).
5 Release the handbrake and check that the rear wheels rotate freely.
6 The handbrake should be fully applied when the lever has been pulled through between four and eight notches.
7 Lower the car to the floor.

19 Handbrake cable - renewal

1 Raise the rear of the car, support it securely and remove the roadwheel from the side on which the cable is to be renewed.
2 Remove the brake drum as described in Section 6.
3 Remove the brake shoes.
4 Fit a 12.0 mm ring spanner over the cable spigot to compress the retainer and release it from the backplate (photo).

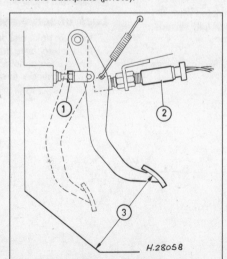
Fig. 9.10 Brake pedal height setting diagram (Sec 20)

1 Pushrod locknut   3 174.0 mm (6.8 in)
2 Stop-light switch

5 Refer to Chapter 11 and remove the centre console.
6 Unscrew and remove the handbrake cable adjuster nut and disconnect the cable from the equaliser.
7 Remove the heatshield from the floor and disconnect the cable from its supporting guides and remove it.
8 Fit the new cable, apply grease to the cable guides.
9 Refit the brake shoes and drum as described in Section 6. Refit the roadwheel .
10 Apply the footbrake several times to set the shoes and self-adjuster mechanism and then adjust the cable as described in Section 18.
11 Lower the car to the floor. Tighten the wheel nuts.

20 Handbrake warning light switch - removal and refitting

1 Disconnect the battery earth lead.
2 Remove the centre console, as described in Chapter 11 or Chapter 13.
3 Remove the switch from the base of the handbrake lever.
4 Refitting is a reverse of the removal procedure, but check the switch operation before the centre console is finally fitted in position.

21 Brake pedal - setting

1 To check the brake pedal height, first remove the rubber cover from the pedal pad and peel back the floor carpet from under the pedal.
2 Refer to Fig. 9.10 and measure the height (3) from the underside of the pedal to the floor.
3 If it is not as specified, release the locknut on the stop-light switch and unscrew the switch clear of the brake pedal.
4 Release the pushrod locknut and rotate the pushrod until the pedal height is correct. Tighten the locknut.
5 Screw in the stop-light switch until its plunger is fully depressed then unscrew the switch exactly half a turn and tighten the locknut (photo).
6 Refit the pedal pad and the carpet.

21.5 Brake stop-light switch

9

22 Brake pedal - removal and refitting

1 Working inside the car remove the facia lower access panel (Chapter 11).
2 Disconnect the pedal return spring and the pushrod clevis fork from the pedal arm.

3 Unscrew the pivot cross-shaft nut and withdraw the shaft until the brake pedal can be removed. The clutch and brake pedals pivot on a common cross-shaft (see Chapter 5, Section 5).
4 On cars with automatic transmission, the brake pedal pivots on a shorter cross-shaft otherwise the arrangement is similar.
5 Refit by reversing the removal operations.

23 Brake stop-light switch - removal and refitting

1 Disconnect the battery earth lead.
2 Disconnect the switch wiring, then remove the locknut and draw the switch out of the pedal bracket.
3 Refitting is the reverse of the removal procedure, but check and adjust the switch (see Section 21) before finally tightening the locknut.

Fault finding - braking system

Before diagnosing faults from the following chart, check that any braking irregularities are not caused by:
  Uneven and incorrect tyre pressures
  Wear in the steering mechanism
  Defects in the suspension and dampers
  Misalignment of the body

Pedal travels a long way before the brakes operate
☐ Incorrect pedal adjustment
☐ Brake shoes set too far from the drums (seized adjusters)

Stopping ability poor, even though pedal pressure is firm
☐ Linings, discs or drums badly worn or scored
☐ One or more wheel hydraulic cylinders seized, resulting in some brake
☐ shoes not pressing against the drums (or pads against disc)
☐ Brake linings contaminated with oil
☐ Wrong type of linings fitted (too hard)
☐ Brake shoes wrongly assembled
☐ Servo unit not functioning

Car veers to one side when the brakes are applied
☐ Brake pads or linings on one side are contaminated with oil
☐ Hydraulic wheel cylinder on one side partially or fully seized
☐ A mixture of lining materials fitted between sides
☐ Brake discs not matched
☐ Unequal wear between sides caused by partially seized wheel cylinders

Pedal feels spongy when the brakes are applied
☐ Air is present in the hydraulic system

Pedal feels springy when the brakes are applied
☐ Brake linings not bedded into the drums (after fitting new ones)
☐ Master cylinder or brake backplate mounting bolts loose
☐ Severe wear in brake drums causing distortion when brakes are applied
☐ Disc out of true

Pedal travels right down with little or no resistance and brakes are virtually non-operative
☐ Leak in hydraulic system resulting in lack of pressure for operating
☐ wheel cylinders
☐ If no signs of leakage are apparent the master cylinder internal seals are
☐ failing to sustain pressure

Binding, juddering, overheating
☐ One or a combination of reasons given above
☐ Shoes installed incorrectly with reference to leading and trailing ends
☐ Broken shoe return spring
☐ Drum out-of-round
☐ Disc distorted
☐ Incorrect pedal adjustment

Lack of servo assistance
☐ Vacuum hose disconnected or leaking
☐ Non-return valve defective or incorrectly fitted
☐ Servo internal defect
☐ Master cylinder to servo flange seal ineffective

Chapter 10 Suspension and steering

For modifications, and information applicable to later models, see Supplement at end of manual

Contents

Degrees of difficulty

Easy, suitable for novice with little experience	**Fairly easy,** suitable for beginner with some experience	**Fairly difficult,** suitable for competent DIY mechanic	**Difficult,** suitable for experienced DIY mechanic	**Very difficult,** suitable for expert DIY or professional

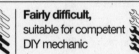

Specifications

Type

Front suspension	Independent, MacPherson strut with torsion bar springing and anti-roll bar
Rear suspension	Independent with trailing arms, telescopic shock absorbers and coil springs. Axle beam location by Panhard rod
Steering	Rack and pinion with rake adjustable safety steering column

Front suspension settings

Vehicle height - centre of roadwheel to wheel arch	372.0 to 392.0 mm (14.7 to 15.4 in)
Hub end play	0.05 mm (0.002 in)

Rear suspension settings

Vehicle height* - centre of roadwheel to wheelarch	353.8 to 373.8 mm (13.9 to 14.7 in)

Non-adjustable, if not within the specified tolerance, suspect weak coil springs

Steering

Steering wheel diameter	377.0 mm (14.8 in)
Number of turns, lock to lock	4
Ratio	19 : 1
Turning circle (between kerbs)	10.0 m (33.0 ft)
Camber	1° negative to 1° positive
Castor	1° 25' to 3° 25' positive
Steering axis inclination	12° 15' to 13° 15'
Toe	Parallel ± 0.7 mm (0.028 in)
Steering angles:	
Inner wheel	39° 35' to 43° 35'
Outer wheel	32° 23' to 36° 23'
Lubricant	Fluid grease (Duckhams Adgear 00)

Rear wheel alignment (non-adjustable) ....

Parallel to 4.0 mm (0.16 in) toe-in

10

Torque wrench settings

	Nm	lbf ft
Front suspension		
Anti-roll bar clamp bolts	22	16
Anti-roll bar end nuts	22	16
Lower arm balljoint nut	44	32
Driveshaft nut	185	137
Strut pinch-bolt	65	48
Strut top mounting nuts	39	29
Strut spindle nut	44	32
Suspension arm to radius arm bolts	39	29
Radius arm to body	81	60
Front crossmember bolts	75	55
Torque tube retainer bolts	22	16
Rear suspension		
Panhard rod nut and bolt	55	41
Rear axle beam bolts	65	48
Shock absorber lower mounting bolt	55	41
Shock absorber upper mounting	22	16
Rear hub nut	185	137
Swing bearing nuts	55	41
Trailing arm pivot bolts	55	41
Stub axle to axle beam nuts	45	33
Steering		
Tie-rod end balljoint nuts	44	32
Tie-rod locknut	44	32
Steering shaft coupling pinch bolts	30	22
Steering column upper bracket bolts	22	16
Steering column upper bracket nuts	12	9
Steering rack adjuster screw locknut	25	18
Tie-rod to rack locknut	75	55
Steering gear mounting bolts	40	30
Steering wheel nut	50	37
Steering rake adjuster domed locknut	7.0	5.0
Roadwheel nuts	80	59

1 General description

The front suspension is of MacPherson strut independent type with torsion bar springing.

Each strut is located between the upper wing valance and the hub carrier.

An anti-roll bar is fitted.

The rear suspension is of trailing link beam type incorporating telescopic gas-filled shock absorbers and coil springs.

A tubular axle beam is fitted and this is positively located transversely by a Panhard rod.

The steering is of rack and pinion type with a collapsible safety column.

The steering wheel is adjustable for rake.

2 Maintenance

1 At the specified intervals, check all suspension flexible bushes for wear.
2 Occasionally check the condition and security of all steering and suspension nuts, bolts and components.

3 Inspect the struts and shock absorbers for signs of fluid leakage. If anything more than a slight weep from the top gland is evident, then the unit must be renewed.
4 If the car tends to roll on bends or dip under heavy braking, check the action of the struts and shock absorbers by pressing the corner of the car downwards and then releasing it. The up and down momentum of the car should be damped out immediately. If the car oscillates up and down several times, the condition of the particular unit should be checked after removal from the car as described in Sections 4 and 11.
5 Inspect the steering rack bellows for splits and loss of lubricant. Look particularly closely at the bottom of the bellows pleats when the steering is at full lock. Splits here can often pass unnoticed.
6 With the help of an assistant, check for wear in the steering tie-rod end balljoints. Move the steering wheel quickly a few degrees in each direction and observe the balljoints for shake or lost movement. If evident renew the tie-rod ends as described in Section 18.
7 Check the front suspension lower arm balljoint by inserting a lever carefully between the arm and the hub carrier and checking for vertical movement.
8 Renewal of the lower arm balljoint will mean

the purchase of the complete radius arm with balljoint.
9 At the specified intervals, check the front wheel alignment (Sec 27).

3 Anti-roll bar - removal and refitting

Front

1 Remove the front crossmember as described in Section 7.
2 Unscrew the bolts which secure the anti-roll bar mounting bush clamps to the body.
3 Unscrew the end bolts and disconnect the anti-roll bar from the radius arms. Note the fitted sequence of the spacer cushions and cups.
4 Refitting is a reversal of removal, tighten nuts and bolts to the specified torque. See also Section 6, paragraph 8.

Rear (Vitesse and Sprint)

5 Remove the rear hub on each side of the car, as described in Chapter 8.
6 On the left-hand side of the car, remove the nuts so that the brake backplate can be detached and tied to one side. Take care that the brake hoses and handbrake cable are not twisted or strained.

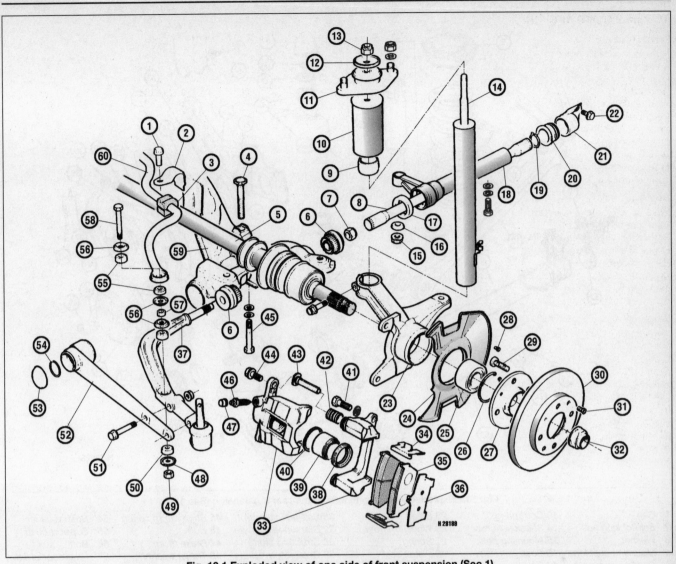

Fig. 10.1 Exploded view of one side of front suspension (Sec 1)

1 Bolt	11 Strut top mounting	21 Torque tube	31 Screw	41 Caliper bolt	51 Bolt
2 Clamp	12 Washer	retainer	32 Driveshaft nut	42 Dust excluding	52 Lower suspension
3 Flexible bush	13 Self-locking nut	22 Bolt	33 Caliper bracket	boot	arm
4 Vehicle height	14 Strut	23 Hub carrier	34 Brake pad clip	43 Guide bolt	53 Cap
adjusting tool	15 Vehicle height	24 Disc shield	35 Brake pad	44 Caliper bolt	54 Circlip
5 Driveshaft	adjusting nut	25 Hub bearing	36 Shim	45 Crossmember bolt	55 Cushion
6 Radius arm bush	16 Washer	26 Circlip	37 Radius arm	46 Bleed screw	56 Washer
7 Self-locking nut	17 Seal	27 Hub flange	38 Dust excluding	47 Bleed screw cap	57 Collar
8 Torsion bar	18 Torque tube	28 Screw	boot	48 Washer	58 Bolt
9 Bump stop	19 Circlip	29 Wheel stud	39 Piston	49 Nut	59 Crossmember
10 Dust cover	20 Cap	30 Brake disc	40 Piston seal	50 Rubber cushion	60 Anti-roll bar

7 Repeat this procedure on the right-hand side of the car, after first removing the end cap from the axle tube.

8 Remove the nuts securing the roll bar front control link. Remove the bushes and the rear link.

9 Remove the two bolts securing the anti-roll bar flange to the axle tube. Tap the end flange to relieve any stiffness.

10 Using a long rod as a drift, suitably protected at the end to prevent damage, carefully drive out the anti-roll bar from the axle tube.

11 Refitting is essentially the reverse of the removal procedure, noting the following points:

(a) *Generously lubricate the inside of the axle tube and the anti-roll bar end bush with grease.*

(b) *Twist the end of the anti-roll bar slightly prior to centralising the bolt holes.*

(c) *Refer to Chapter 8 when tightening the hub bearings.*

4 Front suspension strut - removal and refitting

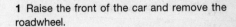

1 Raise the front of the car and remove the roadwheel.

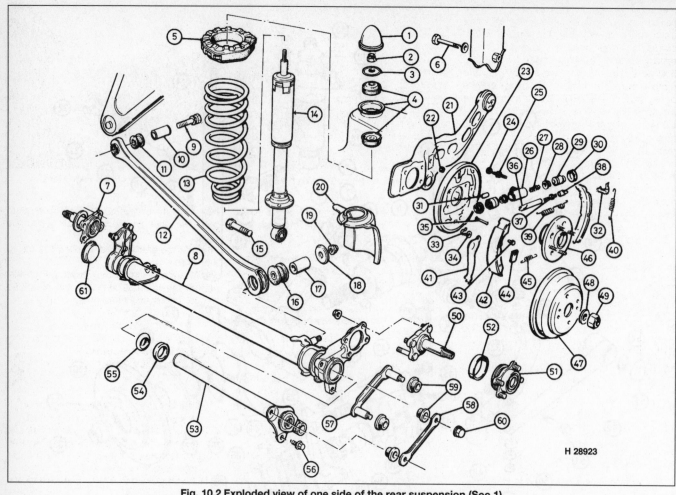

Fig. 10.2 Exploded view of one side of the rear suspension (Sec 1)

1 Cap	13 Coil spring	25 Bleed screw	36 Self-adjuster strut	45 Shoe return spring	54* Bush retainer
2 Self-locking nut	14 Shock absorber	26 Wheel cylinder	37 Star wheel adjuster	46 Hub	55* Support bush
3 Washer	15 Mounting bolt	27 Spring	38 Strut end fitting	47 Brake drum	56* Bolt
4 Mounting cushions	16 Bush	28 Piston seal	39 Shoe return spring	48 Thrust washer	57* Rear control link
5 Spring upper seat	17 Sleeve	29 Piston	40 Self-adjuster spring	49 Hub nut	58* Front control link
6 Pivot bolt	18 Washer	30 Dust excluder	41 Shoe lever for	50 Stub axle (RH)	59* Link bushes
7 Stub axle (LH)	19 Self -locking nut	31 Blanking plug	handbrake	51 Swing bearing	60* Nut
8 Axle tube	20 Shield	32 Self-adjuster lever	42 Brake shoe	52* Swing bearing	61* End cap
9 Pivot bolt	21 Trailing arm	33 U-clip	43 Pin	shield	*Vitesse and Sprint
10 Sleeve	22 Wheel cylinder nut	34 Washer	44 Shoe steady spring	53* Anti-roll bar	only
11 Bush	23 Brake backplate	35 Shoe steady pin	clip	(stabiliser)	
12 Panhard rod	24 Cap			assembly	

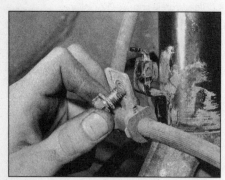

4.2 Disconnecting brake hose from strut

4.3 Front strut top mounting nuts. Allen key in spindle socket shown for information purposes only

2 Support the lower suspension arm on a jack and disconnect the brake hydraulic hose from the support bracket on the suspension strut (photo) .

3 Working within the engine compartment, unscrew the strut top mounting nuts and then lower the jack under the lower suspension arm to separate the strut from the wing valance (photo).

4 Unscrew the clamp pinch-bolt from the base of the strut and slide the hub carrier off the strut. Be prepared for reaction from the torsion bar, so make sure that the car and the suspension is well supported. Withdraw the strut from the car. Alternatively, disconnect the driveshaft from the hub, remove the brake caliper and disconnect the lower arm and track rod end balljoints; the strut and hub carrier can then be removed together and separated on the bench (photo).

5 Unscrew the self-locking spindle nut and remove the top mounting, tubular shield and bump stop. The spindle can be held against rotation using an Allen key in its socket.

6 Fully extend and retract the strut piston rod. If it is jerky, noisy, or offers little or no resistance, the strut must be renewed. It is a sealed unit and cannot be dismantled.

7 To refit the strut, first assemble the top mounting, shield and bump stop. Screw on the self-locking nut, again holding the spindle from turning using an Allen key.

8 Offer the strut up under the wing and tighten the nuts holding it to the valance.

9 Connect the lower end of the strut to the hub carrier making sure that the tab on the strut locates in the clamp slot. Tighten the pinch-bolt to the specified torque (photo).

10 If the hub carrier was removed with the strut, reconnect it as described in Chapter 8, Section 6.

11 Secure the brake hose to the strut bracket.

12 Refit the roadwheel and lower the vehicle. Tighten the wheel nuts.

4.4 Removing front strut and hub carrier

4.9 Strut to clamp alignment

3 Unbolt the radius arm from the lower suspension arm and then unscrew the bolt which holds the anti-roll bar to the radius arm.

Caution: Ensure that the jack supporting the lower suspension arm at the balljoint is securely positioned, otherwise the tension of the torsion bar may cause the lower suspension arm to jump suddenly away from the swivel hub as the balljoint is released

4 Unscrew the nut and withdraw the radius arm from its bushes (photo) .

5 The bushes can be renewed, but wear in the radius arm balljoint can only be rectified by the purchase of a new arm complete.

6 Refit the radius arm into its bushes and screw on the nut finger tight.

7 Connect the radius arm to the lower suspension arm and tighten the bolts to the specified torque.

8 Reconnect the anti-roll bar, making sure that the end fitting components are in the correct sequence.

Caution: To ensure that there is adequate clearance between the driveshaft boot and the radius arm, the anti-roll bar securing bolt must be fitted with the bolt head uppermost (photo).

9 Reconnect the lower suspension arm balljoint to the hub carrier and tighten the nut to the specified torque. Should the taper pin turn as the nut is being tightened, locate a

jack under the balljoint and force it upwards to press the taper pin into the conical seat of the eye.

10 Refit the roadwheel and lower the car to the floor.

11 With the weight of the car on the wheels, tighten the radius arm nut to the specified torque. Tighten the wheel nuts.

7 Front crossmember - removal and refitting

1 Raise the front of the car, support it securely and remove the front roadwheels.

2 Support both lower suspension arms and disconnect the balljoints from the hub carriers. Unscrew the nuts to do this and use a suitable balljoint splitter tool.

3 Unbolt the steering rack and move it to one side.

4 Remove the downpipe and front section of the exhaust pipe.

5 Release the engine rear mounting from the crossmember, at the same time supporting the engine under the sump pan.

6 Disconnect the gearchange rod and the steady rod from the transmission.

7 Unscrew the bolts from the torque tube end retainers. Remove the retainers and the rubber caps.

8 Unscrew the fixing bolts and release the anti-roll bar from the crossmember.

5 Front hub carrier - removal and refitting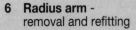

The operations are described in Chapter 8, Section 6.

6 Radius arm - removal and refitting

1 Raise the front of the car, support it securely and remove the roadwheel .

2 Support the lower suspension arm on a jack and disconnect the balljoint from the hub carrier using a balljoint splitter tool (photo).

10

6.2 Disconnecting suspension lower arm balljoint

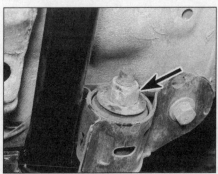
6.4 Radius arm nut (arrowed)

6.8 Correct fitting of anti-roll bar securing bolt (with bolt head uppermost)

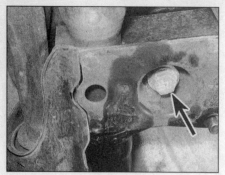

7.9 Crossmember bolt (arrowed)

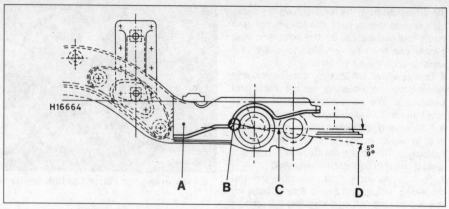

H16664

Fig. 10.4 Crossmember index mark scribing diagram (Sec 8)

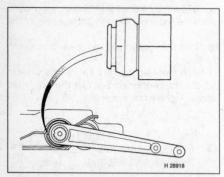

Fig. 10.3 Suspension lower arm bush and crossmember alignment marks (Sec 8)

A Crossmember front face
B Index mark
C Centre line of lower arm recess

D Suspension lower arm centre line at 5° to 9° in relation to centre line of bush recess

9 The crossmember may now be unbolted and removed (photo).

10 To strip the crossmember, unbolt and remove the engine mounting.

11 Unscrew and remove the vehicle height adjustment nuts and bolts.

12 Extract the torsion bar circlips and withdraw the bar complete with torque tube, see Section 9.

13 Remove the radius arm and press out the lower suspension arms and bushes (Section 8).

14 Refitting is a reversal of removal, tighten all nuts and bolts to the specified torque and check the vehicle height on completion as described in Section 10. The method of setting the angle of the lower suspension arm is given in the next Section and fitting the torsion bar (Section 9).

8 Front suspension lower arm and bush - removal and refitting

1 Remove the front crossmember as described in the preceding Section.

2 Remove the vehicle height adjustment nut.

3 Extract the circlip from the rear end of the torsion bar and withdraw the torque tube.

4 Unbolt the lower suspension arm from the radius arm.

5 Remove the cap from the front end of the torsion bar, tap the bar slightly forward and extract the circlip.

6 Push the torsion bar through the crossmember and remove it.

7 Press the lower suspension arm from the crossmember.

8 Renew the lower suspension arm with bush as an assembly.

9 Refitting is a reversal of removal, but the new lower suspension arm bush should have its outer casing scribed to indicate the centre line of the arm. When pressing the arm and bush into the crossmember, align the mark on the bush with the one on the crossmember. If the crossmember mark is not visible, make one as shown in Fig. 10.4 and set the lower suspension arm bush mark in alignment with it before pressing them into the crossmember.

10 The torsion bar should be fitted after reference to the next Section.

9 Torsion bar - removal and refitting

1 Raise the front end of the car, support it securely and remove the roadwheels.

2 Remove the vehicle height adjusting nut.

3 Remove the rubber cap from the front end of the torsion bar (photo).

4 Unbolt and remove the torque tube retainer

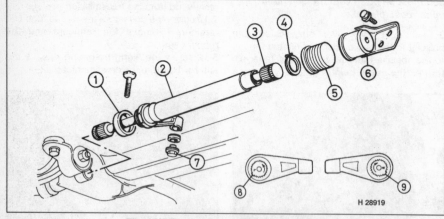

Fig. 10.5 Torsion bar components (Sec 9)

1 Sealing ring
2 Torque tube
3 Torsion bar
4 Circlip
5 Cap
6 Torque tube retainer
7 Vehicle height adjuster nut
8 Master spline alignment (LH bar)
9 Master spline alignment (RH bar)

9.3 Removing torsion bar front cap

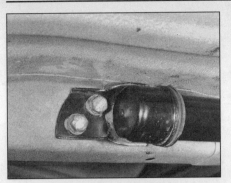
9.4A Torque tube retainer

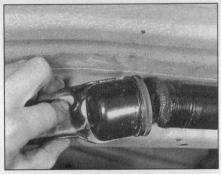
9.4B Removing torque tube retainer

9.5 Torsion bar front circlip

from the rear end of the tube. Remove the cap, extract the circlip (photos).
5 Tap the torsion bar forward just 12.5 mm (0.5 in) to expose the front circlip then extract it (photo).
6 Remove the torsion bar complete with torque tube towards the rear of the car.
7 Commence reassembly by greasing the torsion bar splines and the torque tube seals.
8 Insert the torsion bar into the torque tube so that the rear master spline is aligned (photos).
9 Fit the torsion bar/torque tube assembly making sure that the front master splines engage.

HAYNES HINT *It can be helpful if the end of the torsion bar and the rim of the lower arm splined hole are marked with white paint to indicate the relative positions of the master splines.*

10 Tap the torsion bar towards the front of the car only enough to be able to fit the front circlip.
11 Tap the torsion bar towards the rear of the car and fit the rear circlip (photo).
12 Bolt on the torque tube retainer and replace the rubber cap.
13 Screw on the height adjuster nut and fit the torque tube front cap.
14 Fit the roadwheel and lower the car to the floor. Tighten the wheel nuts.

15 Check and adjust the vehicle ride height, see next Section.

10 Vehicle ride height - adjustment

1 Have the car on a level surface with tyre pressures correct and the front roadwheels in the straight-ahead position.
2 The car should have a full fuel tank, but otherwise be unladen (kerb weight).
3 Bounce the car up and down two or three times to settle the suspension.
4 Measure between the centres of both front wheel hubs vertically to the wheel arch wing edge. If this is not as given in Specifications, raise the front wheels off the floor and turn the height adjusting nut clockwise to increase the height or anti-clockwise to reduce it (photo).
5 One complete turn of the nut will alter the vehicle height by 5.0 mm (0.197 in).
6 Lower the car and re-check the height.
7 The difference in vehicle ride height from side to side should not exceed 10.0 mm (0.39 in).

11 Rear shock absorber and spring - removal and refitting

1 Raise the rear of the car, support it securely and remove the roadwheel.

9.8A Torque tube splines

2 Locate a jack under the rear axle beam and take its weight.
3 Open the luggage boot and take off the cap from the shock absorber top mounting.
4 Unscrew the self-locking nut from the spindle and take off the rubber cushion and retaining plate. Hold the spindle against rotation by inserting an Allen key in its socket (photo).
5 Gently lower the axle beam jack until all tension is relieved in the coil spring.
6 Unbolt the shock absorber lower mounting and then lower the jack again. Withdraw the shock absorber and spring from the car (photos).
7 Remove the spring and the shock absorber protective shield (photo).
8 Prise off the split collar and remove the sleeve upwards from the shock absorber.

10

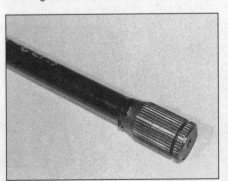
9.8B Torsion bar master spline

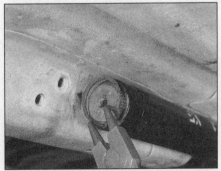
9.11 Torsion bar rear circlip

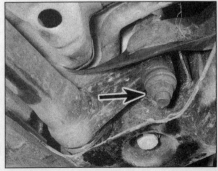
10.4 Vehicle height adjusting nut (arrowed)

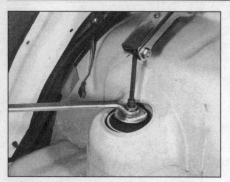

11.4 Unscrewing rear shock absorber top mounting nut

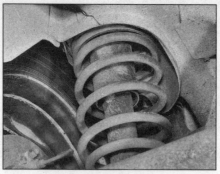

11.6A Rear coil spring

11.6B Rear shock absorber lower mounting bolt

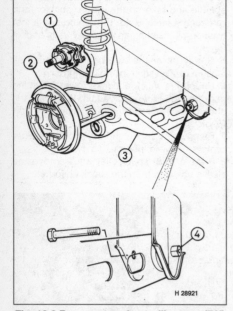

Fig. 10.6 Rear suspension trailing arm (RH) (Sec 12)

1 Swing bearing
2 Brake backplate
3 Trailing arm
4 Trailing arm front mounting

11.7 Rear shock absorber lower shield

9 Remove the bump stop.
10 Grip the shock absorber lower mounting in the jaws of a vice and holding the unit vertically, fully extend and retract it several times. If there is any jerkiness, seizure or lack of resistance, renew the shock absorber complete.
11 Refitting is a reversal of removal, but note the following.
12 The smaller diameter spring coils are at the lower end.
13 Tighten the upper mounting nut and lower mounting bolt to the specified torque only after the roadwheel has been fitted and the car lowered to the floor.

12 Rear suspension trailing arm - removal and refitting

1 Jack up the rear of the car, support it securely and remove the roadwheel.
2 Refer to Chapter 8 and remove the hub.
3 Refer to Chapter 9 and remove the brake shoes.
4 Disconnect the rear wheel cylinder hydraulic hose and cap the end of the hose to prevent loss of fluid.
5 If the right-hand side is being dismantled, unscrew the four nuts which hold the brake backplate and the trailing arm to the swing bearing. If the left-hand side is being dismantled, unbolt the components from the stub axle.
6 Unscrew and remove the mounting bolt from the front end of the trailing arm and withdraw the assembly.

7 Refitting is a reversal of removal, bleed the brakes on completion as described in Chapter 9.

13 Panhard rod - removal and refitting

1 Raise the rear of the car and support it securely.
2 Unscrew the Panhard rod nut from the axle beam (photo).
3 Unbolt the Panhard rod from the body bracket (photo).
4 Slide the Panhard rod from the stud on the axle beam and remove it.
5 Refitting is a reversal of removal. Tighten nuts and bolts to the specified torque.

14 Rear axle beam - removal and refitting

1 Raise the rear of the car and support it securely under the body jacking points.
2 Remove both rear roadwheels.
3 Disconnect both shock absorber lower mountings.
4 Disconnect the Panhard rod from the axle beam.
5 Support the axle beam on a trolley jack.
6 Remove the left-hand brake drum (Chap-

13.2 Panhard rod at axle beam

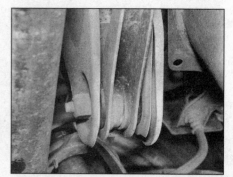

13.3 Panhard rod connection to body bracket

ter 9, Section 6). Working through the holes in
the hub, remove the four nuts which secure
the axle beam to the left-hand stub axle.

7 On the right-hand side, remove the four
nuts which secure the stub axle to the axle
beam.

8 Free the axle beam from the stub axles,
lower the trolley jack and remove the axle
beam.

9 Refitting is a reversal of removal. Tighten all
nuts and bolts to the specified torque.

15 Rear stub axle -
removal and refitting

1 Raise and securely support the rear of the
car.

2 Remove the roadwheel.

3 Remove the brake drum (Chapter 9) and the
hub (Chapter 8).

4 Release the brake hose from its clip on the
trailing arm.

5 Unscrew the nuts which hold the brake
backplate and trailing arm to the stub axle
(left-hand side) or to the swing bearing (right-
hand side). On the right-hand side, also
remove the four nuts which secure the stub
axle to the axle beam.

6 Support the brake backplate and trailing
arm. Free the stub axle (and swing bearing,
when applicable) and remove it.

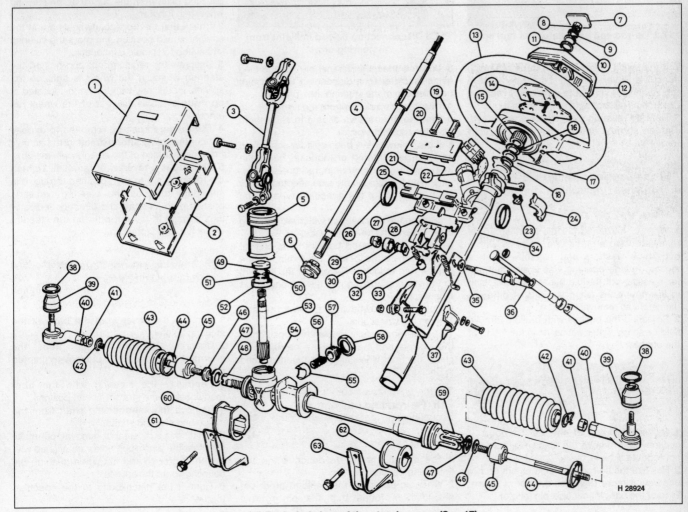

Fig. 10.7 Exploded view of the steering gear (Sec 17)

Note: *The steering gear illustrated is for models up to VIN 150427. A non-adjustable gear was fitted from VIN 150428*

1 Steering column upper shroud
2 Steering column lower shroud
3 Intermediate shaft
4 Steering shaft
5 Cover
6 Lower bearing
7 Blanking plate
8 Nut
9 Circlip
10 Washer
11 Thrust ring
12 Horn push
13 Steering wheel
14 Contact plate
15 Upper bearing
16 Washer
17 Wave washer
18 Spacer
19 Bending plate guide rail
20 Bending plate guide
21 Retaining spring
22 Steering lock/ignition switch
23 Horn contact
24 Bracket
25 Bending plate
26 Rubber band
27 Column bracket
28 Bending plate base
29 Self-locking nut
30 Collar
31 Stopper
32 Spring
33 Tube
34 Steering column tube
35 Washer
36 Rake lever
37 Column pivot
38 Dust excluder clip
39 Dust excluder
40 Tie-rod and balljoint
41 Locknut
42 Bellows clip
43 Bellows
44 Clip
45 Tie-rod
46 Lockplate
47 Stop washer
48 Rack
49 Dust seal
50 Circlip
51 Circlip
52 Pinion bearing
53 Pinion shaft
54 Rack housing
55 Rack damper slipper
56 Spring
57 Adjuster screw
58 Locknut
59 Rack end bush
60 Mounting insulator
61 Mounting clamp
62 Mounting insulator
63 Mounting clamp

10

17.2 Tie-rod end castellated nut and split pin

7 If the swing bearing needs to be renewed, consult a Rover dealer or other specialist. If the bearing is available separately, special press tools will be required for fitting it.
8 Refit by reversing the removal operation. Tighten all nuts and bolts to the specified torque.

16 Suspension arm flexible bushes - renewal

1 Worn or hardened flexible bushes can be renewed using a press or a long bolt with a nut, thick washers and suitable distance pieces. A wide-opening vice is also suitable for pressing out flexible bushes and pressing in the new ones using sockets of different diameters as removal tools.
2 Smearing the bushes with brake hydraulic fluid or soapy water will assist in the fitting of the bushes.

17 Steering rack bellows - renewal

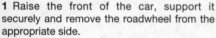

1 Raise the front of the car, support it securely and remove the roadwheel from the appropriate side.
2 Release the tie-rod end locknut, but do not unscrew it more than one quarter of a turn. Extract the balljoint nut split pin (photo).

17.3 Disconnecting tie-rod balljoint from steering arm

3 Unscrew the balljoint taper pin nut and then using a splitter tool, disconnect the balljoint from the eye of the steering arm (photo).
4 Unscrew the balljoint from the tie-rod.
5 Release the bellows clips and slide them from the rack housing.
6 If the bellows have been split for some time and dirt has entered or lubricant has been lost, clean away contaminated grease after extending the rack on the side affected. Apply fresh lubricant of the specified type to the rack teeth.
7 Slide on the new bellows with their retaining clips. Grease the tie-rod threads.
8 Screw on the tie-rod balljoint to its original position where the locknut will require only a quarter turn to lock it. Reconnect the balljoint to the steering arm, tighten the nut and insert a new split pin.
9 Refit the roadwheel and lower the car. Tighten the wheel nuts.
10 However carefully the refitted position of the tie-rod end balljoint was carried out, check the front wheel alignment as described in Section 27.

18 Tie-rod end balljoint - renewal

1 The operations are as described in the preceding Section.
2 When screwing on the balljoint taper pin nut, if it is found that the pin rotates

preventing tightening of the nut, force the tie-rod end upwards using a jack. This will drive the taper pin further into the conical seat of the steering eye and prevent rotation.

19 Steering wheel - removal and refitting

1 Using a small screwdriver, prise out the blanking plate from the centre of the steering wheel hub (photo).
2 Check that the front roadwheels are in the straight-ahead position and mark the steering wheel hub to spindle relationship.
3 Unscrew the retaining nut and pull off the steering wheel. If the wheel is tight on the splines, jar it lightly with the hands, located at opposite sides at the rear of the wheel rim (photo).
4 The horn pad can be removed to expose the contact plate after extracting the screws from the rear face of the steering wheel hub.
5 Refitting is a reversal of removal. Tighten the retaining nut to the specified torque. It is important that, as the steering wheel is pushed onto its shaft, the direction indicator lugs engage in the cut-outs on the steering wheel hub boss (photo).

20 Steering intermediate shaft - removal and refitting

1 Remove the cover from the base of the steering column.
2 Unscrew the pinch-bolts from the intermediate shaft universally-jointed couplings.
3 Centralise the steering with the front roadwheels in the straight-ahead position.
4 Remove the intermediate shaft from the pinion and steering shafts.
5 Refitting is a reversal of removal, but make sure that the pinch-bolt holes are aligned with the shaft groove and flat when pushing the couplings onto the splines.
6 Tighten the pinch-bolts to the specified torque.

19.1 Removing blanking plate from steering wheel

19.3 Unscrewing steering wheel nut

19.5 Steering wheel hub cut-outs

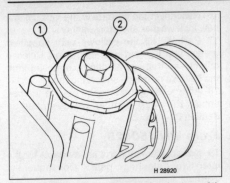

Fig. 10.8 Steering rack damper locknut (1) and adjuster screw (2) (Sec 21)

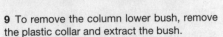

22.2A Unscrewing shroud screw

22.2B Shroud retaining clip

21 Steering rack damper - adjustment (up to VIN 150427)

1 If free play exceeds 10.0 mm (0.40 in) when measured at the steering wheel rim or knocking is heard when traversing rough surfaces, adjust the rack damper in the following way.
2 Raise the front of the car, support it securely with the roadwheels hanging free.
3 Attach a spring balance to the outer end of a steering wheel spoke and check the pull required to turn the steering wheel. This should not exceed 1.5 kg (3.3 lb). A figure just below this is ideal.
4 To adjust, centralise the steering, slacken the rack damper locknut and tighten the adjuster screw until it is felt to contact the coil spring. Check the steering wheel pull as previously described, adjusting the screw by a quarter turn at a time until the specified pull is obtained.
5 Tighten the locknut without altering the position of the adjuster screw.

22 Steering column - removal, overhaul and refitting

1 Remove the steering wheel as previously described.
2 Extract the screws, remove the steering column lower shroud and then unclip and remove the upper shroud (photos).
3 Disconnect the battery and the wiring plugs at the side of the steering column which serve the ignition and combination switches.
4 Remove the combination switch and indicator self-cancelling sleeve from the top of the steering column.
5 Remove the intermediate shaft cover and unscrew the pinch-bolt which secures the universal joint coupling to the steering shaft.
6 Unbolt the steering column lower bracket.
7 Unbolt the steering column upper bracket and bending plate.
8 Withdraw the column from the car.

9 To remove the column lower bush, remove the plastic collar and extract the bush.
10 Grease the new bush and push it into the column tube as far as it will go.
11 Align the nib on the plastic collar with the hole in the column tube and fit the collar.
12 To renew the top bush, extract the circlip and remove the washer.
13 Turn the ignition key to the 1 position. Remove the bottom bush as previously described and pull the shaft from the column tube.
14 From the top of the column, remove the thrust ring, top bush and horn contact.
15 Grease the new top bush and smear the shaft with grease to prevent rust.
16 Reassembly is a reversal of removal, but make sure that the concave side of the washer under the circlip is towards the circlip.
17 To refit the steering column, reverse the removal operations. Make sure that the bending and holder plates are not distorted. Renew if they are and fit them so that the arrow on the plate is uppermost and pointing towards the bottom of the column.
18 Tighten all nuts and bolts to the specified torque.

23 Steering column rake adjustment mechanism - overhaul

1 With the steering column removed from the car, take off the hanger springs and rubber bands which retain the bending and holder plates.
2 Release the screw and remove the stopper clip from the rake mechanism.
3 Unscrew and remove the domed locknut (29) (Fig. 10.7) collar (30) and stopper (31). Note that the locknut has a left-hand thread.
4 Remove the adjuster lever assembly (36).
5 Lubricate the sliding surfaces with grease, assemble the lever, stopper and collar without damaging the O-ring.
6 Fit the hanger springs and domed locknut, tightening to 7.0 Nm (5.0 lbf ft), with the collar pushed towards the locknut.
7 Check the force required to operate the adjustment lever. This should be between

5.9 and 9.0 kg (11.0 and 20.0 lb) when checked on a spring balance. If not as specified, slide the collar towards the stopper and slightly tighten or slacken the domed locknut.
8 Finally slide the collar towards the locknut and fit the stopper clip.
9 Fit the bending and holder plates with their spring and rubber bands.

24 Steering column lock - removal and refitting

1 Remove the steering column as described in Section 22.
2 Secure the column in the jaws of a vice and remove the lock fixing bolts. Do this by drilling them out or using a screw extractor. To remove the ignition switch from the lock, refer to Chapter 12.
3 Locate the new lock on the column and tighten the new shear head bolts finger tight. Check that the steering lock is correctly aligned with the hole in the column.
4 Insert the key into the lock and check for smooth operation of the lock tongue in the column cut-out.
5 Tighten the bolts until their heads shear off.

25 Steering rack - removal and refitting

1 Remove the cover from the base of the steering column and unscrew the pinch-bolt from the lower universal joint coupling.
2 Raise the front of the car, support it securely and remove the front roadwheels.
3 Disconnect the tie-rod end balljoints from their steering arms as described in Section 18.
4 Turn the steering to full left-hand lock.
5 Slide the safety clip off the roll pin which connects the gearchange remote control rod to the selector shaft of the transmission. Drive out the roll pin.
6 Disconnect the steady rod from the transmission.
7 Disconnect the front section of the exhaust pipe from the rest of the system.

10

8 Remove the retainers and pinion shaft dust seal from the car floor.
9 Unbolt the rack housing mounting clamps, lower the housing to clear the pinion shaft and then turn the housing through 180° (photo).
10 Move the housing towards the left-hand side of the car until the right-hand tie-rod clears the exhaust pipe. Then lower the steering gear and withdraw it from the right-hand side of the car.
11 Refitting is a reversal of removal, but centralise the rack and steering wheel before connecting the intermediate shaft coupling.
12 Tighten all nuts and bolts to the specified torque. Check the front wheel alignment on completion.

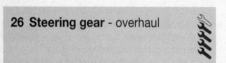

26 Steering gear - overhaul

Up to VIN 150427

1 If the steering gear is well worn it is recommended that a new or factory reconditioned unit is fitted.
2 For those wishing to overhaul the original unit, proceed in the following way. Remove the gear (Section 25).
3 Clean away external dirt and clamp the rack housing in the jaws of a vice.
4 Release the bellows clips and pull them away from the rack housing.
5 Release the tie-rod lockwasher tabs (46) (Fig. 10.7). Hold the rack still by means of its flats and unscrew the tie-rods.
6 Unscrew the locknut and remove the rack damper components.
7 Extract the pinion dust seal and the circlip

25.9 Steering rack mounting clamp bolts (arrowed)

then withdraw the pinion shaft from the housing.
8 Slide the rack out of the pinion gear end of the rack housing.
9 Remove the mounting insulator followed by the rack end bush.
10 Clean and renew all components which appear worn.
11 Reassembly is a reversal of dismantling. Pack the pinion bearing with grease and smear grease onto the inner surface of the rack end bush. Do not fill the outer slots with grease or the air passages will be restricted.
12 The mounting insulator bush should be positioned between 1.0 and 3.0 mm from the end of the rack housing.
13 Apply specified grease to the teeth of the rack and then insert the rack from the pinion gear end of the housing.
14 Press 25 to 35g of specified grease into the pinion shaft opening. Insert the pinion, fit the circlip and dust seal.
15 Reassemble the rack damper components having been smeared with grease.

16 Reconnect the tie-rods to the rack using a new lock washer and stop washer.
17 Partially fill the bellows with specified grease and fit them with their clips. Release one clip so that any air can be removed from the bellows by gently squeezing them.
18 After refitting the steering gear to the car, adjust the rack damper as described in Section 21.

From VIN 150428

19 No replacement parts are available for the later-type steering gear. Consequently, overhaul is not possible.

27 Steering angles and front wheel alignment

1 Accurate front wheel alignment is essential to provide good steering and roadholding characteristics and to ensure slow and even tyre wear. Before considering the steering angles, check that the tyres are correctly inflated, that the front wheels are not buckled, the hub bearings are not worn or incorrectly adjusted and that the steering linkage is in good order, without slackness or wear at the joints.
2 Wheel alignment consists of four factors:
Camber, is the angle at which the road wheels are set from the vertical when viewed from the front or rear of the vehicle. Positive camber is the angle (in degrees) that the wheels are tilted outwards at the top from the vertical.
Castor, is the angle between the steering axis and a vertical when viewed from each side of the vehicle. Positive castor is indicated when the steering axis is inclined towards the rear of the vehicle at its upper end.
Steering axis inclination, is the angle when viewed from the front or rear of the vehicle between vertical and an imaginary line drawn between the top and bottom strut mountings.
Toe, is the amount by which the distance between the front inside edges of the roadwheel rims differs from that between the rear inside edges. If the distance between the front edges is less than that at the rear, the wheels are said to toe-in. If the distance

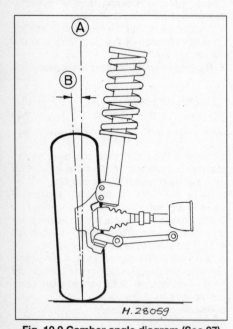

Fig. 10.9 Camber angle diagram (Sec 27)

A Vertical   B Camber angle (positive)

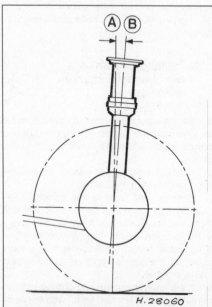

Fig. 10.10 Castor angle diagram (LH) (Sec 27)

A Vertical   B Castor angle (positive)

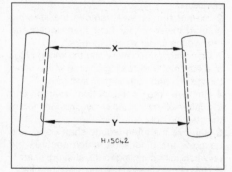

Fig. 10.11 Front wheel alignment diagram (Sec 27) showing toe-in

Y – X = toe-in

between the front inside edges is greater than that at the rear, the wheels toe-out.

3 Owing to the need for precision gauges to measure the small angles of the steering and suspension settings, it is preferable that measuring of camber and castor is left to a service station having the necessary equipment.

4 The camber, castor and steering axis inclination angles are set in production and cannot be adjusted. Where they differ from those specified, suspect collision damage or gross wear in the steering or suspension components.

5 To check the front wheel alignment, first make sure that the lengths of both tie-rods are equal when the steering is in the straight-ahead position. Adjust if necessary by releasing the tie-rod end locknuts and turning the tie-rods until the lengths of the exposed threads are equal on each side.

6 Obtain a tracking gauge. These are available in various forms from accessory stores or one can be fabricated from a length of steel tubing suitably cranked to clear the sump and bellhousing and having a setscrew and locknut at one end.

7 With the gauge, measure the distance between the two wheel inner rims (at hub height) at the rear of the wheel. Push the vehicle forward to rotate the wheel through 180° (half a turn) and measure the distance between the wheel inner rims, again at hub height, at the front of the wheel. This last measurement should differ from the first by the appropriate toe-in or toe-out according to specification (see Specifications Section).

8 Where the toe-in or toe-out is found to be incorrect, release the tie-rod balljoint locknuts and turn the tie-rods equally. Only turn them a quarter of a turn at a time before re-checking the alignment. Do not grip the threaded part of the tie-rod/balljoint during adjustment and make sure that the gaiter outboard clip is released otherwise the gaiter will twist as the tie-rod is rotated. Turn each tie-rod in the same direction when viewed from the centre line of the car otherwise the rods will become unequal in length. This would cause the steering wheel spoke position to alter and cause problems on turns with tyre scrubbing. On completion, tighten the tie-rod locknuts without disturbing their setting, check that the balljoint is at the centre of its arc of travel and then retighten the bellows clip.

28 Rear wheel alignment

These angles are set in production of the car and any deviation from those specified must be due to collision damage or gross wear in the suspension components.

Fault finding - front suspension

Vehicle wanders
- [ ] Incorrect wheel alignment
- [ ] Worn lower suspension arm balljoints

Heavy or stiff steering
- [ ] Incorrect front wheel alignment
- [ ] Incorrect tyre pressures

Wheel wobble or vibration
- [ ] Roadwheels out of balance
- [ ] Roadwheel buckled
- [ ] Incorrect front wheel alignment
- [ ] Faulty strut
- [ ] Weak torsion bar

Excessive pitching or rolling on corners or during braking
- [ ] Faulty strut
- [ ] Weak or broken torsion bar

Tyre squeal when cornering
- [ ] Incorrect front wheel alignment
- [ ] Incorrect tyre pressures

Abnormal tyre wear
- [ ] Incorrect tyre pressures
- [ ] Incorrect front wheel alignment
- [ ] Worn hub bearing

Fault finding - rear suspension

Poor roadholding and wander
- [ ] Faulty shock absorber
- [ ] Weak coil spring
- [ ] Worn hub bearing
- [ ] Worn trailing arm bush

10

Fault finding - steering

Note: *Before diagnosing steering faults, be sure that trouble is not due to incorrect or uneven tyre pressures, inappropriate tyre combinations, or braking system or suspension defects*

Car pulls to one side
- ☐ Incorrect steering geometry
- ☐ Collision damage

Car wanders when driven straight-ahead
- ☐ Play in steering gear
- ☐ Wear in steering balljoints

Heavy or stiff steering
- ☐ Lack of lubricant in steering gear or balljoints
- ☐ Incorrect steering geometry
- ☐ Collision damage

Play at steering wheel
- ☐ Wear in steering rack or balljoints
- ☐ Loose steering shaft coupling pinch-bolt or worn splines
- ☐ Worn steering column/shaft universal joints

Vibration at steering wheel
- ☐ Roadwheels out of balance or loose
- ☐ Tyre damage
- ☐ Loose driveshaft-to-hub nuts

Rattles from steering when traversing rough surfaces
- ☐ Steering damper defective or in need of adjustment
- ☐ Loose steering column mounting bolts
- ☐ Loose steering column/shaft coupling pinch-bolts
- ☐ Loose steering rack housing mounting bolts
- ☐ Worn steering column bearings

Excessive or uneven tyre wear
- ☐ Incorrect steering geometry
- ☐ Worn steering components
- ☐ Collision damage

Chapter 11 Bodywork and fittings

For modifications, and information applicable to later models, see Supplement at end of manual

Contents

Degrees of difficulty

| **Easy,** suitable for novice with little experience | | **Fairly easy,** suitable for beginner with some experience | | **Fairly difficult,** suitable for competent DIY mechanic | | **Difficult,** suitable for experienced DIY mechanic | | **Very difficult,** suitable for expert DIY or professional | |

Specifications

Body dimensions are given in the introductory Section of this Manual.

Torque wrench settings	Nm	lbf ft
Bumper bracket to body bolts	22	16
Door hinge bolts	22	16
Front seat track bolts	22	16
Rear seat back rest bolts	10	7
Seat belt anchor bolts	32	24

1 General description

The Rover 200 Series consists of six four-door Saloon models with either a 1342 cc or 1 598 cc engine.

The body is of all-steel unitary construction with a level of trim and equipment dependent upon the model specified in the vehicle range.

2 Maintenance - bodywork and underframe

The general condition of a vehicle's bodywork is the one thing that significantly affects its value. Maintenance is easy, but needs to be regular. Neglect, particularly after minor damage, can lead quickly to further deterioration and costly repair bills. It is important also to keep watch on those parts of the vehicle not immediately visible, for instance the underside, inside all the wheel arches, and the lower part of the engine compartment.

The basic maintenance routine for the bodywork is washing - preferably with a lot of water, from a hose. This will remove all the loose solids which may have stuck to the vehicle. It is important to flush these off in such a way as to prevent grit from scratching the finish. The wheel arches and underframe need washing in the same way, to remove any accumulated mud, which will retain moisture and tend to encourage rust. Paradoxically enough, the best time to clean the underframe and wheel arches is in wet weather, when the mud is thoroughly wet and soft. In very wet weather, the underframe is usually cleaned of large accumulations automatically, and this is a good time for inspection.

Periodically, except on vehicles with a wax-based underbody protective coating, it is a good idea to have the whole of the underframe of the vehicle steam-cleaned, engine compartment included, so that a thorough inspection can be carried out to see what minor repairs and renovations are necessary. Steam-cleaning is available at many garages, and is necessary for the removal of the accumulation of oily grime, which sometimes is allowed to become thick in certain areas. If steam-cleaning facilities are not available, there are some excellent grease solvents available which can be brush-applied; the dirt can then be simply hosed off. Note that these methods should not be used

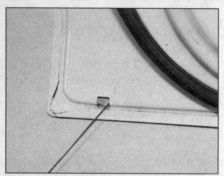

2.4A Clearing door drain

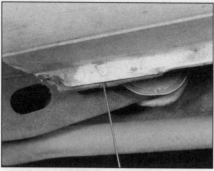

2.4B Clearing sill drain

2.5A Oiling a door hinge

2.5B Applying grease to bonnet lock

on vehicles with wax-based underbody protective coating, or the coating will be removed. Such vehicles should be inspected annually, preferably just prior to Winter, when the underbody should be washed down, and any damage to the wax coating repaired. Ideally, a completely fresh coat should be applied. It would also be worth considering the use of such wax-based protection for injection into door panels, sills, box sections, etc, as an additional safeguard against rust damage, where such protection is not provided by the vehicle manufacturer.

After washing paintwork, wipe off with a chamois leather to give an unspotted clear finish. A coat of clear protective wax polish will give added protection against chemical pollutants in the air. If the paintwork sheen has dulled or oxidised, use a cleaner/polisher combination to restore the brilliance of the shine. This requires a little effort, but such dulling is usually caused because regular washing has been neglected. Care needs to be taken with metallic paintwork, as special non-abrasive cleaner/polisher is required to avoid damage to the finish. Always check that the door and ventilator opening drain holes and pipes are completely clear, so that water can be drained out (photos). Brightwork should be treated in the same way as paintwork. Windscreens and windows can be kept clear of the smeary film which often appears, by the use of proprietary glass cleaner. Never use any form of wax or other body or chromium polish on glass.

Periodically oil all hinges and apply grease to the catches (photos).

3 Maintenance - upholstery and carpets

Mats and carpets should be brushed or vacuum-cleaned regularly, to keep them free of grit. If they are badly stained, remove them from the vehicle for scrubbing or sponging, and make quite sure they are dry before refitting. Seats and interior trim panels can be kept clean by wiping with a damp cloth. If they do become stained (which can be more apparent on light-coloured upholstery), use a little liquid detergent and a soft nail brush to scour the grime out of the grain of the material. Do not forget to keep the headlining clean in the same way as the upholstery. When using liquid cleaners inside the vehicle, do not over-wet the surfaces being cleaned. Excessive damp could get into the seams and padded interior, causing stains, offensive odours or even rot.

> **HAYNES HINT** *If the inside of the vehicle gets wet accidentally, it is worthwhile taking some trouble to dry it out properly, particularly where carpets are involved.* **Do not leave oil or electric heaters inside the vehicle for this purpose.**

4 Minor body damage - repair

Note: *For more detailed information about bodywork repair, Haynes Publishing produce a book by Lindsay Porter called "The Car Bodywork Repair Manual". This incorporates information on such aspects as rust treatment, painting and glass-fibre repairs, as well as details on more ambitious repairs involving welding and panel beating.*

Repairs of minor scratches in bodywork

If the scratch is very superficial, and does not penetrate to the metal of the bodywork, repair is very simple. Lightly rub the area of the scratch with a paintwork renovator, or a

very fine cutting paste, to remove loose paint from the scratch, and to clear the surrounding bodywork of wax polish. Rinse the area with clean water.

Apply touch-up paint to the scratch using a fine paint brush; continue to apply fine layers of paint until the surface of the paint in the scratch is level with the surrounding paintwork. Allow the new paint at least two weeks to harden, then blend it into the surrounding paintwork by rubbing the scratch area with a paintwork renovator or a very fine cutting paste. Finally, apply wax polish.

Where the scratch has penetrated right through to the metal of the bodywork, causing the metal to rust, a different repair technique is required. Remove any loose rust from the bottom of the scratch with a penknife, then apply rust-inhibiting paint to prevent the formation of rust in the future. Using a rubber or nylon applicator, fill the scratch with bodystopper paste. If required, this paste can be mixed with cellulose thinners to provide a very thin paste which is ideal for filling narrow scratches. Before the stopper-paste in the scratch hardens, wrap a piece of smooth cotton rag around the top of a finger. Dip the finger in cellulose thinners, and quickly sweep it across the surface of the stopper-paste in the scratch; this will ensure that the surface of the stopper-paste is slightly hollowed. The scratch can now be painted over as described earlier in this Section.

Repairs of dents in bodywork

When deep denting of the vehicle's bodywork has taken place, the first task is to pull the dent out, until the affected bodywork almost attains its original shape. There is little point in trying to restore the original shape completely, as the metal in the damaged area will have stretched on impact, and cannot be reshaped fully to its original contour. It is better to bring the level of the dent up to a point which is about 3 mm below the level of the surrounding bodywork. In cases where the dent is very shallow anyway, it is not worth trying to pull it out at all. If the underside of the dent is accessible, it can be hammered out gently from behind, using a mallet with a wooden or plastic head. Whilst doing this, hold a suitable block of wood firmly against the outside of the panel, to absorb the impact from the hammer blows and thus prevent a large area of the bodywork from being "belled-out".

Should the dent be in a section of the bodywork which has a double skin, or some other factor making it inaccessible from behind, a different technique is called for. Drill several small holes through the metal inside the area - particularly in the deeper section. Then screw long self-tapping screws into the holes, just sufficiently for them to gain a good purchase in the metal. Now the dent can be pulled out by pulling on the protruding heads of the screws with a pair of pliers.

The next stage of the repair is the removal of the paint from the damaged area, and from an inch or so of the surrounding "sound" bodywork. This is accomplished most easily by using a wire brush or abrasive pad on a power drill, although it can be done just as effectively by hand, using sheets of abrasive paper. To complete the preparation for filling, score the surface of the bare metal with a screwdriver or the tang of a file, or alternatively, drill small holes in the affected area. This will provide a really good "key" for the filler paste.

To complete the repair, see the Section on filling and respraying.

Repairs of rust holes or gashes in bodywork

Remove all paint from the affected area, and from an inch or so of the surrounding "sound" bodywork, using an abrasive pad or a wire brush on a power drill. If these are not available, a few sheets of abrasive paper will do the job most effectively. With the paint removed, you will be able to judge the severity of the corrosion, and therefore decide whether to renew the whole panel (if this is possible) or to repair the affected area. New body panels are not as expensive as most people think, and it is often quicker and more satisfactory to fit a new panel than to attempt to repair large areas of corrosion.

Remove all fittings from the affected area, except those which will act as a guide to the original shape of the damaged bodywork (eg headlight shells etc). Then, using tin snips or a hacksaw blade, remove all loose metal and any other metal badly affected by corrosion. Hammer the edges of the hole inwards, in order to create a slight depression for the filler paste.

Wire-brush the affected area to remove the powdery rust from the surface of the remaining metal. Paint the affected area with rust-inhibiting paint, if the back of the rusted area is accessible, treat this also.

Before filling can take place, it will be necessary to block the hole in some way. This can be achieved by the use of aluminium or plastic mesh, or aluminium tape.

Aluminium or plastic mesh, or glass-fibre matting, is probably the best material to use for a large hole. Cut a piece to the approximate size and shape of the hole to be

filled, then position it in the hole so that its edges are below the level of the surrounding bodywork. It can be retained in position by several blobs of filler paste around its periphery.

Aluminium tape should be used for small or very narrow holes. Pull a piece off the roll, trim it to the approximate size and shape required, then pull off the backing paper (if used) and stick the tape over the hole; it can be overlapped if the thickness of one piece is insufficient. Burnish down the edges of the tape with the handle of a screwdriver or similar, to ensure that the tape is securely attached to the metal underneath.

Bodywork repairs - filling and respraying

Before using this Section, see the Sections on dent, deep scratch, rust holes and gash repairs.

Many types of bodyfiller are available, but generally speaking, those proprietary kits which contain a tin of filler paste and a tube of resin hardener are best for this type of repair. A wide, flexible plastic or nylon applicator will be found invaluable for imparting a smooth and well-contoured finish to the surface of the filler.

Mix up a little filler on a clean piece of card or board - measure the hardener carefully (follow the maker's instructions on the pack), otherwise the filler will set too rapidly or too slowly. Using the applicator, apply the filler paste to the prepared area; draw the applicator across the surface of the filler to achieve the correct contour and to level the surface. As soon as a contour that approximates to the correct one is achieved, stop working the paste - if you carry on too long, the paste will become sticky and begin to "pick-up" on the applicator. Continue to add thin layers of filler paste at 20-minute intervals, until the level of the filler is just proud of the surrounding bodywork.

Once the filler has hardened, the excess can be removed using a metal plane or file. From then on, progressively-finer grades of abrasive paper should be used, starting with a 40-grade production paper, and finishing with a 400-grade wet-and-dry paper. Always wrap the abrasive paper around a flat rubber, cork, or wooden block - otherwise the surface of the filler will not be completely flat. During the smoothing of the filler surface, the wet-and-dry paper should be periodically rinsed in water. This will ensure that a very smooth finish is imparted to the filler at the final stage.

At this stage, the "dent" should be surrounded by a ring of bare metal, which in turn should be encircled by the finely "feathered" edge of the good paintwork. Rinse the repair area with clean water, until all of the dust produced by the rubbing-down operation has gone.

Spray the whole area with a light coat of primer - this will show up any imperfections in the surface of the filler. Repair these

imperfections with fresh filler paste or bodystopper, and once more smooth the surface with abrasive paper. Repeat this spray-and-repair procedure until you are satisfied that the surface of the filler, and the feathered edge of the paintwork, are perfect. Clean the repair area with clean water, and allow to dry fully.

 HAYNES HiNT *If bodystopper is used, it can be mixed with cellulose thinners to form a really thin paste which is ideal for filling small holes.*

The repair area is now ready for final spraying. Paint spraying must be carried out in a warm, dry, windless and dust-free atmosphere. This condition can be created artificially if you have access to a large indoor working area, but if you are forced to work in the open, you will have to pick your day very carefully. If you are working indoors, dousing the floor in the work area with water will help to settle the dust which would otherwise be in the atmosphere. If the repair area is confined to one body panel, mask off the surrounding panels; this will help to minimise the effects of a slight mis-match in paint colours. Bodywork fittings (eg chrome strips, door handles etc) will also need to be masked off. Use genuine masking tape, and several thicknesses of newspaper, for the masking operations.

Before commencing to spray, agitate the aerosol can thoroughly, then spray a test area (an old tin, or similar) until the technique is mastered. Cover the repair area with a thick coat of primer; the thickness should be built up using several thin layers of paint, rather than one thick one. Using 400-grade wet-and-dry paper, rub down the surface of the primer until it is really smooth. While doing this, the work area should be thoroughly doused with water, and the wet-and-dry paper periodically rinsed in water. Allow to dry before spraying on more paint.

Spray on the top coat, again building up the thickness by using several thin layers of paint. Start spraying at one edge of the repair area, and then, using a side-to-side motion, work until the whole repair area and about 2 inches of the surrounding original paintwork is covered. Remove all masking material 10 to 15 minutes after spraying on the final coat of paint.

Allow the new paint at least two weeks to harden, then, using a paintwork renovator, or a very fine cutting paste, blend the edges of the paint into the existing paintwork. Finally, apply wax polish.

5 Major body damage - repair

1 This sort of work should be left to your Austin Rover dealer or specialist body repair works.
2 It is essential to have the body aligned on special jigs to ensure that the specified

11

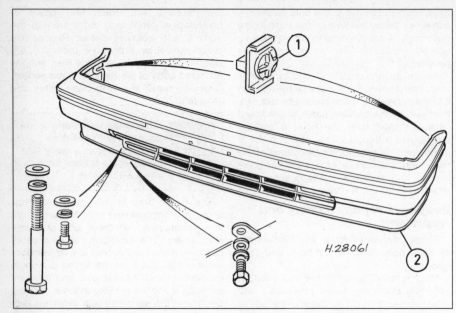

Fig. 11.1 Front bumper locating clip (1) and bumper (2) (Sec 6)

7.2 Front spoiler bracket

steering and suspension settings are maintained during repair.

3 This is of course beyond the scope of the home mechanic and if not carried out correctly will give rise to unroadworthy behaviour and severe tyre wear.

6 Front bumper - removal and refitting

1.3 models

1 On 1.3 models, unbolt and remove the splash panels from under the front end of the car.
2 Unscrew the two lower bumper mounting bolts.
3 Unscrew the two bolts which hold the bumper to the brackets.

1.6 models

4 Unscrew the two bolts which hold the bumper to the body crossmember.

All models

5 Working through the bumper grille, remove the bumper clamp bolts.
6 Support the bumper and ease it forward.
7 Disconnect the headlamp washer hose (where fitted) and remove the bumper from the car.
8 Refitting is a reversal of removal.

7 Front spoiler - removal and refitting

1 Turn the steering to full lock and remove the two self-tapping screws from the flange of the front wheel arch.
2 Unscrew the three screws which hold the spoiler brackets to the lower edge of the bumper (photo).
3 Extract the three screws which hold the top edge of the spoiler to the bumper.
4 Lift the spoiler from the car.
5 Refitting is a reversal of removal.

8 Bonnet - removal and refitting

1 Open the bonnet and support it on its stay.
2 Mark the position of the hinges on the underside of the bonnet. Use a pencil or masking tape to prevent scoring the paint, as this could encourage rust (photo).
3 Release the washer hose from its clip and disconnect it. With the help of an assistant, unscrew the hinge bolts, disconnect the stay and lift the bonnet from the car (photo).
4 Refitting is a reversal of removal, but do not fully tighten the hinge bolts until the bonnet has been gently lowered and its alignment checked. There should be an equal gap at each side between wing and bonnet. Move the bonnet if necessary after releasing the hinge bolts.
5 It is acceptable to fit shims under the hinges to make the near end of the bonnet flush with the wing top surfaces.
6 Adjust the bonnet lock and bump stops to provide firm positive closure as described in the next Section (photo).

9 Bonnet lock and cable

1 The bonnet lock may be moved within the limits of its elongated bolt holes so that the bonnet shuts smoothly and positively. This

8.2 Bonnet hinge

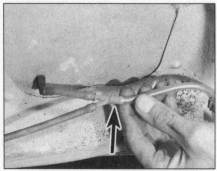
8.3 Washer hose connector (arrowed)

8.6 Bonnet bump stop

9.1 Bonnet lock

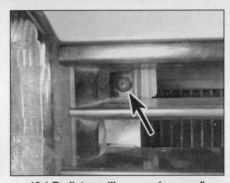
10.1 Radiator grille screw (arrowed)

10.2 Withdrawing radiator grille

should be carried out in conjunction with adjusting the rubber bump stops. These should be screwed in or out so that the bonnet will be flush with the tops of the wings and not rattle when closed (photo).

2 The bonnet cable is not adjustable, but may be renewed after disconnecting it from the lock and release lever and withdrawing it through the bulkhead grommet into the engine compartment.

10 Radiator grille -
removal and refitting

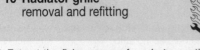

1 Extract the fixing screws from between the slots of the grille (photo) .
2 Pull the grille sharply from the spring clips (photo).
3 Refitting is a reversal of removal.

11 Front wing -
removal and refitting

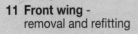

1 Remove the front bumper (Section 6).
2 Remove the front direction indicator (Chapter 12).

11.3 Underwing protective shield bolt (arrowed)

3 Raise the front of the car and remove the roadwheel. Remove the underwing protective plastic shield (photo).
4 Open the bonnet.
5 Unscrew the row of bolts from the top edge of the wing (photo).
6 Open the front door and remove the wing upper fixing bolt which is accessible between the rear edge of the wing and the leading edge of the door (photo).
7 Extract the fixing screw from the front and rear lower edges of the wing (photo).
8 Remove the wing and recover the rubber buffer from halfway down the rear edge. If the wing is stuck tight, cut along the mastic joint using a sharp knife.

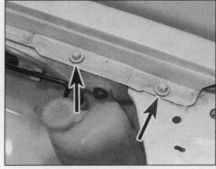
11.5 Front wing bolts (engine compartment) (arrowed)

9 Before fitting the new wing, clean away all old jointing mastic and apply a bead of new material.
10 Once the wing has been fitted, apply protective coating to its underside and finish the outer surface to match the body colour.

12 Door interior trim panel -
removal and refitting

1 Extract the screws and remove the armrest (photos).
2 Extract the screw and remove the

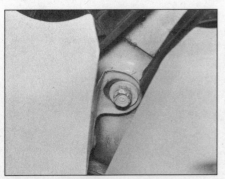
11.6 Front wing bolt (pillar)

11.7 Front wing bolt (sill) (arrowed)

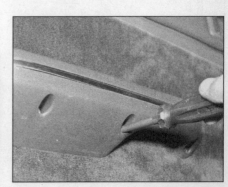
12.1A Extracting door armrest screw

11

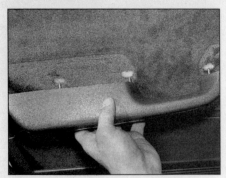

12.1B Removing door armrest

12.2A Extracting door lock remote control escutcheon plate screw

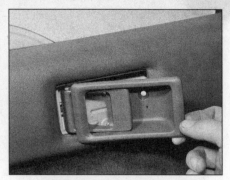

12.2B Removing escutcheon plate

12.3 Door window regulator handle

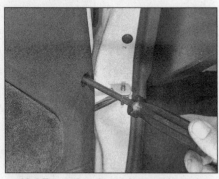

12.4 Extracting door trim panel screw

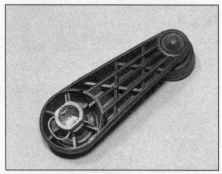

12.8 Window regulator handle ready for fitting

escutcheon plate from the remote control handle (photos).

3 On cars without power-operated windows, extract the the spring clip and take off the window regulator handle. The clip can be removed using a piece of wire with a hook at its end or a strip of rag pulled in either direction under the handle boss (photo).

4 Extract the trim panel fixing screws (photo).

5 Insert the fingers or a broad blunt blade between the trim panel and the door and release the clips.

6 Remove the trim panel. On cars with

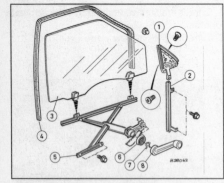

Fig. 11.2 Front door window components (Sec 13)

1 Escutcheon plate
2 Glass channel
3 Glass
4 Glass channel weatherseal
5 Glass regulator
6 Regulator handle escutcheon
7 Clip
8 Regulator handle

electrically-powered windows, disconnect the multi-pin plug as the panel is withdrawn.

7 Peel away the waterproof sheet for access to the door interior.

8 Refitting is a reversal of removal. To fit the regulator handle, position the spring clip on the handle and fit it to the splined shaft of the regulator simply by striking it with the hand (photo).

13 Front door - dismantling and reassembly

Window glass

1 Remove the exterior rear view mirror, see Section 28.

13.4 Front door with trim panel removed

2 Unclip and remove the door waist outer weather sealing strip.

3 Remove the door trim panel as described in the preceding Section and peel away the weatherproof sheet.

4 Remove the front speaker from the door (photo).

5 Temporarily refit the regulator handle and lower the glass until the glass bottom slide channel bolts are visible (photo).

6 If power-operated windows are fitted, use jump leads to energise the winding motors.

7 Extract the slide channel bolts and lift the glass upwards, turning it as necessary to remove it from the door waist slot.

Window winder regulator

8 With the door glass removed as previously described, unscrew the regulator mounting

13.5 Door glass regulator arms and glass bottom channel

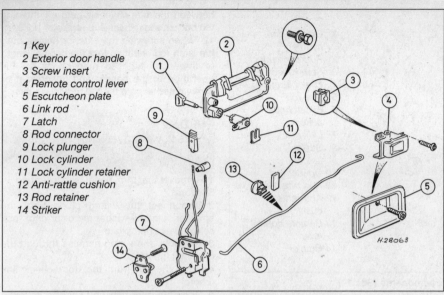

1 Key
2 Exterior door handle
3 Screw insert
4 Remote control lever
5 Escutcheon plate
6 Link rod
7 Latch
8 Rod connector
9 Lock plunger
10 Lock cylinder
11 Lock cylinder retainer
12 Anti-rattle cushion
13 Rod retainer
14 Striker

H.28063

Fig. 11.3 Front door lock components (Sec 13)

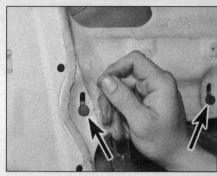

13.8 Regulator mounting bolts (arrowed)

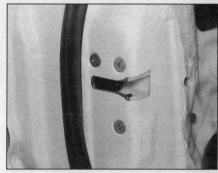

13.11 Door latch screws

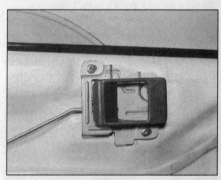

13.12 Door lock remote control handle

bolts and manoeuvre the regulator through the lower aperture in the door (photo).

Door lock

9 Unscrew the exterior handle bolts which are accessible from inside the door cavity.
10 Pull out the forked spring retainer and take out the lock cylinder at the same time disconnecting the link rod.
11 Extract the screws from the edge of the door and push the latch and rod inside the door cavity. Measure the exposed threads on the latch rod and unscrew the exterior handle from it. Withdraw the latch from the door cavity (photo).
12 The lock remote control rod can be removed after extracting the fixing screws (photo).

Refitting

13 Refitting is a reversal of removal, but observe the following points.
14 When fitting the glass, set it centrally between the side guides before tightening the bottom slide channel bolts.
15 When screwing the exterior handle onto

the latch rod, set it so that the original length of thread is exposed. Then check for full movement of the handle and unscrew or screw it further onto the rod to achieve this.

14 Rear door - dismantling and reassembly

Door glass

1 Remove the trim panel as described in Section 12.
2 Lower the glass fully.
3 Extract the sash screws, tilt the sash and remove the quarter-light (photo) .
4 Adjust the position of the glass by temporarily fitting the regulator handle until the glass to regulator fixing screws are visible. Extract the screws and manoeuvre the glass up and out of the door waist slot.

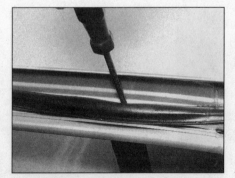

14.3 Rear door sash top screw located under weatherseal

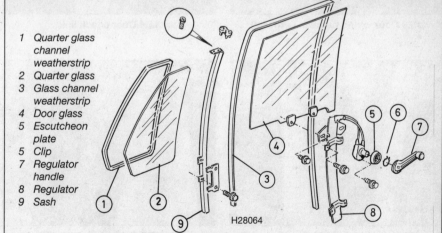

1 Quarter glass channel weatherstrip
2 Quarter glass
3 Glass channel weatherstrip
4 Door glass
5 Escutcheon plate
5 Clip
7 Regulator handle
8 Regulator
9 Sash

H28064

Fig. 11.4 Rear door window components (Sec 14)

11

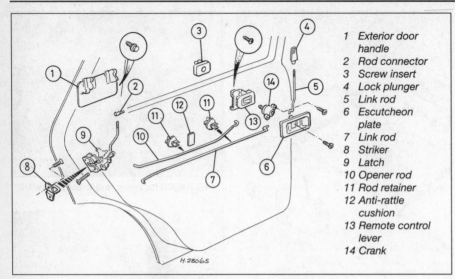

1 Exterior door handle
2 Rod connector
3 Screw insert
4 Lock plunger
5 Link rod
6 Escutcheon plate
7 Link rod
8 Striker
9 Latch
10 Opener rod
11 Rod retainer
12 Anti-rattle cushion
13 Remote control lever
14 Crank

Fig. 11.5 Rear door lock components (Sec 14)

Window regulator

5 With the door glass removed as previously described, unbolt the regulator and remove it through the lower aperture of the door.

Door lock

6 Working through the door cavity, unscrew the door exterior handle fixing bolts.
7 Remove the lock crank and disconnect the link rods.
8 Extract the latch screws from the door edge and push the latch and rods inside the door. Measure the length of exposed thread on the latch rod and then withdraw the exterior handle until it can be unscrewed from the latch rod.
9 Remove the latch and rods from the door.

Refitting

10 Refitting is a reversal of removal, but observe the following points.
11 When fitting the glass, centralise it between the side channels before tightening the bottom slide channel to regulator bolts.
12 When screwing the exterior handle onto the latch rod, set it so that the original length of thread is exposed then check for full operation of the handle and unscrew it or screw it further onto the rod to achieve this.

15 Door - removal and refitting

1 Remove the trim panel as described in Section 12.
2 Disconnect the wiring plugs from the speaker, window winder motor or door lock solenoid as appropriate.
3 Withdraw the wiring harness through the grommet (photo).
4 Drive the pin from the door check link (photo).
5 Open the door fully and support its lower edge on blocks or jacks covered with pads of rags.
6 Extract the circlips from the door hinge pins and drive out the pins. Lift the door from the car (photo).
7 Refitting is a reversal of removal. Any adjustment of the door can be made by releasing the hinge bolts and moving the door within the limits of the pillar bolt holes (photo).
8 Close the door gently and check that the striker is correctly located. If not, release the striker screws and move its position on the body pillar as necessary (photo).

16 Luggage boot lid - removal and refitting

1 Open the lid fully and mark the position of the hinges on the underside of it (photo).
2 With the help of an assistant, support the weight of the lid, unscrew the hinge bolts and remove the lid from the car.
3 Refitting is a reversal of removal, but do not fully tighten the hinge bolts until the lid has been closed gently and checked for

15.3 Door wiring harness (arrowed)

15.4 Door check link

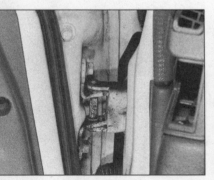

15.6 Door hinge

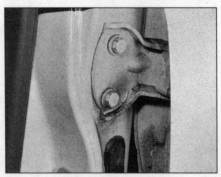

15.7 Door hinge bolts

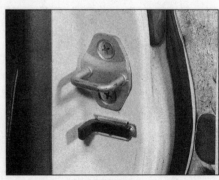

15.8 Door striker

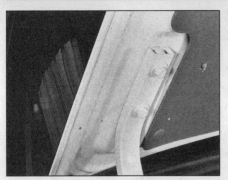

16.1 Luggage boot lid hinge

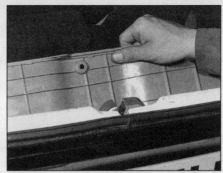

16.4A Removing luggage boot lock cover

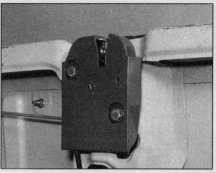

16.4B Luggage boot lid lock

alignment. If an equal gap does not exist on both sides of the lid, move it as necessary within the limits of the elongated hinge bolt holes and then tighten the bolts.

4 As the lid is closed, the lock should engage smoothly and positively. If it does not, release the striker or lock bolts or both and adjust for alignment and closure (photo).

5 If for any reason the boot lid counter-balance torsion rod must be removed, then the end of the rod must be released from its anchorage slot. Do this using a large adjustable spanner or a long lever. *Exercise caution as the rod is under considerable torsion (photo).*

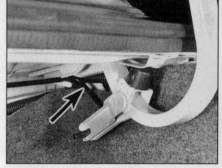

16.4C Luggage boot lid lock striker

16.5 Luggage boot lid lock hinge and torsion rod (arrowed)

17 Luggage boot lock and controls - removal and refitting

Lock

1 Open the boot lid and disconnect the remote control cable from it.

2 Unscrew the lock fixing screws, withdraw the lock until the link rod from the lock cylinder can be disconnected and the lock removed from the car.

Control cable and lever

3 Working inside the car, remove the boot control lever cover and housing from the side of the driver's seat (photo).

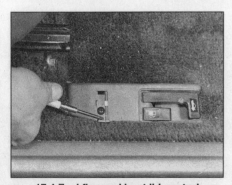

17.4 Fuel flap and boot lid control levers

4 Unbolt the lever bracket and disconnect the control cable from the lever.

5 Remove the rear seat cushion (Section 25), and the sill mouldings from the front and rear right-hand door openings.

6 Peel back the floor carpet to expose the control cable.

7 Remove the fixing tape and pull the cable through into the luggage boot. Disconnect the cable from the lock and its locating clips.

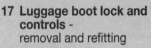

Fig. 11.6 Luggage boot lid lock (Sec 17)

1 Striker
2 Lock cylinder
3 Latch
4 Lock control cable
5 Link rod

Lock cylinder

8 Open the luggage boot, remove the nuts which hold the rear number plate panel and remove the panel.

9 Pull out the lock cylinder forked retaining clip, disconnect the cylinder link rod.

10 Unscrew the cylinder fixing bolt and then rotate the cylinder to disengage the retaining lugs. Remove the cylinder.

Refitting

11 The refitting of all components is a reversal of removal.

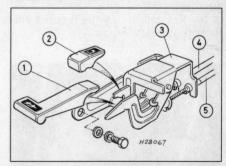

Fig. 11.7 Boot and fuel filler flap remote control (Sec 17)

1 Release lever (luggage boot)
2 Release lever (fuel flap)
3 Lever mounting bracket
4 Cable (fuel flap)
5 Cable (luggage boot)

11

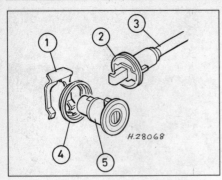

Fig. 11.8 Fuel filler flap lock (Sec 18)

1 Cylinder retaining clip   3 Control cable
2 Latch   4 Bezel   5 Lock cylinder

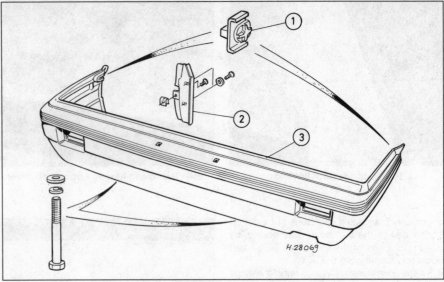

Fig. 11.9 Rear bumper (Sec 20)

1 Locating clip   2 End cover   3 Bumper

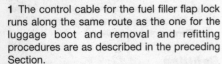

18.2 Fuel filler flap lock

18 Fuel filler flap lock and controls - removal and refitting

1 The control cable for the fuel filler flap lock runs along the same route as the one for the luggage boot and removal and refitting procedures are as described in the preceding Section.
2 To remove the cable release lock tongue, open the flap, pull out the forked retaining clip and withdraw the assembly into the luggage boot (photo).
3 The lock cylinder can be removed after extracting the retaining clip.

19 Rear spoiler - removal and refitting

1 Open the luggage boot lid, unscrew the five spoiler retaining nuts and lift the spoiler away.
2 Refitting is a reversal of removal.

20 Rear bumper - removal and refitting

1 Extract the three screws from each wheel arch which secure the bumper to the rear wing panel.
2 Unbolt the bumper brackets from the body.
3 Open the luggage boot lid and disconnect the bumper lamps wiring harness plug.
4 Release the grommet from the body panel and feed the wiring through the hole in the panel.
5 Remove the bumper.
6 Refitting is a reversal of removal.

21 Windscreen and heated rear screen - renewal

1 Removal and refitting of the front and rear screens should be left to a professional screen replacement specialist.
2 The glass is flush-mounted, and removal requires the use of a hot knife or wire to release the sealant.

22 Centre console - removal and refitting

1 On cars with manual transmission, unscrew and remove the gear lever knob.
2 Remove the rear flap and centre cover from the centre console (photos) .
3 Extract the five fixing screws from the centre console (photo).
4 If a radio speaker balance control is fitted withdraw the centre console only far enough

22.2A Centre console rear flap

22.2B Centre console top screw (arrowed)

22.3 Centre console side screw (arrowed)

23.3 Facia under cover

23.10A Facia end cap

23.10B Facia end fixing bolt (arrowed)

to be able to disconnect the wiring multi-pin plug before lifting the console over the handbrake lever.

5 Refitting is a reversal of removal.

23 Facia panel - removal and refitting

1 Disconnect the battery.
2 Remove the steering wheel (Chapter 10).
3 Remove the facia under cover access panel from around the steering column by extracting the screws (photo).
4 Remove the glove box (two screws).
5 Remove the ashtray.
6 Remove the radio (Chapter 12).
7 Prise out the clock and then disconnect its multi-plug.
8 Refer to Chapter 12 and remove the instrument panel.
9 Extract the screw which secures the bonnet release lever to its bracket and move the lever to one side.
10 Remove the caps from both ends of the facia panel. Do this by prising them out sideways (photos).
11 Remove the two blanking caps from the lower centre of the facia panel to expose the facia lower mounting bolts (photos).
12 Remove the facia centre air vent. Do this by prising out with a thin blade inserted at the sides of the central switch (photos).

13 On 1.3 models, remove the choke knob and disconnect the cable from the facia as described in Chapter 3.
14 Pull off the heater control lever knobs and release the heater control escutcheon plate retainers. Withdraw the plate until the illumination bulb can be disconnected.
15 Extract the three screws which retain the heater control lever mounting base and separate it from the facia.
16 On 1.3 models, release the facia wiring harness multi-plugs at the fusebox.
17 On 1.6 models, unscrew the two nuts which hold the fusebox to its bracket.
18 Release the facia wiring harness multi-plug from the fusebox and the main harness.

23.11A Facia lower screw blanking cap

19 Disconnect the heater blower wiring harness.
20 Disconnect the steering column bracket earth leads. Set the steering column in its lowest rake position.
21 Unscrew all the facia fixing bolts and with the help of an assistant, remove the facia panel sideways from the car.
22 Refitting is a reversal of removal.

24 Front seat - removal and refitting

1 Push the seat fully forwards and unscrew the bolts which hold the rear end of the seat track to the floor (photo).

23.11B Facia lower fixing screw (arrowed)

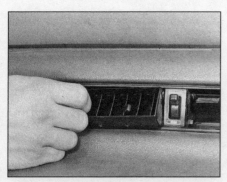

23.12A Removing facia centre air vent

23.12B Facia air vent removed showing retaining lugs

23.12C Facia fixing screw behind air vent (arrowed)

11

24.1 Front seat slide bolt

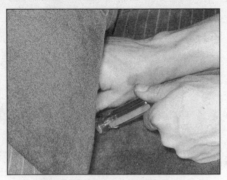

25.1 Removing rear seat screw

25.2 Rear seat cushion retaining hook (arrowed)

25.3 Rear seat back retaining bolt

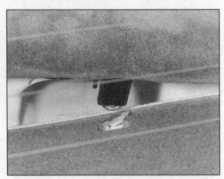

25.5 Rear seat back locating tongues

backrest, unscrew the bolt which holds it to the wheel arch (photo).

4 If the backrest is fitted with an opening hatch to facilitate the carrying of long articles of luggage, then the backrest top rail will have to be removed.

5 Raise the backrest to disengage its locating tongues, and remove it from the car (photo).

6 Refitting is a reversal of removal.

2 Push the seat fully back and unscrew the track front end bolts.

3 Lift the seat from the car.

4 Refitting is a reversal of removal.

25 Rear seat - removal and refitting

Seat cushion

1 Extract the screw from the centre of the joint between the cushion and the backrest (photo).

2 Pull the rear edge of the cushion upwards and then release the retaining hooks at the front lower edge of the cushion. Remove the cushion (photo).

Backrest

3 From each side of the lower edge of the

26 Seat belts - maintenance, removal and refitting

1 Periodically inspect the seat belts for fraying or other damage. If evident, renew the belt (photo).

2 The belts may be cleaned using warm water and liquid detergent. Do not use solvents of any kind.

3 If the car is involved in a front end collision and the belts have restrained the front or rear seat occupants, renew the belts.

4 Before unbolting the seat belt anchor bolts, remove the centre pillar lower trim panel (photo).

5 When refitting, always maintain the original fitted sequence of washers and spacers.

6 Set the floor stalk at 45° to the floor before tightening its bolt (photo) .

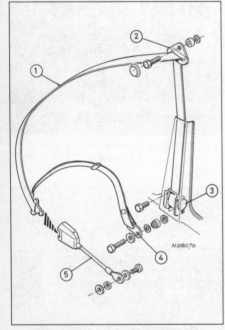

Fig. 11.10 Front seat belt (Sec 26)

1 Belt
2 Upper anchor plate
3 Retracting reel
4 Lower anchor plate
5 Floor stalk

26.1 Seat belt pillar clip

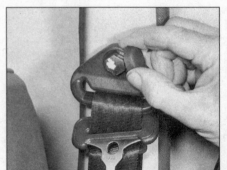

26.4 Seat belt anchor bolt cap

26.6 Seat belt floor stalk

27 Interior grab handles - removal and refitting

1 Prise up the screw covers. remove the screws and the grab rails (photo).

28 Rear view mirrors - removal and refitting

Interior

1 The interior mirror is bonded directly to the windscreen glass. Removal will require the use of a hot air gun.
2 A new mirror is supplied complete with a self-bonding patch.

Exterior

3 Slide the mirror control knob from the operating rod (photo).
4 Prise out the triangular escutcheon plate, to expose the mirror fixing screws (photos).
5 Remove the screws and withdraw the mirror. Disconnect the wiring plug on electrically-operated mirrors.
6 Refitting is a reversal of removal.

29 Headlining - removal and refitting

1 The headlining is of moulded type and in consequence can be removed more easily than is the case with conventional linings.
2 Working inside the car, remove the sun visors, the front pillar trim, the interior lamp, the roof rear trim and the grab handles.
3 Remove the upper seat belt anchor bolts.
4 Release the body pillar upper trims and wedge them away from the pillars at the tops.
5 Remove the headlining side moulding strips.
6 Remove the headlining clips and then with the help of an assistant, remove the headlining from the car interior.
7 Fitting the headlining is a reversal of removal, but a new one will require cross-cuts to be made for the sun visor mounting.

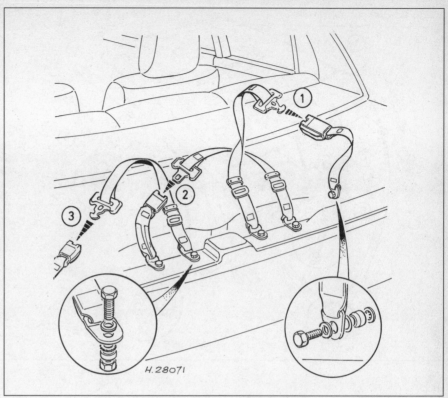
Fig. 11.11 Rear seat belts (Sec 26)

1 Right-hand belts   2 Centre belts   3 Left-hand belts

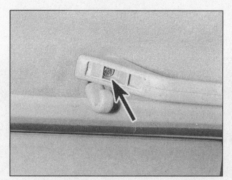
27.1 Grab handle screw (arrowed)

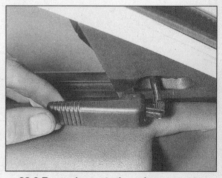
28.3 Removing exterior mirror remote control handle

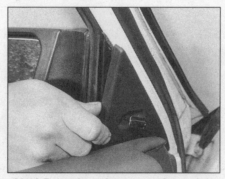
28.4A Removing mirror escutcheon plate

28.4B Exterior mirror fixing screws (arrowed)

11

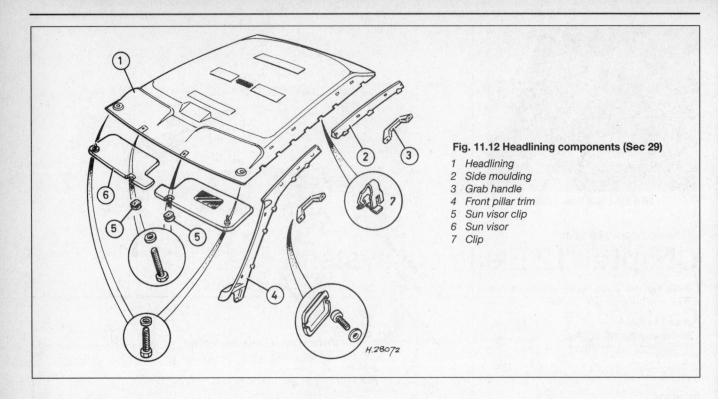

Fig. 11.12 Headlining components (Sec 29)

1 Headlining
2 Side moulding
3 Grab handle
4 Front pillar trim
5 Sun visor clip
6 Sun visor
7 Clip

H.28072

Chapter 12 Electrical system

For modifications, and information applicable to later models, see Supplement at end of manual

Contents

Degrees of difficulty

| **Easy,** suitable for novice with little experience | **Fairly easy,** suitable for beginner with some experience | **Fairly difficult,** suitable for competent DIY mechanic | **Difficult,** suitable for experienced DIY mechanic | **Very difficult,** suitable for expert DIY or professional |

Specifications

System type . . . . 12 volt negative earth, battery, alternator and pre-engaged starter motor

Battery . . . . 45Ah, maintenance-free

Alternator
Regulated voltage . . . . 13.9 to 15.1 volt
Output at 14 volt and 6000 rev/min 55A
Minimum brush length:
  Hitachi . . . . 5.0 mm (0.2 in)
  Lucas . . . . 10.0 mm (0.4 in)
Drivebelt deflection under load:
  1.3, new belt . . . . 4.0 to 6.5 mm (0.18 to 0.26 in) under load of 98 N (22 lbf)
  1.3, used belt . . . . 7 to 10 mm (0.28 to 0.39 in) under same load
  1.6, new or used belt . . . . 7 to 12 mm (0.28 to 0.47 in) under load of 44N (10 lbf)

Starter motor
Minimum brush length . . . . 10.0 mm (0.4 in) Lucas, 12 mm (0.5 in) Hitachi

12

Fuses

Number	Circuit protected	Rating (A)
1	Rear fog warning lamp	10
2	Wipers, washers	15
3	Direction indicators, reverse lamp	10
4	Alternator	10
5	LH headlamp (dipped beam)	10
6	RH headlamp (dipped beam)	10
7	LH headlamp (main beam)	10
8	RH headlamp (main beam)	10
9	Horn and stop lamps	15
10	Hazard warning lamps	10
11	Interior lamp, clock, cigar lighter	15
12	Tail, rear number plate and instrument illumination	15
13	Radiator cooling fan	15
14	Heater booster fan, heated rear window relay	20
15	Radio	10
16	Heated rear window	15
17	Central locking	15
18	Headlamp washer	15
19	Electric window (front right)	15
20	Electric window (front left)	15
21	Electric window (rear right)	15
22	Electric window (rear left)	15
23	Spare	

Continuous current fuses colour coding

Red	10A
Blue	15A
Yellow	20A

Fusible links

Main	55A
Link	45A

Bulbs

Lamp	Wattage	Number
Headlamp (Halogen)	60/55	GLB472
Front parking lamp	4	GLB 233
Stop/tail lamp	25/5	GLB380
Direction indicator and reverse lamps	21	GLB 382
Rear number plate lamp	5	GLB 501
Interior lamp	5	BNP4 195
Luggage boot lamp	3.4	GLB 758
Cigar lighter illumination	2.2	G LB 643
Instrument panel, warning lamps	1.4	GLB 286
Instruments	3	GLB 504
Switch warning lamp	1.4	GLB 748
Heater controls, ashtray illumination	1.4	GLB 286
Rear fog warning lamp	21	GLB 382

Wiper blades

Champion X-4503

Torque wrench settings

	Nm	lbf ft
Alternator mounting bolt	45	33
Alternator adjuster link bolt	24	18
Starter mounting bolts	45	33
Wiper arm domed nut	14	10

1 General description

The electrical system is of 12 volt negative earth type and consists of a battery, an alternator, pre-engaged starter motor and the usual lamps and accessories.

On certain models, central door locking and power-operated windows are fitted.

2 Battery - maintenance and charging

1 A maintenance-free type battery is fitted which requires no topping up of the electrolyte.
2 Keep the top of the battery clean and the terminals tight and smeared with petroleum jelly to reduce corrosion.
3 The battery will not normally require charging from the mains supply, but if only very short journeys are made with much use being made of the starter and electrical accessories then a regular charge from an outside source may be required.
4 Before charging the battery, remove it from the car as described in the next Section.
5 Connect the leads correctly, ensuring no sparks or naked flame are allowed near the battery during charging as the hydrogen being produced could cause an explosion.

3.1 Battery, showing close proximity of distributor cap on 1.3 models

4.8 Alternator adjuster link

4.9 Alternator drivebelt

3 Battery - removal and refitting

1 Open the bonnet and disconnect the battery negative (-) lead then the positive (+) lead in that order (photo).
2 Unscrew the nuts from the battery retaining bar and unhook the down rods and lift the components away.
3 Lift the battery carefully from its tray and mounting platform.
4 Refitting is a reversal of removal.

4 Alternator - precautions and maintenance

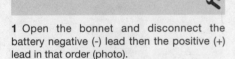

1 The alternator can be damaged if the following precautions are not observed.
2 Never connect the battery leads incorrectly.
3 Never run the engine with the alternator multi-plug disconnected.
4 Do not pull off a battery lead as a means of stopping the engine.
5 When charging the battery from the mains, disconnect it from the car's electrical system or remove it.
6 When using electric welding equipment on the car, always disconnect both battery leads and the alternator multi-plug.
7 Do not operate the starter motor if the engine earth lead is not connected.
8 Regularly inspect the condition of the alternator drivebelt and if frayed or cut, renew

it. To do this, slacken the alternator mounting and adjuster link bolts and move the alternator as far as it will go towards the engine. Slip the belt off the pulleys. If it is tight, press the belt against the rim of a pulley while the crankshaft pulley bolt is turned. The belt will then ride up the pulley rim and come off (photo). **Note:** *On 1.6 litre models the access to adjust and remove the alternator belt is from below. This is done after raising and supporting the right-hand front of the car.*
9 Fit the new belt using the same method (photo).
10 To tension the drivebelt, pull the alternator away from the engine as far as it will come and nip up the adjuster link bolt. At the mid-point of the longest run of the belt, it should deflect by the specified amount under finger pressure. If further tension is required, prise the alternator away from the engine using a piece of wood or the handle of a hammer. Keep the prising force applied while the adjuster link bolt is tightened.
11 Once the belt tension is correct, tighten the alternator mounting bolt.
12 Drivebelt tension should be checked and adjusted at the intervals specified in Routine Maintenance. If a new belt has been fitted, check its tension after the first few miles of operation.
13 Apart from keeping the outside of the casing clean and the connecting leads secure, no further maintenance is required to the alternator.
14 If an air conditioner is fitted, then the compressor drivebelt will have to be removed (see Chapter 2) before the alternator drivebelt can be removed.

5 Alternator - removal and refitting

1 Disconnect the battery.
2 Disconnect the leads from the rear of the alternator. On 1.6 models, release the dipstick guide tube from the camshaft cover.
3 Remove the drivebelt as described in the preceding Section.
4 Remove the alternator mounting and adjuster link bolts and remove the unit from the engine compartment (photo).
5 Refitting is a reversal of removal, tension the drivebelt as described in the preceding Section.

6 Alternator - overhaul

1 Renewal of the brushes should be the limit of overhaul work to the alternator. If the unit has covered a high mileage, exchange it for a new or factory reconditioned assembly. Renewal of several internal components will prove more expensive than the price of a complete alternator.

Hitachi

2 To renew the brushes, unscrew the nuts and take off the rear cover (photos) .
3 Remove the brush holder with brushes. If the brushes have worn down or nearly down

5.4 Alternator mounting bolt

6.2A Alternator rear cover

6.2B Removing alternator rear cover

12

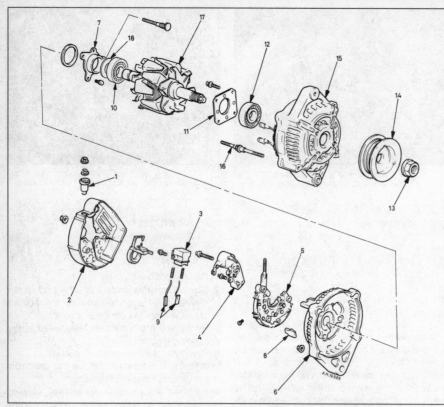

6.3A Removing alternator brush holder

6.3B Alternator brush holder with brushes

Fig. 12.1 Exploded view of Hitachi alternator (Sec 6)

1 Terminal insulator	6 Rear housing	10 Bearing	15 Stator
2 Rear end cover	7 Bearing housing	11 Bearing retainer	16 Tie-bolt
3 Brush holder	and oil seal	12 Bearing	17 Rotor
4 Voltage regulator	8 Insulator	13 Pulley nut	18 Spacer
5 Diode assembly	9 Brushes	14 Pulley	

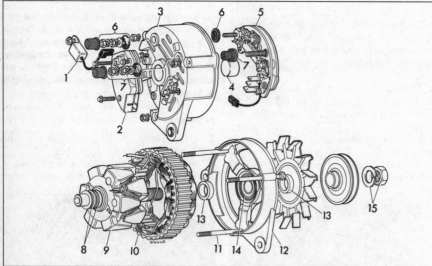

Fig. 12.2 Components of the Lucas type alternator (Sec 6)

1 Suppressor	7 Terminal parts (10.0 mm)	12 Drive end bracket
2 Regulator/brush box	8 Slip rings	13 Spacer
3 Slip ring end bracket	9 Rotor	14 Bearing
4 Bearing	10 Stator	15 Pulley nut and spring
5 Rectifier	11 Tie-bolts	washer
6 Terminal parts (8.0 mm)		

to their limit (see Specifications) then the brush holder assembly must be renewed (photo).

4 While the brush holder is out, take the opportunity to clean the slip rings with a fuel-soaked rag or very fine glasspaper if they are severely discoloured.

5 Fit the brush holder and the rear cover.

Lucas

6 The brush holder/voltage regulator unit can be removed from the rear of the alternator after undoing its securing screws. Disconnect the lead as the unit is withdrawn.

7 Inspect the brushes and clean the slip rings as described in paragraphs 3 and 4.

8 If new brushes can be obtained separately, the old brushes can be unsoldered and the new ones soldered into place. Some skill with a soldering iron is required.

9 Reconnect the brush holder/voltage regulator unit and secure it with the screws.

7 Starter motor - testing, removal and refitting

1 Failure of the starter motor to operate at all or to turn too slowly to start the engine may be due to a discharged battery or loose leads at the battery terminals.

2 Check the leads at the starter motor terminals for security.

3 Listen for the starter motor solenoid 'clicking' when the ignition key is turned to the

7.5 Starter motor solenoid terminals

7.7 Starter motor location

8.3 Removing starter motor dust cover

start position. If this cannot be heard when the battery is known to be fully charged, suspect a faulty solenoid.

4 To remove the starter motor, disconnect the battery negative lead.

5 Disconnect the starter motor leads. On 1.6 automatic transmission models, disconnect the knock sensor multi-plug (photo).

6 On 1.6 manual transmission models, remove the air cleaner.

7 Unscrew the mounting bolts and withdraw the starter motor from the flywheel or torque converter (automatic transmission) housing (photo) .

8 Refitting is a reversal of removal.

8 Starter motor (Hitachi) - overhaul

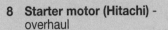

1 If the starter motor has given good service over a high mileage then overhaul work should be limited to the operations described in this Section. The renewal of other internal components, bearings etc., will not prove an economic proposition and it will be better to exchange the starter for a new or factory reconditioned unit.

2 Disconnect the link cable from the solenoid and then unscrew the nuts which hold the solenoid to the starter motor.

3 Prise off the dust cover from the centre of the starter motor rear cover. On some starters the dust cover is held by two screws (Fig. 12.3) (photo).

4 Remove the U-shaped lockplate, coil spring

and washer. Some versions have an E-clip and washer (photos).

5 Unscrew the tie-bolts.

6 Withdraw the end cover and drivegear end bracket from the field coil housing (photo).

7 Inspect the brushes in the brush holder. If the brushes have worn down to or nearly down to their wear limit (see Specifications), then they must be renewed by unsoldering the old ones and soldering on the new.

HAYNES HiNT

When using the soldering iron on the field coil brushes, use a pair of pliers as a heat sink as shown, to prevent damage to the field coils.

Do not allow solder to run down the brush leads or their flexibility will be ruined.

8 Inspect the commutator, if discoloured clean it with a petrol moistened cloth or if very dirty use very fine glasspaper.

9 Check that the mica separators of the commutator are undercut to the correct depth. If not, use a thin hacksaw blade keeping the corners of the undercut square.

8.4A Removing starter motor E-clip

10 A worn or faulty pinion/clutch assembly may be renewed by tapping the stop collar up the armature shaft to expose the jump ring. Remove the ring and slide the pinion assembly off the shaft.

11 Use a new jump ring when refitting. The collar can be drawn down over the jump ring using a small two-legged puller.

12 Reassembly is a reversal of dismantling. Apply a smear of molybdenum disulphide grease to the bearings and friction surfaces.

13 Check that the brushes slide freely in their guides and use a hooked piece of wire to lift them onto the commutator as the holder is located (photo) .

14 When the starter is fully reassembled, slide the drive pinion along the armature shaft and using a feeler gauge, check the clearance between the end of the pinion and its stop. This should be between 0.1 and 4.0 mm (0.004 and 0.157 in). If the clearance is outside this tolerance, change the stop for one of different thickness.

8.4B Starter motor thrust washer

8.6 Removing starter motor end cover

8.13 Releasing a brush spring

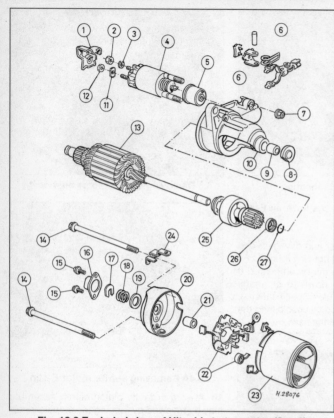

Fig. 12.3 Exploded view of Hitachi starter motor (Sec 8)

1 Cover	10 Drivegear end	18 Coil spring
2 Nut	bracket	19 Washer
3 Spring washer	11 Washer	20 End cover
4 Solenoid	12 Nut	21 Bearing
5 Cover	13 Armature	22 Brush holder plate
6 Engagement lever	14 Tie-bolt	23 Field coils and yoke
7 Mounting nut	15 Screw	24 Clip
8 End cap	16 End cap	25 Pinion/clutch
9 Bearing	17 U-shaped	26 Stop collar
	lockplate	27 Jump ring

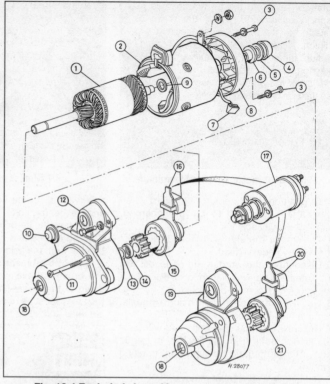

Fig. 12.4 Exploded view of Lucas starter motor (Sec 9)

1 Armature	11 Bracket screws	17 Solenoid
2 Field coils and	12 Drive end bracket	18 Bush
yoke	(manual	19 Drive end bracket
3 Tie-bolt	transmission)	(automatic
4 End cap	13 Jump ring	transmission)
5 Spire washer	14 Thrust collar	20 Engagement lever
6 Bush	15 Drive/clutch	(automatic
7 Field brush	assembly (manual	transmission)
8 Commutator end	transmission)	21 Drivegear/clutch
bracket	16 Engagement lever	(automatic
10 Cap	(manual	transmission)
	transmission)	

9 Starter motor (Lucas) - overhaul

1 Refer to paragraph 1 of the preceding Section.
2 With the starter motor removed from the car, clean away external dirt.
3 Disconnect the lead from the solenoid STA terminal.
4 Extract the two solenoid securing screws, withdraw the solenoid and disconnect the solenoid plunger from the engagement lever.
5 Refer to Fig. 12.4 and remove the end cap and spare washer. The latter will be destroyed and must be renewed.
6 Mark the relationship of the field coil yoke to the drive end bracket by scribing a line across the joint.
7 Unscrew the two tie-bolts and withdraw the end bracket to expose the brushes. Release

the field brushes from the brush box and remove the end bracket.
8 Renew the brushes and the drive assembly if necessary as described in the preceding Section.
9 The face type commutator may be cleaned with very fine glasspaper, but do not attempt to undercut its mica segments.
10 Once the starter motor has been reassembled insert a spacer to set the pinion to dimension A (Fig. 12.5). Press the solenoid

Fig. 12.5 Lucas starter motor pinion setting diagram (Sec 9)

1 Solenoid pressed fully in
2 Adjuster screw
3 Pinion pressed fully in
A Pinion setting dimension
Manual transmission
    44.1 to 44.6 mm (1.746 to 1.754 in)
Automatic transmission
    21.0 to 21.2 mm (0.826 to 0.834 in)

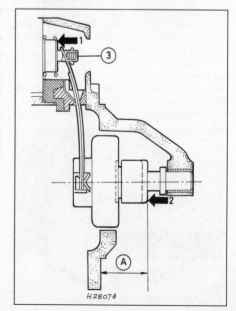

plunger fully into the body and then use a spring balance to check the force being exerted on the temporary spacer by the drive pinion. This should be between 13 and 17 lb. Adjust the screw if necessary using an Allen key to obtain the specified force.
11 Lock the adjuster screw with a suitable sealant on completion.

10 Fuses and relays

1 Three main fusible links are located in the engine compartment. Should one of these blow at any time, do not renew it until the charging circuit has been checked and tested by your dealer or an auto electrical engineer (photo).
2 The fuses which protect all the other electrical circuits in the car are located in the fusebox under the facia panel (photos).
3 The fuse ratings and circuits protected are given in the Specifications Section at the beginning of this Chapter.
4 If a fuse blows, renew it with one of identical rating. Never substitute anything for the correct type of fuse. If the new fuse blows immediately, check and rectify the problem, usually shorting of a wire due to chafed insulation.
5 Relays for the intermittent windscreen wiper and direction indicator/hazard warning

10.1 Fusible links

systems are plugged into the fuse block. Other relays are located in the engine compartment or beside the front footwells and include those for the following circuits:
    Heated rear window
    Power-operated windows
    Headlamp washers
    Air conditioning
    Inlet manifold heater and fuel pump
    (1.6 models)
6 A trailer flasher relay may be found suspended under the instrument panel to the right of the steering column (photo).
7 The location of most relays is indicated in the wiring harness layouts at the end of this Chapter.

11 Switches - removal and refitting

Steering column switch

1 Disconnect the battery negative lead.
2 Remove the steering wheel and the steering column shrouds as described in Chapter 10.
3 Disconnect the switch wiring multi-plugs.
4 Pull the direction indicator cancelling sleeve from the steering shaft.
5 Extract the two screws which hold the switch to its bracket and remove the switch.
6 When refitting, make sure that the cancelling sleeve is pushed fully home.
7 When fitting the steering wheel, check that the lugs engage correctly with the cut-outs in the cancelling cam before tightening the securing nut to the specified torque.

Heated rear window switch

8 Disconnect the battery negative lead.
9 Carefully prise the switch from the facia panel. Disconnect the multi-plug from the switch.
10 Refitting is a reversal of removal.

Rear fog warning lamp switch

11 The operations are as described for the heated rear window switch.

Central door lock switch

12 Have the driver's door window fully raised and disconnect the battery.
13 Remove the door trim panel and waterproof sheet as described in Chapter 11.
14 Disconnect the switch wiring multi-plug.
15 Extract the fixing screws and remove the switch from the door.
16 Refitting is a reversal of removal, but make sure that the switch operating arm is correctly engaged with the peg on the door lock.

Power-operated window switch

17 Disconnect the battery and then remove the door trim panel as described in Chapter 11.
18 Disconnect the wiring plug and extract the screws which hold the switch to the trim panel.
19 Refitting is a reversal of removal.

Instrument panel lamp dimmer switch (rheostat)

20 Disconnect the battery and remove the facia panel access under cover.
21 Reach up behind the switch and disconnect the multi-plug.
22 Prise off the switch knob and remove the plain washer.
23 Unscrew the bezel nut and remove the switch from the facia panel.
24 Refitting is a reversal of removal.

Ignition switch

25 Disconnect the battery and remove the steering column shrouds (Chapter 10).
26 insert the ignition key into the lock.
27 Disconnect the wiring harness plug.
28 Extract the two switch fixing screws and remove the switch from the lock.
29 Refitting is a reversal of removal, but make sure that as the switch is fitted to the lock, the tang on the lock barrel enters the recess in the switch.

Heater blower switch

30 This is described in Chapter 2.

10.2A Fuse cover and diagram

10.2B Fuse block
1 *Wiper intermittent relay*
2 *Direction indicator/hazard warning relay*

10.6 Trailer flasher relay

11.31 Glovebox lamp switch

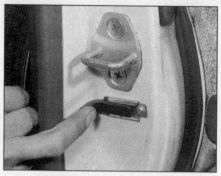
11.32 Courtesy lamp switch

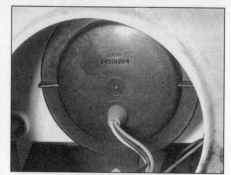
12.2A Headlamp rear cover

Glovebox lamp switch

31 Access is obtained by removing the glovebox. Disconnect the wiring plugs and pull the switch from its mounting bracket while holding the retaining tags squeezed inwards (photo).

Courtesy lamp switch

32 These are of sliding type and control the interior lamp (photo).
33 Extract the screw which holds the switch to the body pillar, withdraw the switch and disconnect the leads.
34 Tape the leads to the body to prevent them from slipping into the pillar interior.
35 When refitting the switch, smear the contacts with petroleum jelly to prevent corrosion.

12 Exterior bulbs - renewal

Headlamp

1 Open the bonnet.
2 Rotate the cover on the back of the headlamp in an anti-clockwise direction and withdraw it until the connector plug can be pulled from the bulb spade terminals (photos).
3 Prise back the spring clips and remove the bulb (photos).
4 Fit the new bulb, avoiding touching the glass with the fingers. If it is inadvertently touched, clean it with methylated spirit.

5 When fitting the rear cover, make sure that the drain hole is at the bottom.

Front parking lamp

6 This bulb is a push fit in the headlamp reflector. Access to it is as described for the headlamp bulb.

Front direction indicator lamp

7 Extract the lens fixing screws and pull the lens gently from the car (photo).
8 Twist the bulbholder to remove and then take out the bulb which is of bayonet fitting type (photo).

Rear lamp bulbs

9 Working inside the luggage boot, turn the

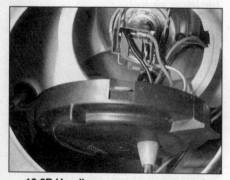
12.2B Headlamp rear cover removed

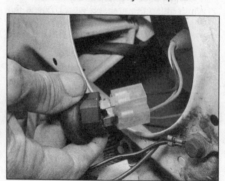
12.2C Headlamp wiring plug

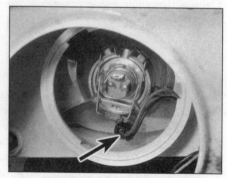
12.3A Front parking lamp bulb

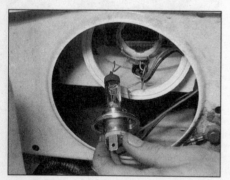
12.3B Headlamp halogen type bulb

12.7 Removing front direction indicator lamp lens screw

12.8 Front indicator bulb and holder

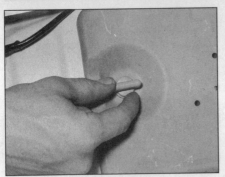

12.9 Rear lamp cluster cover plate

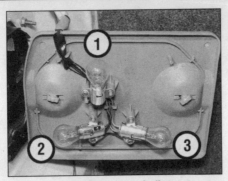

12.10 Rear lamp bulbs

1 Direction indicator   2 and 3 Stop/tail

12.12 Rear number plate lamp and bulb

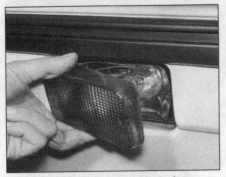

12.14A Rear fog guard lamp lens

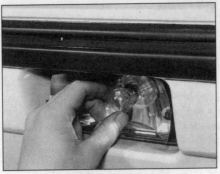

12.14B Rear fog guard lamp bulb

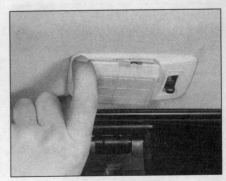

13.1 Interior lamp lens

quick release retainers through half a turn and remove the cover plate (photo).

10 Remove the bayonet fitting type bulb noting that the twin filament stop/tail bulb has offset pins and it will only fit in its holder in one position (photo).

Rear number plate lamp

11 Press the lamp in the forward direction and remove it from the bumper.

12 Twist the bulbholder in an anti-clockwise direction to release it from the lamp body (photo).

13 The bulb is of wedge base type and is simply pulled from its holder.

Reverse and rear fog warning lamps

14 Access to the bulbs is obtained by extracting the screws and taking off the lens. The bulb is of bayonet fitting type (photos).

13 Interior bulbs - renewal

Interior lamp

1 Prise the lens carefully from the lamp (photo).

2 Pull the festoon type bulb from its contacts and push the new one into place.

3 Refit the lens.

Switch illuminating lamps

4 Reach up behind the heated rear window or rear fog warning switch and push it from the facia panel.

5 Pull off the wiring plug and then turn the bulbholder in an anti-clockwise direction to remove it.

6 Renew the bulb, refit the holder and the switch.

Ashtray lamp

7 Remove the ashtray.

8 Extract the screws from the ashtray carrier and lower the carrier.

9 Twist the bulbholder in an anti-clockwise direction and renew the wedge type bulb.

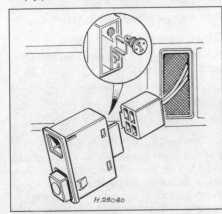

Fig. 12.6 Push-button switch and bulb (Sec 13)

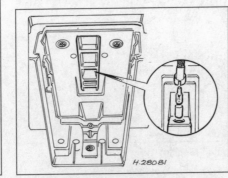

Fig. 12.7 Ashtray lamp bulb (Sec 13)

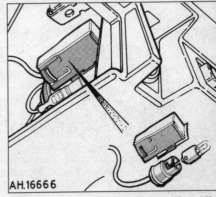

Fig. 12.8 Cigar lighter lamp bulb (Sec 13)

12

13.14A Instrument panel bulb renewable after instrument panel withdrawn

13.14B Instrument panel bulb renewable without removing instrument panel

13.14C Instrument panel bulb renewable without removing instrument panel

13.15 Luggage boot lamp

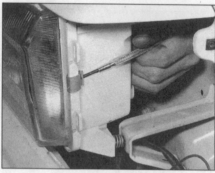

14.1 Headlamp lens clip

15.4 Extracting a headlamp upper fixing screw

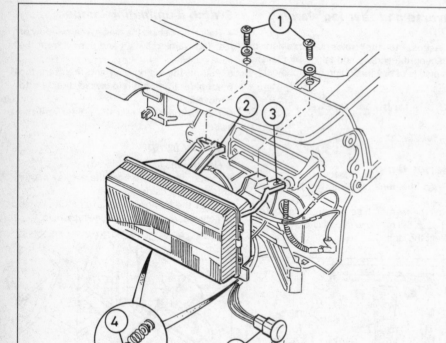

Fig. 12.9 Headlamp unit (Sec 14)

1 Upper fixing screws
2 Beam alignment screw (horizontal)
3 Beam alignment screw (vertical)
4 Headlamp lower fixing screws
5 Wiring connector plug

Cigar lighter lamp

10 Withdraw the lighter element.
11 Remove the ashtray and lower the ashtray carrier.
12 Slacken the locking ring and rotate the lighter unit until the hood can be squeezed and released from the unit.
13 Remove the bulbholder from the hood.
14 Renew the bulb which is of bayonet fitting type.

Warning and instrument panel lamps

15 The instrument panel must be released and pulled forward for access to these lamps. Refer to Section 17. Some upper bulbs are accessible after removal of the hood from the instrument panel (see Section 17) (photos).

Glove compartment lamp

16 Open the glove compartment and prise out the lens (photo).

14 Headlamp lens -
removal and refitting

1 In the event of damage to the headlamp lens, only a complete headlamp assembly is obtainable from Rover dealers or Lucas electrical factors. If a second-hand lens can be obtained, it can be fitted after releasing the spring clips, removing the old lens and clipping the new lens into place (photo).

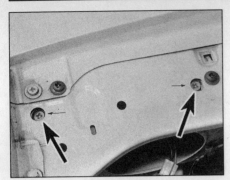

16.2 Headlamp beam alignment screws (arrowed)

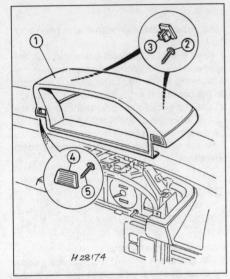

Fig. 12.10 Instrument panel hood (Sec 17)

1 Hood   4 Blanking plate
2 Screw   5 Screw
3 Blanking plate

15 Headlamp - removal and refitting

1 Refer to Chapter 11 and remove the radiator grille and the front bumper.
2 Remove the front parking lamp lens.

17.1A Instrument panel hood front screw blanking plate

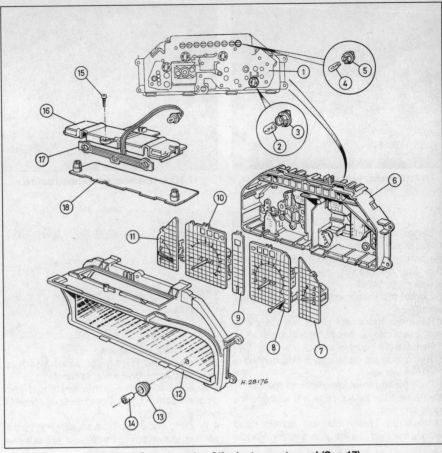

Fig. 12.11 Components of the instrument panel (Sec 17)

1 Printed circuit
2 Bulb
3 Bulbholder
4 Bulb
5 Bulbholder
6 Instrument panel
7 Fuel gauge
8 Speedometer
9 Blanking panel
10 Tachometer
11 Coolant temperature gauge
12 Lens and frame
13 Grommet
14 Speedometer odometer reset knob
15 Fixing screw
16 Lens cover
17 Illumination circuit board
18 Instrument illumination lens

3 Disengage the wiring multi-plug.

4 Extract the two lower and two upper headlamp fixing screws. Remove the unit (photo).

5 Refitting is a reversal of removal. Check the headlamp beam alignment.

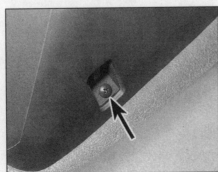

17.1B Instrument panel hood screw

16 Headlamp beam alignment

1 It is recommended that this is carried out by a service station having the necessary optical beam setting equipment.

2 In an emergency, the adjustment screws shown in the photograph may be turned to give an acceptable light pattern (photo).

17 Instrument panel - removal and refitting

1 Prise out the blanking plates which cover the hood securing screws. These are brittle, so exercise care (photos).

2 Extract the screws now exposed and remove the hood.

12

17.1C Instrument panel hood screw blanking plate

17.1D Instrument panel hood screw

17.5 Instrument panel fixing screw (hood removed)

3 Disconnect the battery.
4 Reach behind the instrument panel, press the arm of the speedometer cable retaining clip and disconnect the cable from the speedometer head.
5 Extract the instrument panel fixing screws (photo).
6 Raise the instrument panel until the wiring multi-plugs can be disconnected (photo).
7 Remove the panel (photos).
8 The instrument panel may be dismantled in the following way.
9 Prise the trip reset knob from its spindle.
10 Release the plastic clips and separate the panel and lens.
11 Unscrew the nuts or screws and remove the instruments as necessary. Handle

the printed circuit with care using clean hands.
12 Refitting is a reversal of removal.

18 Speedometer drive cable - renewal

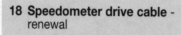

1 Disconnect the battery.
2 Remove the instrument panel hood as described in the preceding Section.
3 Reach behind the instrument panel and disconnect the cable from the speedometer head (photo).
4 Working under the facia panel, remove the access under cover panel and release the

speedometer cable grommet and boot from the bulkhead.
5 Feed the speedometer cable through the bulkhead into the engine compartment.
6 Working at the transmission. pull the boot up the cable and extract the spring clip which retains the cable. On no account remove the bolt or lockplate or the pinion might drop into the transmission (photo).
7 Fit the new cable by reversing the removal operations.

19 Clock - removal and refitting

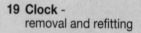

1 Disconnect the battery.
2 Using a small screwdriver, carefully prise the clock from the facia panel until the wiring harness can be disconnected.
3 Refit the clock by reversing the removal operations.
4 The clock normally only displays when the ignition is on, but if the ignition is off, it will display if the button cover panel is pressed in (photo) .
5 To set the clock depress the centre MIN button until the minutes are correct.
6 Depress the left-hand HOUR button until the hour is correct.
7 If it is wished to synchronise the clock with a radio time signal or another clock, set the

17.6 Instrument panel multi-plug

17.7A Instrument panel removed

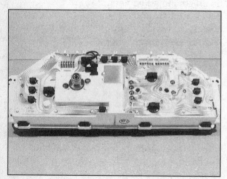

17.7B Rear view of instrument panel

18.3 Speedometer cable connector at head

18.6 Speedometer cable connecting clip at transmission

19.4 Pressing clock setting button cover panel

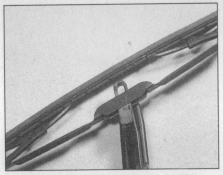

20.3 Wiper blade to arm connection

20.6 Unscrewing wiper arm nut

car clock to within a few minutes before the hour. As the time signal is heard, depress the reset button on the car clock.

20 Windscreen wiper blades and arms - removal and refitting

1 The wiper blades should be renewed as soon as they cease to clean the glass without leaving streaks.
2 Lift the wiper arm from the screen until it locks.
3 Turn the blade through 90°, depress the retaining tab with the thumb nail and slide the blade down the arm until it can be withdrawn over the hook of the arm (photo).
4 Refit the new blade, pushing it fully into the hook until it locks.
5 To remove a wiper arm, have the arm in the parked position. Run some masking tape along the edge of the blades on the glass as a guide to refitting the arms.
6 Unscrew the domed nut and remove the wiper arm from the splined spindle (photo).
7 Refit by reversing the removal procedure.

21 Windscreen wiper motor and linkage - removal and refitting

1 Remove the wiper arms as described in the preceding Section.

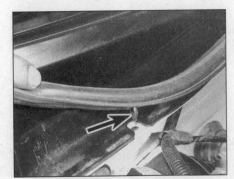

21.2 Weatherstrip with plastic pins

2 Open the bonnet and pull off the rubber weatherstrip from the front edge. The weatherstrip incorporates plastic pins which serve to hold the front edge of the scuttle plastic cover (air scoop) (photo).
3 Prise out the circular plastic blanking plates

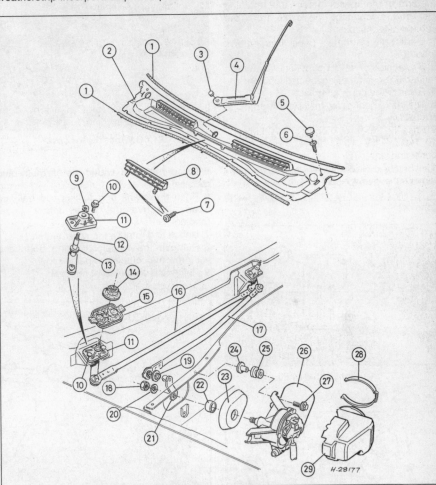

Fig. 12.12 Windscreen wiper components (Sec 21)

1 Weatherseal	9 Circlip	17 Link rod	24 Ferrule
2 Air scoop	10 Bolt	18 Nut	25 Mounting cushion
3 Domed nut	11 Spindle housing	19 Dust seal	26 Wiper motor
4 Wiper arm	12 Splined spindle	20 Spring washer	27 Motor mounting
5 Cover	13 Washer	21 Crank arm	bolt
6 Screw	14 Spindle seal	22 Spacer	28 Spring clip
7 Fixing screw	15 Shield	23 Shield	29 Cover
8 Air intake grille	16 Connecting rod		

12

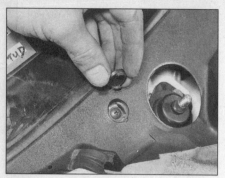

21.3 Scuttle plate screw cover plate

21.4A Scuttle grille

21 .4B Removing scuttle air scoop

21.6A Wiper motor crankarm and link

21.6B Wiper motor cover

just below the windscreen and extract the exposed screws (photo).
4 Remove the scuttle plastic cover (air scoop) (photos).

5 Disconnect the wiper motor multi-plug (photos).
6 Prise the crank arm to link rod balljoint apart. Remove the wiper motor cover (photos).
7 Unbolt and remove the wiper motor.
8 Remove the wheelbox fixing bolts and withdraw the complete wiper linkage.
9 Refitting is a reversal of removal.

22 Washer system

1 Depending upon the car model, a windscreen washer system may be fitted only, or a combined windscreen and headlamp washer system.
2 The reservoir capacity differs between the two systems and two independent electric pumps are used where a windscreen and headlamp washer are fitted.
3 The pumps are detachable from the reservoirs after disconnecting the wiring plugs and tubes.

> **HAYNES HiNT** *When removing a tube from a pump or jet nozzle, warm the tube with a rag soaked in boiling water otherwise the nozzle may fracture.*

4 The jets may be adjusted by inserting a pin into the nozzles.

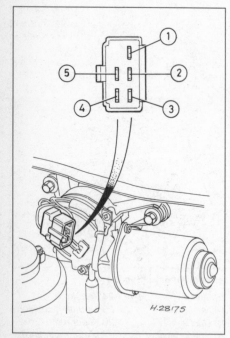

Fig. 12.13 Wiper motor terminals (Sec 21)

1 Blue/yellow   4 Blue/white
2 Blue   5 Green/black
3 Black

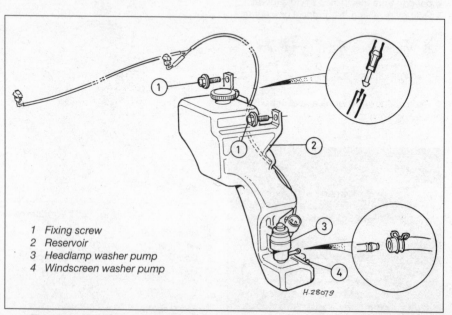

1 Fixing screw
2 Reservoir
3 Headlamp washer pump
4 Windscreen washer pump

Fig. 12.14 Combined windscreen and headlamp washer fluid reservoir (Sec 22)

24.11 Using DIN tools to remove radio/cassette unit

25.2 Extracting aerial mounting base screw

mountings. Draw it from its recess and disconnect the wiring from it.

13 When refitting, connect the wiring, then push the radio home until it clicks into place. Recover the removal tools.

5 Do not use household detergent or cooling system antifreeze in the washer reservoir or the pumps and car paintwork will be damaged.

6 In very cold weather, a little methylated spirit may be added to the reservoir in addition to the normal mixture of water and screen cleaning fluid.

23 Heated rear screen

1 To prevent damage to the elements of the heated rear window, observe the following precautions:

(a) *Clean the interior surface of the glass with a damp cloth or chamois leather, rubbing in the direction that the elements run*

(b) *Avoid scratching the elements with rings on the fingers or contact with articles in the luggage compartment*

(c) *Do not stick adhesive labels over the elements*

2 Should the element be broken, it can be repaired using a conductive silver paint, without the need to remove the glass from the window.

3 The paint is available from many sources and should be applied with a soft brush to a really clean surface. Use two strips of masking tape as a guide to the thickness of the element to be repaired.

4 Allow the new paint to dry thoroughly before switching the heater on.

24 Radio/cassette player - removal and refitting

1 All models are supplied with a windscreen pillar aerial and either a radio or radio/cassette player depending upon the particular vehicle specifications.

2 The leads and connecting plugs at the back of the radio are accessible on certain models without having to remove the receiver if the facia panel under cover is removed and the hand inserted round behind the radio.

3 To remove the radio/cassette player, carry out the following operations.

Standard fitting

4 Disconnect the battery negative lead.

5 On 1.3 models, remove the choke control knob. Undo the retaining nut and release the choke control.

6 On all models, prise the knobs off the heater controls, then prise the heater control plate out of the facia. Move the plate aside without disconnecting the leads from it.

7 Carefully pull off the radio knobs and bezels. Remove the two nuts now exposed and lift off the finisher plate.

8 Open the glovebox to gain access to the rear of the radio. Push the front of the radio into the facia and remove the mounting plate, then pull it outwards and disconnect the aerial plug and multi-plug from it.

9 Refit by reversing the removal operations.

DIN fitting

10 Two DIN removal tools will be needed. These should have been supplied with the radio; if not, they can be obtained from car audio specialists.

11 Insert the removal tools into the holes in the radio face plate (photo).

12 Pull the tools away from each other and into the vehicle to release the radio from its

25 Aerial - removal and refitting

1 Remove the facia undercover from the side on which the aerial is located.

2 Extract the screws from the aerial mounting base at the top of the windscreen pillar (photo).

3 Reach behind the radio and disconnect the aerial lead.

4 Withdraw the aerial and lead upwards out of the pillar. A length of cord should be securely taped to the end of the aerial lead so that it can be drawn through the pillar and used to guide the new aerial lead through the pillar cavity.

5 If a new aerial is fitted, always adjust the aerial trim. This is done by tuning in to a station with low signal strength on the medium wave band. Using a small screwdriver turn the trim screw provided in the radio in or our until the loudest volume is obtained.

26 Electrically-operated windows

1 The system is controlled by a master switch on the driver's door and individual switches on the other doors.

2 The electric motor and regulator mechanism are accessible once the door trim panel has been removed as described in Chapter 11.

3 Always disconnect the battery before working on the components. A fault in the lift motor should be rectified by renewing the motor.

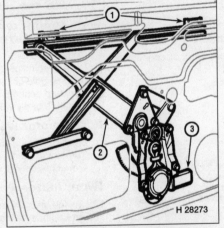

Fig. 12.15 Front door power-operated window mechanism (Sec 26)

1 *Glass lifting pads*   3 *Electric motor*
2 *Regulator unit*

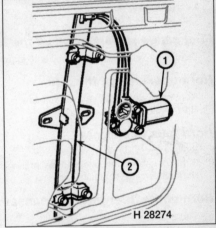

Fig. 12.16 Rear door power-operated window mechanism (Sec 26)

1 *Electric motor*   2 *Regulator*

12

27 Central door locking

1 The master switch which operates all door locks is controlled from the driver's door lock or lock plunger.
2 The lock plunger on the other doors, if lifted, will unlock only the relevant door.
3 Always disconnect the battery before removing any part of the system.

4 To remove the central locking control unit, slide the driver's seat fully to the rear. Unbolt the control unit mounting plate, disconnect the wiring multi-plug and unclip the control unit from the plate. Where more than one control unit is fitted, the central locking unit is on the left-hand side of the mounting plate.
5 Removal and refitting procedures for the door lock motors will be found in the Supplement at the end of this manual.

28 Horns

1 The horns are located below the headlamps within the bumper.
2 Although the horns normally require no attention, if they must be removed, then the headlamps and front bumper must be removed (Section 15). See also Chapter 11.
3 Apply silicone grease to the horn terminals when refitting to prevent corrosion.

Fault finding - electrical system

Alternator not charging*

☐ Drivebelt loose and slipping, or broken
☐ Brushes worn, sticking, broken or dirty
☐ Brush springs weak or broken
*If all appears to be well but the alternator is still not charging, take the car to an automobile electrician for checking of the alternator

Battery will not hold charge for more than a few days

☐ Battery defective internally
☐ Electrolyte level too low or electrolyte too weak due to leakage
☐ Plate separators no longer fully effective
☐ Battery plates severely sulphated
☐ Drivebelt slipping
☐ Battery terminal connections loose or corroded
☐ Alternator not charging properly
☐ Short in lighting circuit causing continual battery drain

Ignition light fails to go out, battery runs flat in a few days

☐ Drivebelt loose and slipping, or broken
☐ Alternator faulty

Fuel gauge gives no reading

☐ Fuel tank empty!
☐ Electric cable between tank sender unit and gauge earthed or loose
☐ Fuel gauge case not earthed
☐ Fuel gauge supply cable interrupted
☐ Fuel gauge unit broken

Fuel gauge registers full all the time

☐ Electric cable between tank unit and gauge broken or disconnected

Horn operates all the time

☐ Horn push either earthed or stuck down
☐ Horn cable to horn push earthed

Horn fails to operate

☐ Blown fuse
☐ Cable or cable connections loose, broken or disconnected
☐ Horn has an internal fault

Horn emits intermittent or unsatisfactory noise

☐ Cable connections loose
☐ Horn incorrectly adjusted

Lights do not come on

☐ If engine not running, battery discharged
☐ Light bulb filament burnt out or bulbs broken
☐ Wire connections loose, disconnected or broken
☐ Light switch shorting or otherwise faulty

Lights come on but fade out

☐ If engine not running, battery discharged

Lights give very poor illumination

☐ Lamp glasses dirty
☐ Reflector tarnished or dirty
☐ Lamps badly out of adjustment
☐ Incorrect bulb with too low wattage fitted
☐ Existing bulbs old and badly discoloured
☐ Electric wiring too thin not allowing full current to pass

Lights work erratically, flashing on and off, especially over bumps

☐ Battery terminals or earth connections loose
☐ Lights not earthing properly
☐ Contacts in light switch faulty

Wiper motor fails to work

☐ Blown fuse
☐ Wire connections loose, disconnected or broken
☐ Brushes badly worn
☐ Armature worn or faulty

Wiper motor works very slowly and takes excessive current

☐ Commutator dirty, greasy or burnt
☐ Drive to spindles bent or unlubricated
☐ Drive spindle binding or damaged
☐ Armature bearings dry or unaligned
☐ Armature badly worn or faulty

Wiper motor works slowly and takes little current

☐ Brushes badly worn
☐ Commutator dirty, greasy or burnt
☐ Armature badly worn or faulty

Wiper motor works but wiper blades remain static

☐ Linkage disengaged or faulty
☐ Drive spindle damaged or worn
☐ Wiper motor gearbox parts badly worn

Chapter 13 Supplement:
Revisions and information on later models

Contents

Degrees of difficulty

Easy, suitable for novice with little experience	**Fairly easy,** suitable for beginner with some experience	**Fairly difficult,** suitable for competent DIY mechanic	**Difficult,** suitable for experienced DIY mechanic	**Very difficult,** suitable for expert DIY or professional

1 Introduction

This Supplement contains information relating to models produced from August 1986 onwards and material which is additional to, or a revision of, that contained in the preceding Chapters. The Sections in this Supplement follow the same order as the Chapters to which they relate, and it is recommended that before any particular operation is undertaken, reference be made to the appropriate Section(s) of the Supplement. In this way, any changes to procedures or components can be noted before referring to the main Chapters.

Project car

The vehicles used in the original preparation of this Supplement and appearing in many of the photographic sequences were a Rover 213 SE Automatic and a Rover 216 EFi Vanden Plas.

2 Specifications

Engine

1.3 engine

Oil pressure:

At 3000 rev/min	3.5 to 4.2 bar (50 to 60 lbf/in²)
Minimum pressure at idle speed of 800 rev/min	0.7 bar (10 lbf/in²)

1.6 engine

Oil pressure (with oil temperature above 40°C/104°F):

At 2500 rev/min	3.75 to 5.5 bar (55 to 80 lbf/in²)
Minimum pressure at idle speed	0.7 bar (10 lbf/in²)

1.6 engine - unleaded with HIF carburettor from 1989

Details as per other 1.6 engine types, but with the following differences:

Engine number prefix	16 HE 58
Compression ratio	9.2:1

Torque wrench settings

	Nm	lbf ft
1.6 engine (from 1987):		
Connecting rod big-end nuts	40	30
Engine/transmission mountings (1.6 engine):		
Right-hand mounting nuts	75	55
Right-hand mounting through-bolt	65	48
Left-hand mounting-to-body bolts	45	33

Cooling system

Antifreeze requirement

1.3 model up to VIN 800 000 (1985 model year)	2.3 litre (4 pints) (50% solution)
1.3 model from VIN 800 000 (1985 model year)	3.2 litre (5.5 pints) (50% solution)
1.6 model	2.1 litre (3.5 pints) (33% solution)

Fuel and exhaust systems

1.6 engine - unleaded with HIF carburettor from 1989 (Engine No. prefix 16 HE 58)

Carburettor specification number	FZX 1478
Fast idle speed	1150 to 1250 rev/min
Fuel octane rating	95 RON (unleaded) or 97 RON (leaded)

Torque wrench setting (1.6 engine from 1987)

	Nm	lbf ft
Exhaust manifold to cylinder head	28	21

Ignition system

1.6 engine - unleaded with HIF carburettor from 1989 (Engine No. prefix 16 HE 58)

Ignition timing:

At 1100 rev/min - vacuum pipe disconnected	11° BTDC
At 1100 rev/min - vacuum pipe connected	28° ± 2° BTDC

Manual transmission

Ratios (Sprint)

As for fuel injection models (see Chapter 6 Specifications)

Driveshafts, hubs, roadwheels and tyres

Roadwheels

Size:

Sprint, 216 SE and Vanden Plas:	
Standard	5J x 13 steel
Optional	5.5J x 14 alloy
Vitesse (later models)	5.5J x 14 alloy

Tyres

Sprint with steel wheel	175/70 SR 13
Sprint with alloy wheel	175/65 TR 14
Vitesse	175/65 TR 14

Tyre pressures in bar (lbf/in²):	Front	Rear
1.3 models	1.8 (26)	1.8 (26)
1.6 models	2.0 (28)	1.8 (26)

Braking system

Disc brakes

Disc diameter - later 1.3 models . . . .   231.0 mm (9.0 in)

Torque wrench setting (from 1987)

	Nm	lbf ft
Caliper mounting bolts	75	55

Suspension and steering

Torque wrench settings (from 1987)

	Nm	lbf ft
Rear suspension:		
Panhard rod nut/bolt	75	55
Trailing arm pivot bolts	61	45
Steering:		
Tie-rod-to-rack locknut	55	40
Tie-rod end balljoint nut	60	44
Steering column coupling bolts	25	18

Bodywork and fittings

Torque wrench setting (from 1987)

	Nm	lbf ft
Seat belt anchorage point bolts	40	30

Electrical system

Starter motor (Lucas)

Type . . . .   Lucas 9M90 (pre-engaged) or Lucas M79 (pre-engaged)
Minimum brush length:
9M90 . . . .   10.0 mm (0.4 in)
M79 . . . .   3.5 mm (0.15 in)
Commutator minimum thickness – 9M90 . . . .   2.0 mm (0.8 in)
Commutator minimum diameter – M79 . . . .   28.8 mm (1.134 in)

Starter motor (Nippondenso)

Minimum brush length . . . .   10.0 mm (0.4 in)

Fuses (August 1986 onwards)

Number	Circuit protected	Rating (amps)
1	Rear fog guard lamps	10
2	Wipers, washers, power window relay	15
3	Direction indicators, reversing lamps	10
4	Alternator, solenoid valve	10
5	LH headlamp (dipped beam)	10
6	RH headlamp (dipped beam)	10
7	LH headlamp (main beam)	10
8	RH headlamp (main beam)	10
9	Horn, stop lamps	15
10	Hazard warning lamps	15
11	Ignition auxiliaries	15
12	Tail, number plate and instrument illumination	15
13	Radiator cooling fan	15
14	Heater fan, heated rear window relay	20
15	Radio	10
16	Heated rear window	20
17	Central locking	15
18	Headlamp washer	20
19	Electric window (front right)	15
20	Electric window (front left)	15
21	Electric window (rear right)	15
22	Electric window (rear left)	15
23	Electric door mirrors	10
24	Electric sunroof	15
25	Spare fuses	15

Capacities

Washer system reservoir - 1.3

Windscreen washer only . . . .   2.2 litres (4.0 pints)
Windscreen/headlamp washer . . . .   5.5 litres (9.5 pints)
Washer system reservoir - 1.6
Windscreen washer only . . . .   2.0 litres (3.5 pints)
Windscreen/headlamp washer . . . .   5.8 litres (10.0 pints)

13

3 Engine (1.3 litre)

Camshaft sprocket and timing belt - refitting

1 The camshaft sprocket used will either be a cast type or a pressed steel type. Although the fitting procedure for both is the same, it should be noted that the steel type does not have an 'UP' timing mark. When refitting the timing belt to this type, it is therefore necessary to align the sprocket timing marks so that they are level with the top surface of the cylinder head, then check that the camshaft is set so that the number 1 cylinder valves are fully closed and the valve rockers are free.

Rocker shafts, camshaft and cylinder head - removal and refitting

2 Proceed as described in Sections 11, 12 and or 13 of Chapter 1 (as applicable), but if a pressed steel type camshaft sprocket is fitted, check it for correct positioning as described in paragraph 1 above before locating the timing belt onto the sprocket.

4 Engine (1.6 litre)

Engine/transmission mountings

When reconnecting the engine/transmission mountings on later models it should be noted that some of the retaining bolt/nut torque wrench settings have been revised. Refer to the Specifications in this Chapter for details.

5 Fuel and exhaust systems

Unleaded fuel - general

1 Unleaded fuel is becoming more widely available in the UK, and in EC countries generally. It is sometimes cheaper than leaded fuel. Its use is desirable on environmental grounds.
2 All 1.3-engined models covered by this manual may be run on unleaded fuel if wished. No modifications are necessary. No harm will result from reverting to leaded fuel if unleaded is not available.
3 Some 1.6 models are capable of running on unleaded fuel, but only if the cylinder head is fitted with suitable valve seat inserts. A fuel advice label is located on the bonnet lock platform.

4 If in any doubt as to which type of fuel to use, consult your Rover dealer for further information.

Tamperproof adjustment screws - caution

5 Certain adjustment points in the fuel system (and elsewhere) are protected by 'tamperproof' caps, plugs or seals. The purpose of such tamperproofing is to discourage, and to detect, adjustment by unqualified operators.
6 In some EC countries (though not yet in the UK) it is an offence to drive a vehicle with missing or broken tamperproof seals.
7 Before disturbing a tamperproof seal, satisfy yourself that you will not be breaking local or national anti-pollution regulations by doing so. Fit a new seal when adjustment is complete when this is required by law.
8 Do not break tamperproof seals on a vehicle which is still under warranty.

Carburettor (1.6 models, later versions) - adjustment

9 When adjusting the throttle lever lost motion gap on later versions of the SU HIF carburettor, adjustment is made on the throttle lever lost motion lugs, and not by a screw as on earlier versions. See Fig. 13.1.

Idle speed and mixture adjustment (fuel injection systems)

10 The procedure in Chapter 3, Section 36 provides basic settings only. If satisfactory running cannot be obtained the vehicle should be professionally adjusted by a Rover dealer or other specialist with the necessary dedicated test equipment.

Fuel cut-off solenoid (fuel injection systems) - general description

11 On later fuel injection systems a fuel cut-off solenoid is mounted in the spill return line. It is wired in series with the fuel temperature switch and, when the fuel temperature switches closes, the cut-off solenoid is energised, closing the spill return line. Fuel pressure in the fuel rail is raised to pump pressure, creating additional fuel availability during hot start conditions, and overcoming vaporisation.

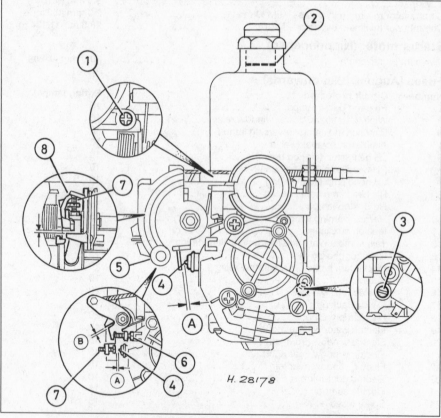

H. 28178

Fig. 13.1 Carburettor (SU HIF) later versions (Sec 5)

1 Idle speed adjustment screw	6 Throttle lever adjustment screw	A Clearance (fast idle pushrod) 0.13 mm (0.005 in) minimum
2 Piston damper oil level	7 Fast idle adjustment screw	B Clearance (lost motion gap) 3.65 to 4.15 mm (0.143 to 0.163 in)
3 Mixture adjustment screw	8 Lost motion adjustment lugs	
4 Fast idle pushrod		
5 Progressive throttle cam		

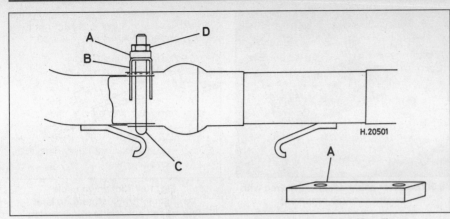

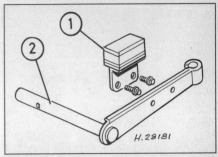

Fig. 13.3 Clutch release arm (2) and damper block (1) – later 1.6 models (Sec 6)

Fig. 13.2 Exhaust vibration counter-measure (1.3 models) (Sec 5)

A Plate (65 x 16 x 5 mm approx)   B Bracket   C U-Bolt   D Nut

Fuel cut-off solenoid - removal and refitting

Caution: Take adequate fire precautions during this procedure

12 Disconnect the battery negative terminal.
13 Disconnect the fuel cut-off solenoid.
14 Remove the screw from the solenoid support bracket on the air cleaner bracket.
15 Remove the fuel hose clips, pull the hoses off the solenoid and lift out the solenoid. Be prepared for fuel spillage.
16 Refit in the reverse sequence, ensuring the connector end of the solenoid forces away from the pressure regulator, and the bracket is uppermost.

Exhaust downpipe vibration (1.3 models)

17 Vibration or resonance in the downpipe spring-loaded balljoint can be cured by attaching a metal plate just in front of the joint, using a standard U-bolt and exhaust bracket. See Fig. 13.2.

6 Clutch

Clutch release arm - 1.6 models

1 The clutch release arm on later models is now fitted with a damper block (see Fig. 13.3). The damper is attached to the arm by two bolts. This fitting does not affect the removal or refitting procedures of any of the clutch system components.

7 Manual transmission

Identification and interchange-ability (1.6 models)

1 Later type manual transmission units differ from early types in respect of certain internal components, and the components are not interchangeable.
2 It is important, therefore, to correctly identify the transmission unit when ordering components for repair purposes.
3 Early transmission units have a gold coloured label and the serial number begins with the figure one. Later types have a white label and the serial number begins with the figure two.

8 Automatic transmission

Transmission fluid (three-speed transmission) - level checking and renewal

1 When checking the automatic transmission fluid level using the procedure described in Chapter 7, Section 3, it should be emphasised that the engine and transmission must be at normal operating temperature, preferably after a short journey.
2 When refilling the transmission after draining, carry out the procedure described in Chapter 7, Section 3, but make a final check of the level with the engine and transmission at normal operating temperature. For clarity the transmission drain plug location is shown in the accompanying photo.

Selector cable (three-speed transmission) - removal and refitting

3 When removing and refitting the selector cable as described in Chapter 7, Section 6, the accompanying photos detail the cable attachment points at the transmission and on the underbody.

Kickdown cable (four-speed transmission) - adjustment

4 The kickdown cable adjustment on later models differs to that described in Chapter 7 as follows, but note that the VIN reference is not available and reference to your Rover dealer will be necessary to decide which adjustment is applicable where this is uncertain.

8.2 Automatic transmission fluid drain plug location (arrowed)

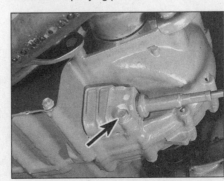

8.3A Selector cable lever attachment at transmission (arrowed)

8.3B Selector cable guide on underbody

13

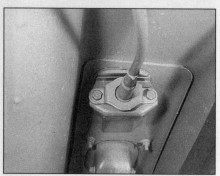

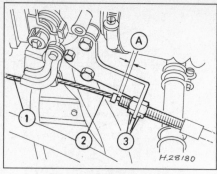

8.3C Selector cable attachment at selector lever

8.3D Selector cable adjuster (viewed with centre console removed)

Fig. 13.4 Kickdown cable arrangement/adjustment on later four-speed automatic transmission model (Sec 8)

1 Throttle cable   3 Adjuster/locknuts
2 Kickdown cable
A Crimped sleeve clearance 0.5 to 1.5 mm (0.02 to 0.04 in)

5 Ensure that the handbrake is fully applied, move the selector lever to the P position, then start the engine and allow it to warm up to its normal operating temperature.

6 With the engine running at its normal idle speed, loosen off the kickdown cable locknuts at the location bracket to release the cable tension (see Fig. 13.4). Measure the clearance between the inner cable crimped sleeve-to-adjuster clearance. This must be between 0.5 to 1.5 mm (0.02 to 0.04 in). If necessary adjust the sleeve to provide this clearance, then retighten the locknuts against the location bracket.

Selector cable (four-speed transmission) - adjustment

7 The information given in paragraph 4 (for the kickdown cable) also applies for the selector cable.

8 Remove the cassette holder by opening it and undoing the two retaining screws.

9 Detach the gear selector knob and remove it together with the spring.

10 Unscrew and remove the upper to lower console retaining screws, release the console, then detach the gear selector plate illumination bulbholder and withdraw the upper console.

11 Loosen the gear selector lever locknut (see Fig. 13.5), move the lever to the '1' position, then rotate the selector lever on the transmission fully anti-clockwise and retighten the cable locknut.

12 Check that the starter motor will only operate when the lever is in the 'P' or 'N' position, then refit the console, gear lever knob (and spring) and the cassette holder.

Selector cable (four-speed transmission) - removal and refitting

13 Before removing the cable, make a sketch of its routing to ensure correct refitting. Remove the centre console.

14 Extract the split pin from the cable clevis pin, then withdraw the clevis pin. Unscrew the cable locknut and withdraw the split olive.

15 In the engine compartment, loosen off the retaining clip and detach the air intake hose from the air cleaner. Detach the air intake hose adaptor from the body crossmember and remove the intake hose.

16 Extract the 'R' clip from the selector cable pin at the lever and collect the two flat washers and the central sleeve.

17 Detach the gaiter from the cable nut, unscrew the nut and release the cable.

18 If a new cable is being fitted, pull back the gaiter from the nut and remove it.

19 Refit in the reverse order of removal. Ensure that the cable is correctly re-routed (as noted during removal). Apply a small amount of grease to the cable pin and lever pivot bush. When reconnecting the cable at the lever end, ensure that the split olive is aligned before tightening the locknut. Lubricate the clevis pin and when fitted, secure it with a new split pin.

20 Check and adjust the cable as described previously in this Section to complete.

Selector lever (four-speed transmission) - removal and refitting

21 Remove the centre console as described in Chapter 11.

22 Position the car over an inspection pit or raise it at the front end and support it on stands.

23 Disconnect the selector cable from the lever as described previously. Recover the split olive.

24 Working underneath the car, disconnect the two selector lever front to floor pan retaining bolts and the four nuts/bolts securing the mounting plate to the floorpan.

25 Pull the lever mounting plate unit up into the car and then remove the console support and rubber seal.

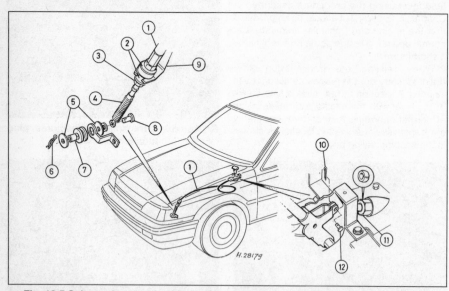

Fig. 13.5 Selector lever and cable on the four-speed automatic transmission (Sec 8)

1 Cable   5 Flat washers   9 Bracket
2 Mounting rubbers   6 'R' clip   10 Split pin
3 Cable nut   7 Sleeve   11 Locknut
4 Gaiter   8 Retaining pin   12 Clevis pin

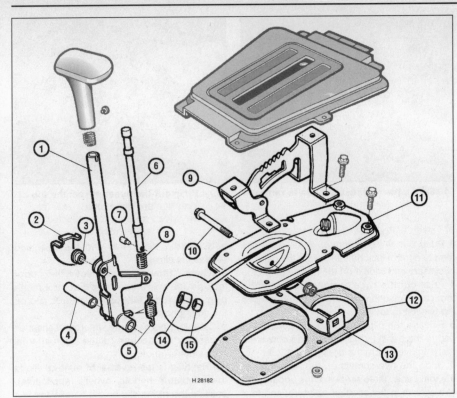

Fig. 13.6 Selector lever components – four-speed automatic transmission (Sec 8)

1 Selector lever	6 Plunger	11 Mounting plate
2 Detent plate	7 Lock pin	12 Rubber seal
3 Detent bush	8 Spring	13 Console support bracket
4 Bush	9 Bracket	14 Locknut
5 Detent plate spring	10 Pivot bolt	15 Olive

26 Detach the spring from the detent plate. Remove the spring, selector bracket detent plate and bush.

27 Undo the lockpin to detach the plunger and spring from the lever.

28 Unscrew and remove the lever pivot bolt, then lift the lever clear of the mounting plate. Remove the lever pivot bush.

29 Refit in the reverse order of removal. Lubricate the pivot bush and the lever end lightly with grease prior to reassembly. Reconnect and adjust the cable as described previously in this Section.

Starter inhibitor/reverse lamp switch (three-speed transmission) - removal and refitting

30 Detach the centre console and move it rearwards and over the selector lever.

31 Detach and withdraw the selector quadrant indicator plate.

32 Detach the wiring connector from the inhibitor switch and the switch from the mounting bracket.

33 When refitting the switch, align the slider with the selector pin and ensure that the earth lead is positioned above the switch. Refit the quadrant indicator plate then check that the starter operates only when the selector lever is in the 'P' or 'N' position. Also check that the reversing light operates when the lever is moved to the 'R' position. Refit the console.

9 Braking system

Brake linings

1 When renewing the brake linings, not only is it important that the linings are renewed on each side of the same axle, but also with the same lining type fitted on each side. Never intermix asbestos and asbestos-free linings of the same axle.

Brake fluid

2 Later models have DOT 4 specification brake fluid and the manufacturers recommend that this fluid is now used when topping-up or renewing the brake fluid on earlier models (which previously used DOT 3 specification fluid).

3 The advantage of the DOT 4 fluid is that it has a higher boiling point than the DOT 3 type, but is compatible to be mixed with the earlier type when topping-up is required.

10 Bodywork and fittings

Front door interior trim panel (August 1986 onwards) - removal and refitting

1 On cars without power-operated windows, extract the spring clip and take off the window regulator handle. The clip can be removed using a piece of wire with a hook at its end or a strip of rag pulled in either direction under the handle boss.

2 Carefully prise out the speaker grille, then undo the four screws and withdraw the speaker. Disconnect the wiring and remove the speaker (photos).

102A Remove the speaker grille from the interior trim panel . . .

10.2B . . . undo the speaker retaining screws . . .

10.2C . . . withdraw the speaker and disconnect the wiring

13

10.3A Prise out the escutcheon plate from the remote control handle . . .

10.3B . . . then rotate the plate to remove

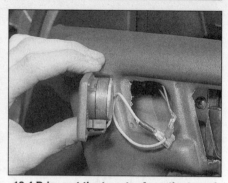

10.4 Prise out the tweeter from the top of the trim panel

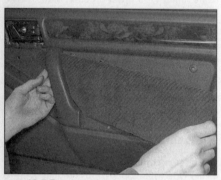

10.5 Remove the centre trim panel

3 Prise out the escutcheon plate from the remote control lock handle, rotate the plate as necessary and slide it off the handle (photos).

4 Prise out the tweeter from the top of the trim panel, disconnect the wiring and remove the tweeter (photo).

5 Release the clips securing the centre trim pad to the panel by pulling the pad outwards, then remove it from the door (photo).

6 Undo the two screws on the rear edge of the trim panel, three screws at the upper front, two screws in the speaker aperture, and four screws in the centre (photos).

7 Insert the fingers or a broad blunt blade

between the trim panel and the door and release the clips.

8 Where fitted, disconnect the door lock/power-operated window control multi-plug, then lift the trim panel upwards and off the door (photo).

9 Carefully peel back the waterproof sheet as necessary for access to the door internal components (photo).

10 Refitting is the reversal of removal. To fit the regulator handle (where applicable), position the spring clip on the handle and fit it to the splined shaft of the regulator simply by striking it with the hand.

10.6A Undo the upper screw on the trim panel rear edge (arrowed)

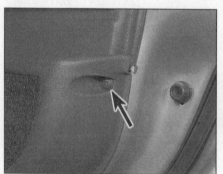

10.6B . . . and the lower screw behind the storage bin (arrowed)

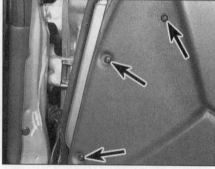

10.6C Undo the three screws at the upper front (arrowed) . . .

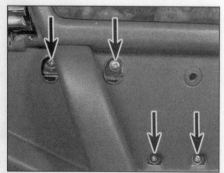

10.6D . . . and the fan screws at the centre (arrowed)

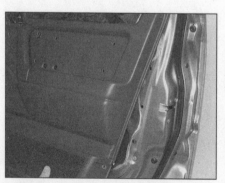

10.8 Release the clips and lift the panel upwards to remove

10.9 Peel back the waterproof sheet for access to the door components

10.13A On automatic transmission models undo the selector lever retaining screw (arrowed) . . .

10.13B . . . lift off the lever and remove the spring (arrowed)

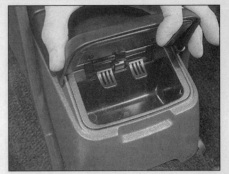

10.14A Remove the ashtray from the rear console . . .

Rear door interior trim panel (August 1986 onwards) - removal and refitting

11 The procedure is the same as for the front door described previously except for fewer panel retaining screws and the absence of door speakers.

Centre console (August 1986 onwards) - removal and refitting

12 Refer to Section 11 of this Supplement and remove the radio/cassette player.
13 On manual transmission models unscrew the gear lever knob. On automatic transmission models undo the screw on the front face of the selector lever (photo). Lift off the selector and remove the spring (photo).
14 Remove the ash tray from the rear console, unclip the access panel and undo the screw securing the rear console upper cover (photos).
15 Where fitted, disconnect the sunroof switch multi-plug, apply the handbrake fully and withdraw the rear console upper cover over the handbrake lever.
16 Undo the two screws at the rear of the front console upper cover (photo).
17 Open the cassette holder lid and undo the two screws from inside the cassette holder (photo). Withdraw the cassette holder from the front console.
18 Undo the two front console upper cover screws from within the cassette holder aperture and lift off the upper cover (photos). Disconnect the panel illumination bulb wiring connectors (where fitted) and remove the upper cover.
19 Undo the two screws at the rear, the centre clamp plate screw, and the three screws on each side at the front securing the front and rear consoles (photos).
20 Lift out the rear console, disconnect the window lift switch wiring (where fitted), and lift out the front console.
21 Refitting is a reversal of removal.

10.14B . . . followed by the upper cover and retaining screw (arrowed)

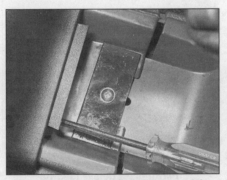

10.16 Undo the screws at the rear of the front console upper cover

10.17 Undo the screws from the inside of the cassette holder and remove the holder

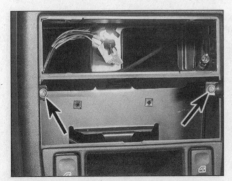

10.18A Undo the two front console upper cover screws (arrowed) . . .

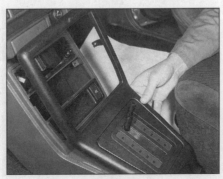

10.18B . . . and lift off the upper cover

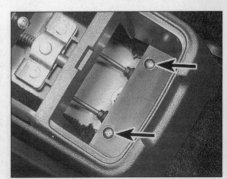

10.19A Undo the two screws at the rear (arrowed) . . .

13

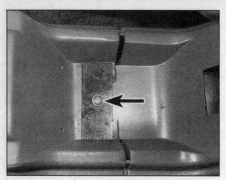

10.19B . . . the centre clamp plate . . .

10.19C . . . and the three screws each side at the front (arrowed)

Facia panel (August 1986 onwards) - removal and refitting

22 The procedure for later models is the same as described in Chapter 11, Section 23, but it is first necessary to remove the centre console as described previously in this Section.

Exterior rear view mirror glass - renewal

Note: *It is assumed that the mirror glass is being removed because it is already broken. This will be the likely result in any case when attempting to remove an unbroken mirror.*

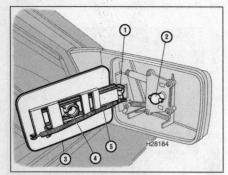

Fig. 13.7 Manually-operated exterior rear view mirror glass details (Sec 10)

1 Mirror arm   4 Socket
2 Ball   5 Retaining spring
3 Mirror glass

Manually-operated mirror

23 Push the mirror glass forward to give access to the mirror ball and socket (Fig. 13.7).
24 Disconnect the ball from the socket, disconnect the retaining spring and withdraw the glass from the mirror arm.
25 Refitting is the reversal of removal.

Electrically-operated mirror

26 Push the mirror glass forward to give access to the mirror glass retaining clips (Fig. 13.8).
27 Release the clips from the retaining ring, disconnect the wiring and remove the glass from the retaining ring.
28 Refitting is the reversal of removal.

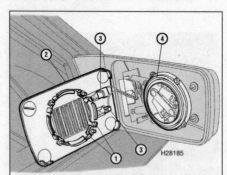

Fig. 13.8 Electrically-operated rear view mirror glass details (Sec 10)

1 Mirror retaining clips   4 Glass retaining
2 Mirror glass   ring
3 Wiring connectors

Luggage boot lock and controls (August 1986 onwards) - general

29 With the provision of the low loading sill and modified boot lid arrangement on later models the layout of the boot lid and controls has also been changed.
30 The lock and lock cylinder have been repositioned from the rear panel to the boot lid itself, and the striker moved from the boot lid to the rear panel (photos).
31 Apart from these location changes the components are unaltered and the procedures contained in Chapter 11 are still applicable.

Headlining - general

32 Should it be necessary to remove the headlining on cars equipped with a sunroof it is recommended that the work be entrusted to a Rover dealer due to the complications involved (see next sub-section).

Sunroof - general

33 A mechanical or electrically-operated sunroof is available as standard or optional equipment on certain models in the range.
34 The sunroof operating mechanism is quite complex and the components removal, refitting and adjustment procedures are equally involved, reflecting this complexity. For the roof to operate smoothly, without water leaks and without excessive wind noise, adjustment is critical, and in some instances special tools are necessary. For these reasons it is recommended that work on the sunroof be entrusted to a suitably equipped dealer, and is considered beyond the scope of the DIY mechanic.

Plastic components

35 With the use of more and more plastic body components by the vehicle manufacturers (eg bumpers. spoilers, and in some cases major body panels), rectification of more serious damage to such items has become a matter of either entrusting repair work to a specialist in this field, or renewing complete components. Repair of such damage by the DIY owner is not really feasible, owing to the cost of the equipment

10.30A Boot lid lock . . .

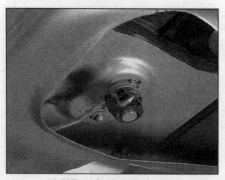

10.30B . . .lock cylinder . . .

10.30C . . .and striker plate locations . . .

and materials required for effecting such repairs. The basic technique involves making a groove along the line of the crack in the plastic, using a rotary burr in a power drill. The damaged part is then welded back together, using a hot-air gun to heat up and fuse a plastic filler rod into the groove. Any excess plastic is then removed, and the area rubbed down to a smooth finish. It is important that a filler rod of the correct plastic is used, as body components can be made of a variety of different types (eg polycarbonate, ABS, polypropylene).

36 Damage of a less serious nature (abrasions, minor cracks etc) can be repaired by the DIY owner using a two-part epoxy filler repair material. Once mixed in equal proportions, this is used in similar fashion to the bodywork filler used on metal panels. The filler is usually cured in twenty to thirty minutes, ready for sanding and painting.

37 If the owner is renewing a complete component himself, or if he has repaired it with epoxy filler, he will be left with the problem of finding a suitable paint for finishing which is compatible with the type of plastic used. At one time, the use of a universal paint was not possible, owing to the complex range of plastics encountered in body component applications. Standard paints, generally speaking, will not bond to plastic or rubber satisfactorily. However, it is now possible to obtain a plastic body parts finishing kit which consists of a pre-primer treatment, a primer and coloured top coat. Full instructions are normally supplied with a kit, but basically, the method of use is to first apply the pre-primer to the component concerned, and allow it to dry for up to 30 minutes. Then the primer is applied, and left to dry for about an hour before finally applying the special-coloured top coat. The result is a correctly-coloured component, where the paint will flex with the plastic or rubber, a property that standard paint does not normally possess.

11 Electrical system

Alternator drivebelt tensioner - 1.3 models (1987 onwards)

1 A positive tensioning device is fitted to these models. Adjust the drivebelt tension as follows.

2 Disconnect the battery negative lead.

3 Slacken the alternator pivot and adjusting link bolts.

4 Turn the tensioning bolt until the belt tension is correct (see Chapter 12 Specifications). Be careful not to over-tension.

5 Tighten the link and pivot bolts. Recheck the belt tension, then reconnect the battery.

Starter motor (later models)

6 A Lucas M79 starter motor is fitted to some

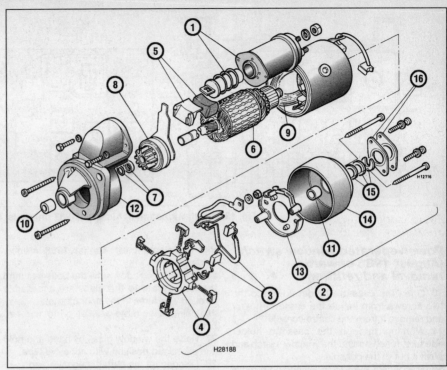

Fig. 13.9 Exploded view of the Lucas M79 starter motor (Sec 11)

1 Solenoid and plunger	6 Armature	12 Drive end bracket – manual
2 Commutator end bracket assembly	7 Jump ring and thrust collar	13 Insulation plate
3 Brushes	8 Drive assembly	14 Commutator end bracket
4 Brush springs	9 Field coils and yoke	15 Circlip and washers
5 Pivot and packing piece	10 Bush – drive end bracket	16 Sealing cup and gasket
	11 Bush – commutator end bracket	

1988-on models. Overhaul and repair procedures are similar to those described for earlier type starter motors in Chapter 12, using the Specifications given in this Supplement and Figs. 13.9 and 13.10.

7 A Nippondenso (ND) starter motor may be found on some 1.3 models. This is similar to the Hitachi motor shown in Chapter 12.

Relays and control units (1987 onwards) - location

8 The location of the various relays in the fusebox is as shown in Fig. 13.11.

9 The location of other relays/control units is as follows:

Passenger compartment

Inertia switch (1.6 models) - behind panel above fusebox
Fuel system ECU (1.6 models) - below left-hand front seat
Door lock control unit (where fitted) - below right-hand front seat
'One touch' window lift control (where fitted) - below right-hand front seat
Sunroof changeover relay - behind sunroof motor access panel

Engine compartment

Ignition ECU (1.6 models) - left-hand front suspension tower

Manifold heater relay 1.6 carburettor models - left-hand suspension tower
Fuel pump relay (1.6 carburettor models) - right-hand suspension tower
Starter solenoid relay (1.6 EFi automatic) - left-hand suspension tower

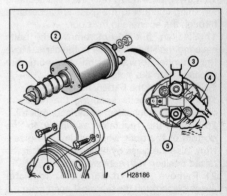

Fig. 13.10 Starter solenoid details – Lucas M79 starter motor (Sec 11)

1 Solenoid plunger
2 Solenoid
3 Battery terminal BAT
4 Solenoid terminal 50
5 Starter terminal STA
6 Retaining screws

13

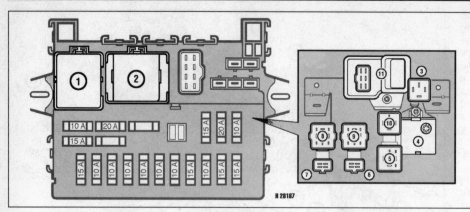

1 Intermittent wiper control
2 Hazard warning/indicator flasher
3 Auxiliary circuits relay
4 Sidelight warning alarm
5 Headlamp dim-dip unit
6 Window lift relay – rear
7 Window lift relay – front
8 Heated rear screen relay
9 Courtesy light delay unit
10 Instrument illumination relay
11 Headlamp washer timer unit

Fig. 13.11 Relay location in fusebox (1987 onwards) (Sec 11)

Power-operated window switch (August 1986 onwards) - removal and refitting

10 Open the cassette holder lid, undo the two screws from inside the cassette holder and remove it from the centre console.
11 Working through the cassette holder aperture, reach behind the window switch and push it out of the console.
12 Disconnect the switch wiring and remove the switch.
13 Refitting is a reversal of removal.

Power-operated window motor and regulator - removal and refitting

Front door

14 Remove the door interior trim panel as described in Chapter 11, or in Section 10 of this supplement for August 1986 models onwards.
15 On early models remove the door speaker if fitted.
16 Lower the window until the bolts securing the lifting channel to the glass are accessible through the aperture in the door.
17 Slacken, but do not remove, the bolts securing the lifting channel to the glass. Move the channel forwards until the bolts are released from the slots.
18 Disconnect the battery negative lead.
19 Undo the bolts securing the regulator channel and mechanism to the door (photo).
20 Lower the regulator assembly to the bottom of the door while holding the glass. Now raise the glass by hand and hold it in the raised position with adhesive tape.
21 Remove the motor and regulator assembly through the rearmost aperture in the door and disconnect the motor wiring.
22 The motor can be removed if necessary after undoing the retaining bolts and releasing the drain tube.
23 Refitting is a reversal of removal.

Rear door

24 Remove the door interior trim panel as described in Chapter 11, or in Section 10 of

this Supplement for August 1986 models onwards.
25 Lower the window until the bolts securing the lifting plate to the glass are accessible through apertures in the door (photo).
26 Using a suitable socket undo the two bolts.
27 Raise the window glass by hand and hold it in the raised position with adhesive tape.
28 Disconnect the battery negative lead.
29 Undo the two lower bolts and two upper nuts securing the regulator channel to the door (photos).
30 Note the location of the motor wiring connectors and disconnect them.
31 Undo the bolts securing the motor and

regulator and remove the assembly from the door.
32 Refitting is the reversal of removal.

Power-operated window control unit - removal and refitting

33 Disconnect the battery negative lead.
34 Move the driver's seat fully rearward.
35 Undo the bolt and withdraw the control unit mounting plate from under the seat.
36 Disconnect the multi-plug connectors, depress the spring clip and remove the control unit from the mounting plate. Where more than one control unit is fitted, the

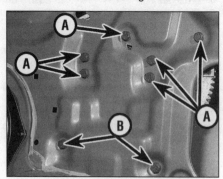

11.19 Front door window regulator mechanism retaining bolts (A) and regulator channel bolts (B)

11.25 Rear door lifting plate-to-glass retaining bolts (arrowed)

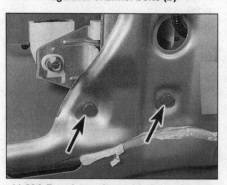

11.29A Regulator channel lower retaining bolts (arrowed) . . .

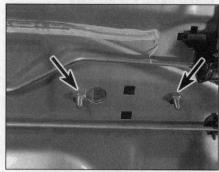

11.29B . . . and upper retaining nuts (arrowed)

power-operated window unit is the one on the right-hand side of the plate.

37 Refitting is a reversal of removal.

Central locking door lock motor - removal and refitting

38 On cars equipped with central locking, the passenger's side front door and both rear door locks are operated by the electric motors attached to the lock mechanism. These are activated by a switch unit attached to the driver's side door lock. Removal and refitting of the switch unit and the system control unit are described in Chapter 12. Removal and refitting of the door lock motors is as follows.

39 Raise the window fully, then disconnect the battery negative lead.

40 Remove the door interior trim panel as described in Chapter 11, or in Section 10 of this Supplement for August 1986 models onwards.

41 Disconnect the motor wiring at the multi-plug connector.

42 If working on the front door, undo the three screws securing the door latch to the door, depress the interior lock button, and move the latch until the motor retaining screws are accessible. Undo the screws and remove the motor.

43 If working on the rear door, depress the interior lock button and, working through the door aperture, undo the motor retaining screws (photo). Remove the motor.

44 Refitting is a reversal of removal.

Dim-dip lighting system (1987 onwards) - general

45 A dim-dip headlamp lighting system is fitted to later models. The system causes the headlamps to light at reduced intensity when both the ignition and the sidelights are switched on.

46 The dim-dip relay is located in the central fusebox, and a resistor is located behind the right-hand headlamp unit, low down in the engine compartment.

47 Where a dim-dip system is fitted, only headlamp bulbs of the recommended wattage should be fitted, or damage to the circuit components may result.

Reversing lamp bulb (August 1986 onwards) - renewal

48 From within the luggage compartment turn the bulbholder anti-clockwise to remove it from the boot lid (photo).

49 Push and turn the bayonet fitting bulb to remove.

50 Refitting is a reversal of removal.

Automatic transmission selector quadrant bulb (August 1986 onwards) - renewal

51 Refer to Section 10 of this Supplement and remove the front centre console upper cover.

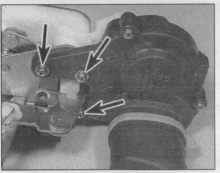

11.43 Central locking rear door lock motor retaining screws (arrowed) – motor lock assembly shown removed for clarity

11.52A Selector quadrant bulb holder locations . . .

52 Withdraw the bulbholder from the rear of the cover and remove the push fit bulb from the bulbholder (photos).

53 Refitting is a reversal of removal.

Clock (later models) - removal and refitting

54 Disconnect the battery earth lead.

55 Using a small screwdriver, carefully prise free the trinket tray from the facia and the electric mirror switch, if fitted.

56 Reaching to the rear of the clock, carefully push it out of its aperture and detach the wiring connector from its rear face.

57 Refit in the reverse order of removal and reset the clock.

Instrument panel light dimmer switch - removal and refitting

58 Disconnect the battery earth lead.

59 Remove the instrument panel lower access facia, then reach through to the rear of the switch and detach the wiring connector.

60 Pull free the knob from the switch, withdraw the plain washer, unscrew and remove the retaining nut. Withdraw the switch.

61 Refit in the reverse order of removal, then check for satisfactory operation on completion.

Radio/cassette player

62 The radio/cassette player fitted to later models has an integral anti-theft security code system. With this unit type, whenever the

11.48 Reversing lamp bulb and holder location in the boot lid

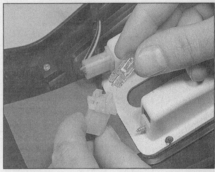

11.52B . . . and removing the selector quadrant bulbs

battery is to be disconnected or the radio/cassette is to be removed, the code must be deactivated. Only the car owner and the original dealer will know the four digit code. The code is pre-set by the owner and the dealer is then advised of the code number. To deactivate the security system code, depress the UP tuning button and switch the radio on. Continue to depress the UP button and correctly enter the security code as follows:

(a) *Depress the number 1 preset button and press one of the arrowed tuner buttons to select the 1st digit of the code. When selected, the digit will show in the display panel. Press the pre-set button to store the number.*

(b) *Now depress one of the arrowed tuner buttons to select the 2nd digit of the code, then when this is registered as entered by the display panel, press the pre-set button to store this number.*

(c) *Repeat the procedure to select the 3rd and 4th digits of the code. When the 4th digit is entered, a twin tone beep will be heard, and this signified that the code is deactivated.*

63 If removing the radio/cassette unit, proceed as described in Section 24 in Chapter 12 (paragraph 10 on). In some instances it may be necessary to remove the end covers to gain access to the release holes. When refitting the unit ensure that any foam padding withdrawn during removal is correctly repositioned.

13

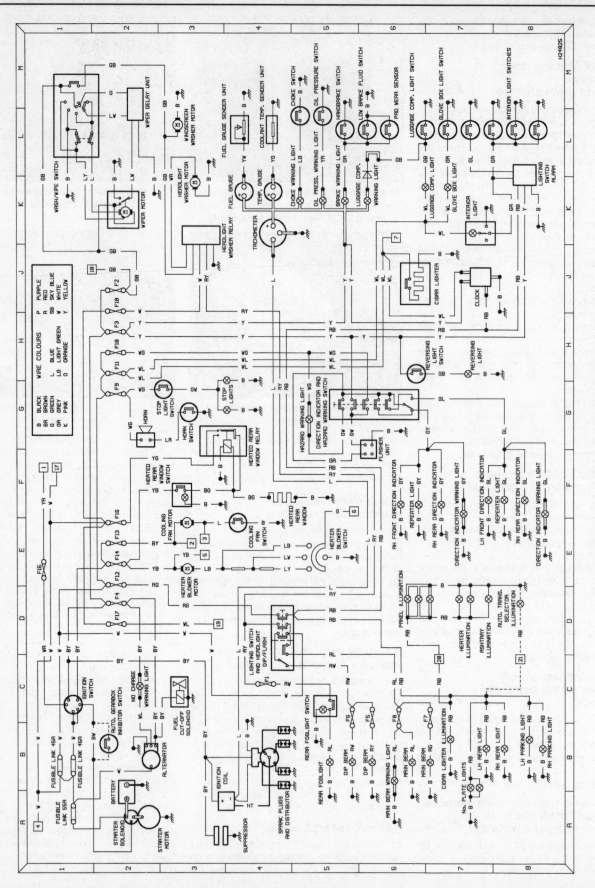

Diagram 1: Main wiring diagram - 1.3 models up to July 1986

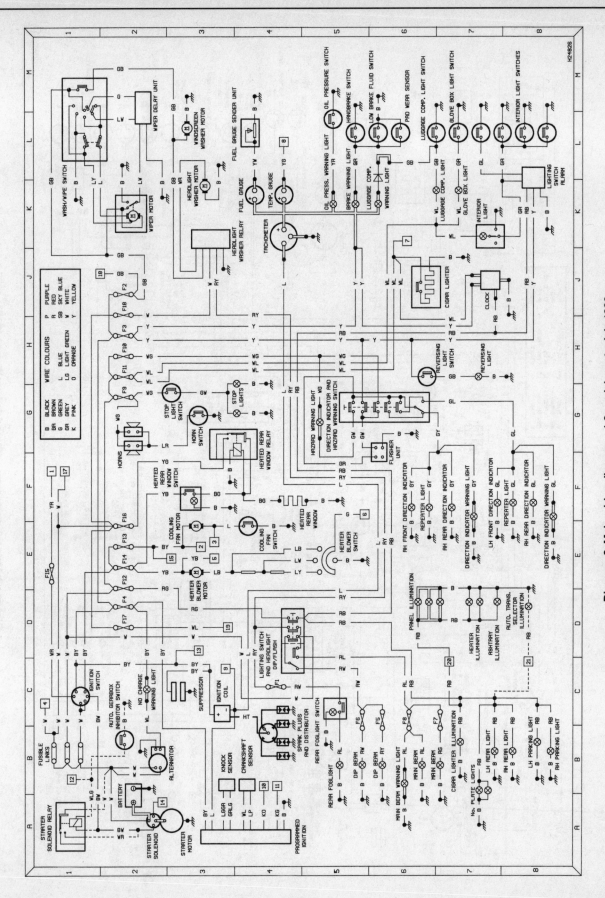

Diagram 2: Main wiring diagram - 1.6 models up to July 1986

14

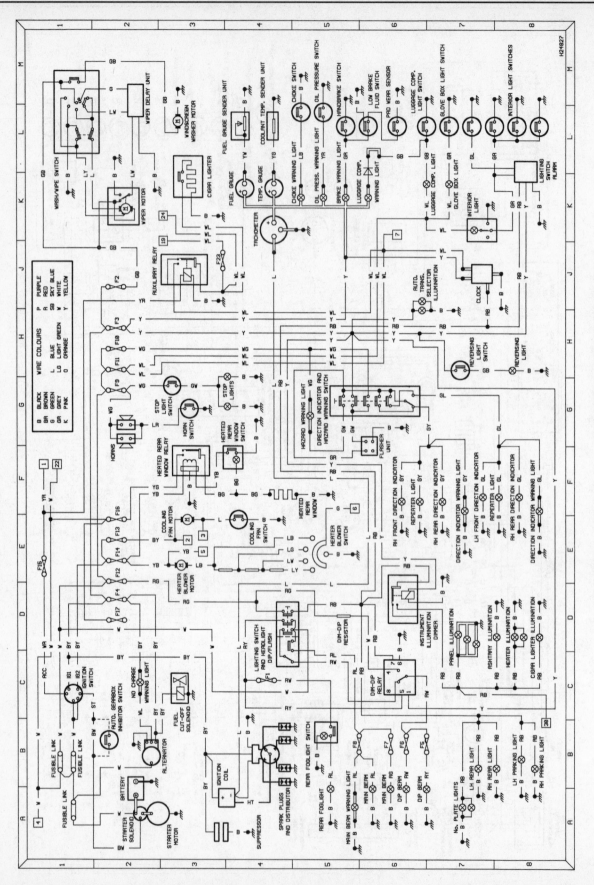

Diagram 3: Main wiring diagram - 1.3 models from August 1986 to 1987

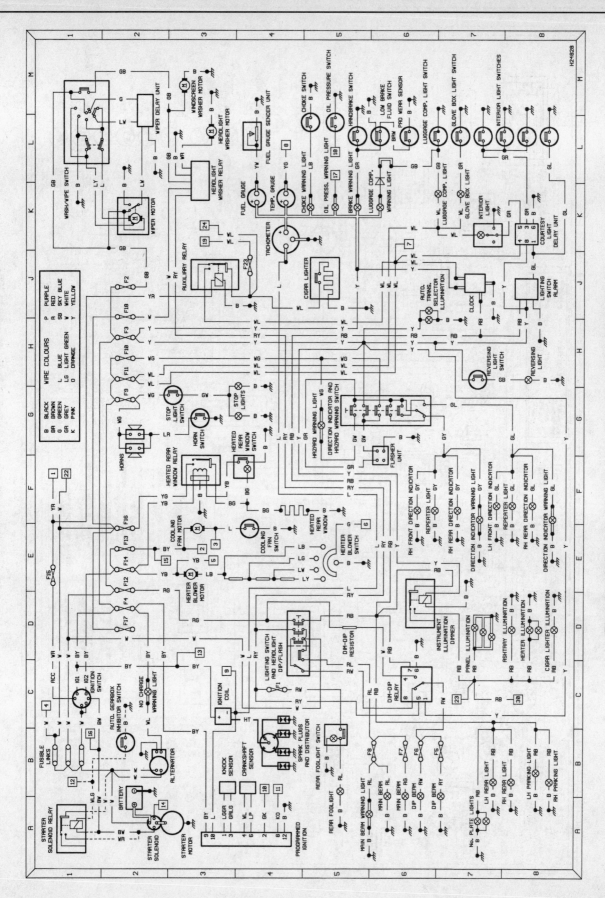

Diagram 4: Main wiring diagram - 1.6 models from August 1986 to 1987

14

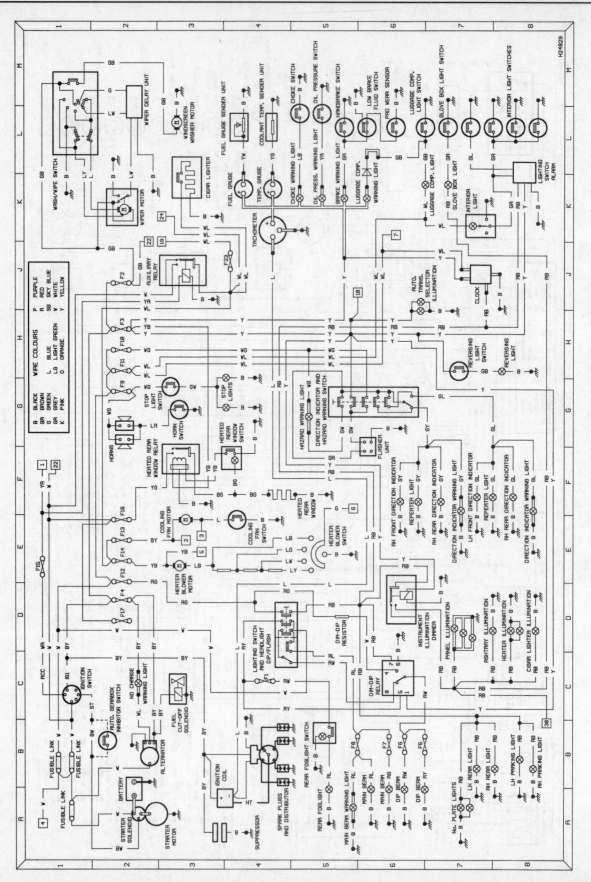

Diagram 5: Main wiring diagram - 1.3 models from 1987

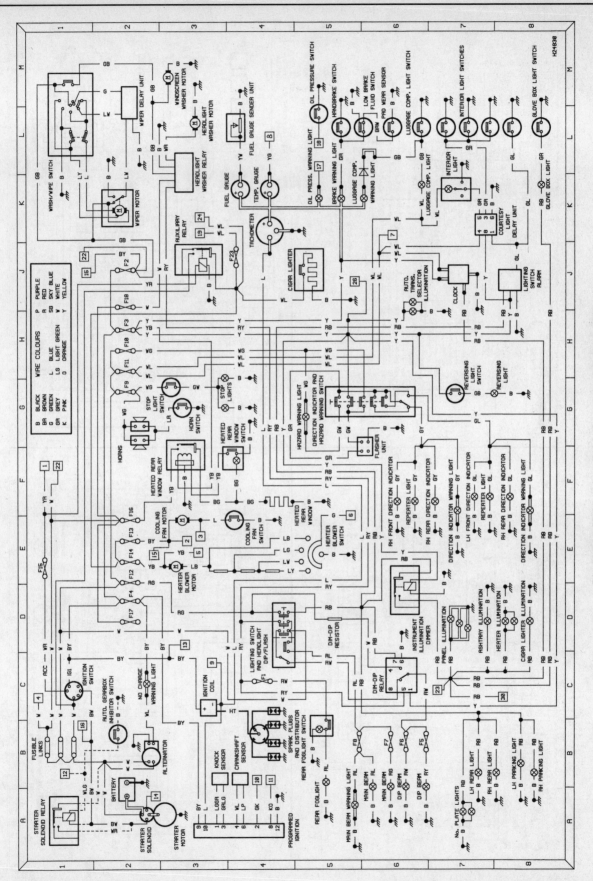

Diagram 6: Main wiring diagram - 1.6 models from 1987

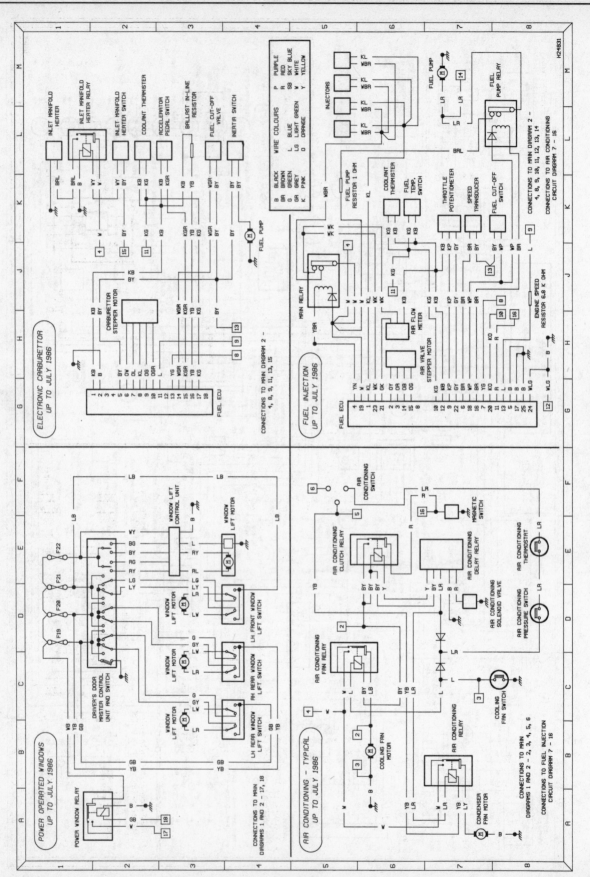

Diagram 7: Supplementary wiring diagrams

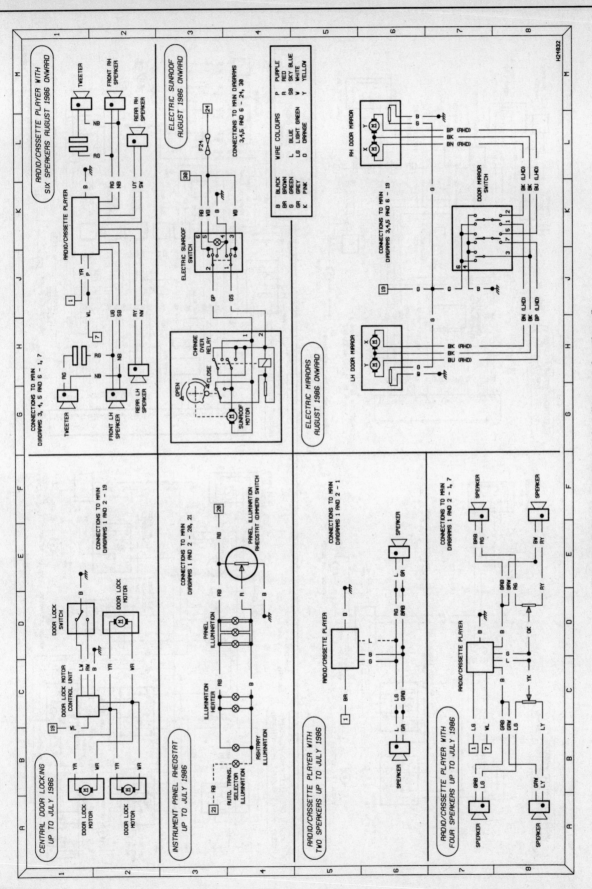

Diagram 8: Supplementary wiring diagrams (continued)

14

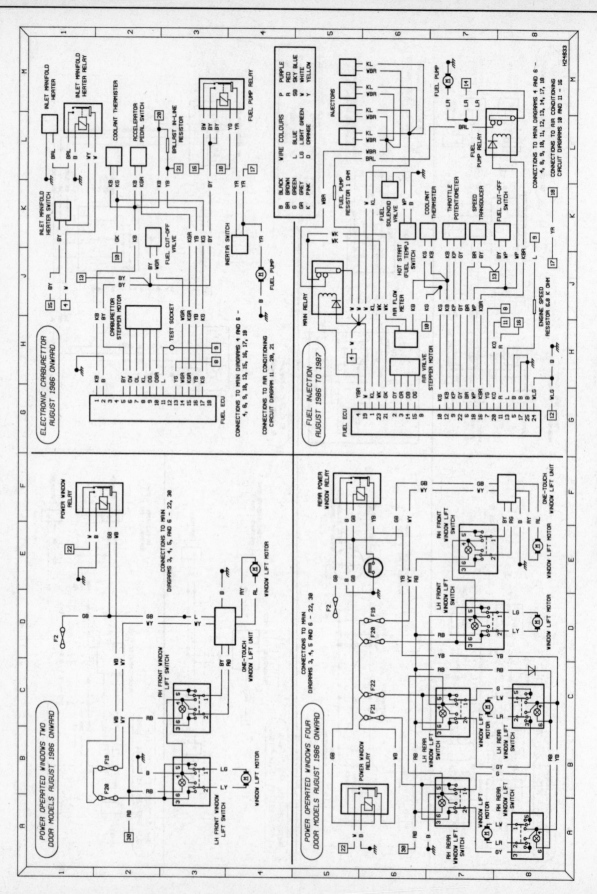

Diagram 9: Supplementary wiring diagrams (continued)

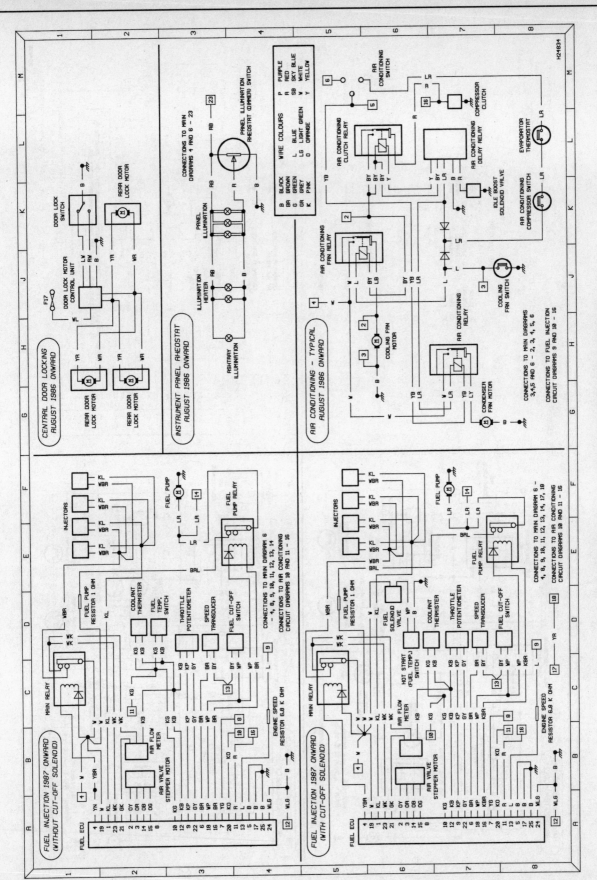

Diagram 10: Supplementary wiring diagrams (continued)

14

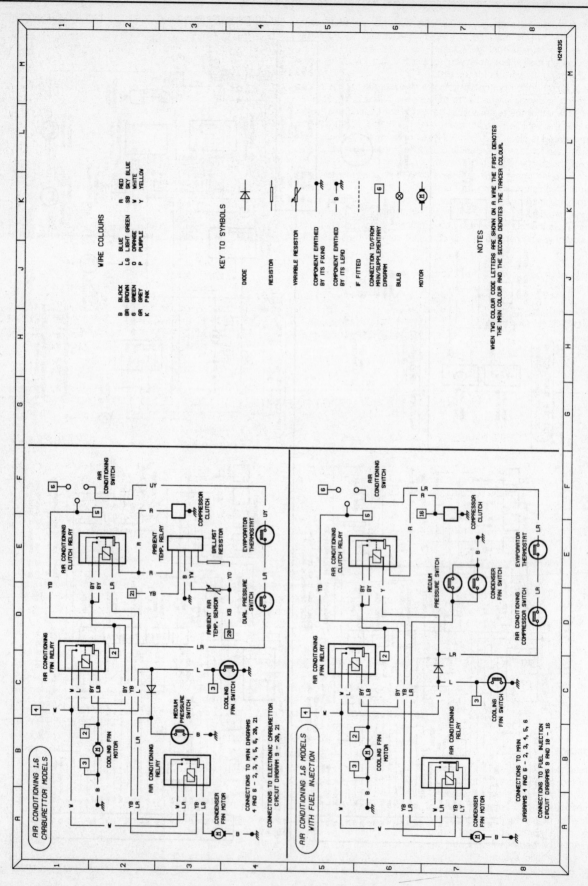

Diagram 11: Supplementary wiring diagrams (continued)

This is a guide to getting your vehicle through the MOT test. Obviously it will not be possible to examine the vehicle to the same standard as the professional MOT tester. However, working through the following checks will enable you to identify any problem areas before submitting the vehicle for the test.

Where a testable component is in borderline condition, the tester has discretion in deciding whether to pass or fail it. The basis of such discretion is whether the tester would be happy for a close relative or friend to use the vehicle with the component in that condition. If the vehicle presented is clean and evidently well cared for, the tester may be more inclined to pass a borderline component than if the vehicle is scruffy and apparently neglected.

It has only been possible to summarise the test requirements here, based on the regulations in force at the time of printing. Test standards are becoming increasingly stringent, although there are some exemptions for older vehicles. For full details obtain a copy of the Haynes publication Pass the MOT! (available from stockists of Haynes manuals).

An assistant will be needed to help carry out some of these checks.

The checks have been sub-divided into four categories, as follows:

1 Checks carried out **FROM THE DRIVER'S SEAT**

2 Checks carried out **WITH THE VEHICLE ON THE GROUND**

3 Checks carried out **WITH THE VEHICLE RAISED AND THE WHEELS FREE TO TURN**

4 Checks carried out on **YOUR VEHICLE'S EXHAUST EMISSION SYSTEM**

---

1 Checks carried out **FROM THE DRIVER'S SEAT**

Handbrake

☐ Test the operation of the handbrake. Excessive travel (too many clicks) indicates incorrect brake or cable adjustment.

☐ Check that the handbrake cannot be released by tapping the lever sideways. Check the security of the lever mountings.

Footbrake

☐ Depress the brake pedal and check that it does not creep down to the floor, indicating a master cylinder fault. Release the pedal, wait a few seconds, then depress it again. If the pedal travels nearly to the floor before firm resistance is felt, brake adjustment or repair is necessary. If the pedal feels spongy, there is air in the hydraulic system which must be removed by bleeding.

☐ Check that the brake pedal is secure and in good condition. Check also for signs of fluid leaks on the pedal, floor or carpets, which would indicate failed seals in the brake master cylinder.

☐ Check the servo unit (when applicable) by operating the brake pedal several times, then keeping the pedal depressed and starting the engine. As the engine starts, the pedal will move down slightly. If not, the vacuum hose or the servo itself may be faulty.

Steering wheel and column

☐ Examine the steering wheel for fractures or looseness of the hub, spokes or rim.

☐ Move the steering wheel from side to side and then up and down. Check that the steering wheel is not loose on the column, indicating wear or a loose retaining nut. Continue moving the steering wheel as before, but also turn it slightly from left to right.

☐ Check that the steering wheel is not loose on the column, and that there is no abnormal

movement of the steering wheel, indicating wear in the column support bearings or couplings.

Windscreen and mirrors

☐ The windscreen must be free of cracks or other significant damage within the driver's field of view. (Small stone chips are acceptable.) Rear view mirrors must be secure, intact, and capable of being adjusted.

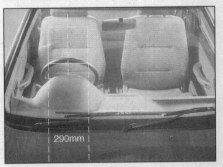

290mm

Seat belts and seats

Note: *The following checks are applicable to all seat belts, front and rear.*

☐ Examine the webbing of all the belts (including rear belts if fitted) for cuts, serious fraying or deterioration. Fasten and unfasten each belt to check the buckles. If applicable, check the retracting mechanism. Check the security of all seat belt mountings accessible from inside the vehicle.
☐ The front seats themselves must be securely attached and the backrests must lock in the upright position.

Doors

☐ Both front doors must be able to be opened and closed from outside and inside, and must latch securely when closed.

2 Checks carried out WITH THE VEHICLE ON THE GROUND

Vehicle identification

☐ Number plates must be in good condition, secure and legible, with letters and numbers correctly spaced – spacing at (A) should be twice that at (B).

☐ The VIN plate and/or homologation plate must be legible.

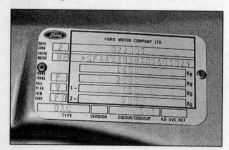

Electrical equipment

☐ Switch on the ignition and check the operation of the horn.
☐ Check the windscreen washers and wipers, examining the wiper blades; renew damaged or perished blades. Also check the operation of the stop-lights.

☐ Check the operation of the sidelights and number plate lights. The lenses and reflectors must be secure, clean and undamaged.
☐ Check the operation and alignment of the headlights. The headlight reflectors must not be tarnished and the lenses must be undamaged.
☐ Switch on the ignition and check the operation of the direction indicators (including the instrument panel tell-tale) and the hazard warning lights. Operation of the sidelights and stop-lights must not affect the indicators - if it does, the cause is usually a bad earth at the rear light cluster.
☐ Check the operation of the rear foglight(s), including the warning light on the instrument panel or in the switch.

Footbrake

☐ Examine the master cylinder, brake pipes and servo unit for leaks, loose mountings, corrosion or other damage.

☐ The fluid reservoir must be secure and the fluid level must be between the upper (**A**) and lower (**B**) markings.

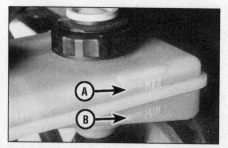

☐ Inspect both front brake flexible hoses for cracks or deterioration of the rubber. Turn the steering from lock to lock, and ensure that the hoses do not contact the wheel, tyre, or any part of the steering or suspension mechanism. With the brake pedal firmly depressed, check the hoses for bulges or leaks under pressure.

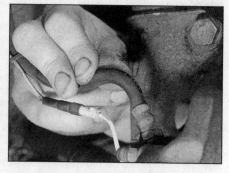

Steering and suspension

☐ Have your assistant turn the steering wheel from side to side slightly, up to the point where the steering gear just begins to transmit this movement to the roadwheels. Check for excessive free play between the steering wheel and the steering gear, indicating wear or insecurity of the steering column joints, the column-to-steering gear coupling, or the steering gear itself.
☐ Have your assistant turn the steering wheel more vigorously in each direction, so that the roadwheels just begin to turn. As this is done, examine all the steering joints, linkages, fittings and attachments. Renew any component that shows signs of wear or damage. On vehicles with power steering, check the security and condition of the steering pump, drivebelt and hoses.
☐ Check that the vehicle is standing level, and at approximately the correct ride height.

Shock absorbers

☐ Depress each corner of the vehicle in turn, then release it. The vehicle should rise and then settle in its normal position. If the vehicle continues to rise and fall, the shock absorber is defective. A shock absorber which has seized will also cause the vehicle to fail.

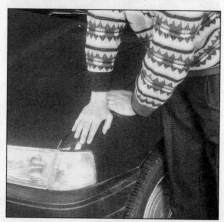

Exhaust system

☐ Start the engine. With your assistant holding a rag over the tailpipe, check the entire system for leaks. Repair or renew leaking sections.

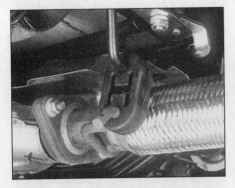

3 Checks carried out
WITH THE VEHICLE RAISED AND THE WHEELS FREE TO TURN

Jack up the front and rear of the vehicle, and securely support it on axle stands. Position the stands clear of the suspension assemblies. Ensure that the wheels are clear of the ground and that the steering can be turned from lock to lock.

Steering mechanism

☐ Have your assistant turn the steering from lock to lock. Check that the steering turns smoothly, and that no part of the steering mechanism, including a wheel or tyre, fouls any brake hose or pipe or any part of the body structure.
☐ Examine the steering rack rubber gaiters for damage or insecurity of the retaining clips. If power steering is fitted, check for signs of damage or leakage of the fluid hoses, pipes or connections. Also check for excessive stiffness or binding of the steering, a missing split pin or locking device, or severe corrosion of the body structure within 30 cm of any steering component attachment point.

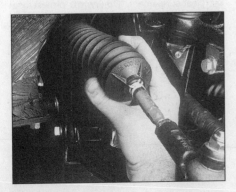

Front and rear suspension and wheel bearings

☐ Starting at the front right-hand side, grasp the roadwheel at the 3 o'clock and 9 o'clock positions and shake it vigorously. Check for free play or insecurity at the wheel bearings, suspension balljoints, or suspension mountings, pivots and attachments.
☐ Now grasp the wheel at the 12 o'clock and 6 o'clock positions and repeat the previous inspection. Spin the wheel, and check for roughness or tightness of the front wheel bearing.

☐ If excess free play is suspected at a component pivot point, this can be confirmed by using a large screwdriver or similar tool and levering between the mounting and the component attachment. This will confirm whether the wear is in the pivot bush, its retaining bolt, or in the mounting itself (the bolt holes can often become elongated).

☐ Carry out all the above checks at the other front wheel, and then at both rear wheels.

Springs and shock absorbers

☐ Examine the suspension struts (when applicable) for serious fluid leakage, corrosion, or damage to the casing. Also check the security of the mounting points.
☐ If coil springs are fitted, check that the spring ends locate in their seats, and that the spring is not corroded, cracked or broken.
☐ If leaf springs are fitted, check that all leaves are intact, that the axle is securely attached to each spring, and that there is no deterioration of the spring eye mountings, bushes, and shackles.

☐ The same general checks apply to vehicles fitted with other suspension types, such as torsion bars, hydraulic displacer units, etc. Ensure that all mountings and attachments are secure, that there are no signs of excessive wear, corrosion or damage, and (on hydraulic types) that there are no fluid leaks or damaged pipes.
☐ Inspect the shock absorbers for signs of serious fluid leakage. Check for wear of the mounting bushes or attachments, or damage to the body of the unit.

Driveshafts (fwd vehicles only)

☐ Rotate each front wheel in turn and inspect the constant velocity joint gaiters for splits or damage. Also check that each driveshaft is straight and undamaged.

Braking system

☐ If possible without dismantling, check brake pad wear and disc condition. Ensure that the friction lining material has not worn excessively, (A) and that the discs are not fractured, pitted, scored or badly worn (B).

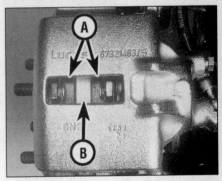

☐ Examine all the rigid brake pipes underneath the vehicle, and the flexible hose(s) at the rear. Look for corrosion or insecurity of the pipes, and for signs of bulging under pressure, chafing, splits or deterioration of the flexible hoses.
☐ Look for signs of fluid leaks at the brake calipers or on the brake backplates. Repair or renew leaking components.
☐ Slowly spin each wheel, while your assistant depresses and releases the footbrake. Ensure that each brake is operating and does not bind when the pedal is released.

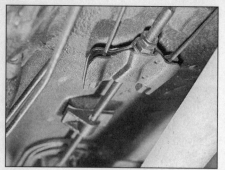

☐ Examine the handbrake mechanism, checking for frayed or broken cables, excessive corrosion, or wear or insecurity of the linkage. Check that the mechanism works on each relevant wheel, and releases fully, without binding.

☐ It is not possible to test brake efficiency without special equipment, but a road test can be carried out later to check that the vehicle pulls up in a straight line.

Fuel and exhaust systems

☐ Inspect the fuel tank (including the filler cap), fuel pipes, hoses and unions. All components must be secure and free from leaks.

☐ Examine the exhaust system over its entire length, checking for any damaged, broken or missing mountings, security of the retaining clamps and rust or corrosion.

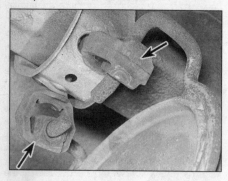

Wheels and tyres

☐ Examine the sidewalls and tread area of each tyre in turn. Check for cuts, tears, lumps, bulges, separation of the tread, and exposure of the ply or cord due to wear or damage. Check that the tyre bead is correctly seated on the wheel rim, that the valve is sound and

properly seated, and that the wheel is not distorted or damaged.

☐ Check that the tyres are of the correct size for the vehicle, that they are of the same size and type on each axle, and that the pressures are correct.

☐ Check the tyre tread depth. The legal minimum at the time of writing is 1.6 mm over at least three-quarters of the tread width. Abnormal tread wear may indicate incorrect front wheel alignment.

Body corrosion

☐ Check the condition of the entire vehicle structure for signs of corrosion in load-bearing areas. (These include chassis box sections, side sills, cross-members, pillars, and all suspension, steering, braking system and seat belt mountings and anchorages.) Any corrosion which has seriously reduced the thickness of a load-bearing area is likely to cause the vehicle to fail. In this case professional repairs are likely to be needed.

☐ Damage or corrosion which causes sharp or otherwise dangerous edges to be exposed will also cause the vehicle to fail.

4 Checks carried out on YOUR VEHICLE'S EXHAUST EMISSION SYSTEM

Petrol models

☐ Have the engine at normal operating temperature, and make sure that it is in good tune (ignition system in good order, air filter element clean, etc).

☐ Before any measurements are carried out, raise the engine speed to around 2500 rpm, and hold it at this speed for 20 seconds. Allow

the engine speed to return to idle, and watch for smoke emissions from the exhaust tailpipe. If the idle speed is obviously much too high, or if dense blue or clearly-visible black smoke comes from the tailpipe for more than 5 seconds, the vehicle will fail. As a rule of thumb, blue smoke signifies oil being burnt (engine wear) while black smoke signifies unburnt fuel (dirty air cleaner element, or other carburettor or fuel system fault).

☐ An exhaust gas analyser capable of measuring carbon monoxide (CO) and hydrocarbons (HC) is now needed. If such an instrument cannot be hired or borrowed, a local garage may agree to perform the check for a small fee.

CO emissions (mixture)

☐ At the time of writing, the maximum CO level at idle is 3.5% for vehicles first used after August 1986 and 4.5% for older vehicles. From January 1996 a much tighter limit (around 0.5%) applies to catalyst-equipped vehicles first used from August 1992. If the CO level cannot be reduced far enough to pass the test (and the fuel and ignition systems are otherwise in good condition) then the carburettor is badly worn, or there is some problem in the fuel injection system or catalytic converter (as applicable).

HC emissions

☐ With the CO emissions within limits, HC emissions must be no more than 1200 ppm (parts per million). If the vehicle fails this test at idle, it can be re-tested at around 2000 rpm; if the HC level is then 1200 ppm or less, this counts as a pass.

☐ Excessive HC emissions can be caused by oil being burnt, but they are more likely to be due to unburnt fuel.

Diesel models

☐ The only emission test applicable to Diesel engines is the measuring of exhaust smoke density. The test involves accelerating the engine several times to its maximum unloaded speed.

Note: *It is of the utmost importance that the engine timing belt is in good condition before the test is carried out.*

☐ Excessive smoke can be caused by a dirty air cleaner element. Otherwise, professional advice may be needed to find the cause.

Introduction

A selection of good tools is a fundamental requirement for anyone contemplating the maintenance and repair of a motor vehicle. For the owner who does not possess any, their purchase will prove a considerable expense, offsetting some of the savings made by doing-it-yourself. However, provided that the tools purchased meet the relevant national safety standards and are of good quality, they will last for many years and prove an extremely worthwhile investment.

To help the average owner to decide which tools are needed to carry out the various tasks detailed in this manual, we have compiled three lists of tools under the following headings: *Maintenance and minor repair*, *Repair and overhaul*, and *Special*. Newcomers to practical mechanics should start off with the *Maintenance and minor repair* tool kit, and confine themselves to the simpler jobs around the vehicle. Then, as confidence and experience grow, more difficult tasks can be undertaken, with extra tools being purchased as, and when, they are needed. In this way, a *Maintenance and minor repair* tool kit can be built up into a *Repair and overhaul* tool kit over a considerable period of time, without any major cash outlays. The experienced do-it-yourselfer will have a tool kit good enough for most repair and overhaul procedures, and will add tools from the *Special* category when it is felt that the expense is justified by the amount of use to which these tools will be put.

Maintenance and minor repair tool kit

The tools given in this list should be considered as a minimum requirement if routine maintenance, servicing and minor repair operations are to be undertaken. We recommend the purchase of combination spanners (ring one end, open-ended the other); although more expensive than open-ended ones, they do give the advantages of both types of spanner.

☐ *Combination spanners: 10, 11, 12, 13, 14 & 17 mm*
☐ *Adjustable spanner - 35 mm jaw (approx)*
☐ *Engine sump/gearbox drain plug key*
☐ *Set of feeler gauges*
☐ *Spark plug spanner (with rubber insert)*
☐ *Spark plug gap adjustment tool*
☐ *Brake bleed nipple spanner*

☐ *Screwdrivers: Flat blade and cross blade – approx 100 mm long x 6 mm dia*
☐ *Combination pliers*
☐ *Hacksaw (junior)*
☐ *Tyre pump*
☐ *Tyre pressure gauge*
☐ *Oil can*
☐ *Oil filter removal tool*
☐ *Fine emery cloth*
☐ *Wire brush (small)*
☐ *Funnel (medium size)*

Repair and overhaul tool kit

These tools are virtually essential for anyone undertaking any major repairs to a motor vehicle, and are additional to those given in the *Maintenance and minor repair* list. Included in this list is a comprehensive set of sockets. Although these are expensive, they will be found invaluable as they are so versatile - particularly if various drives are included in the set. We recommend the half-inch square-drive type, as this can be used with most proprietary torque wrenches. If you cannot afford a socket set, even bought piecemeal, then inexpensive tubular box spanners are a useful alternative.

The tools in this list will occasionally need to be supplemented by tools from the *Special* list:

☐ *Sockets (or box spanners) to cover range in previous list*
☐ *Reversible ratchet drive (for use with sockets) (see illustration)*
☐ *Extension piece, 250 mm (for use with sockets)*
☐ *Universal joint (for use with sockets)*
☐ *Torque wrench (for use with sockets)*
☐ *Self-locking grips*
☐ *Ball pein hammer*
☐ *Soft-faced mallet (plastic/aluminium or rubber)*
☐ *Screwdrivers:*
   Flat blade - long & sturdy, short (chubby), and narrow (electrician's) types
   Cross blade - Long & sturdy, and short (chubby) types
☐ *Pliers:*
   Long-nosed
   Side cutters (electrician's)
   Circlip (internal and external)
☐ *Cold chisel - 25 mm*
☐ *Scriber*
☐ *Scraper*

☐ *Centre-punch*
☐ *Pin punch*
☐ *Hacksaw*
☐ *Brake hose clamp*
☐ *Brake bleeding kit*
☐ *Selection of twist drills*
☐ *Steel rule/straight-edge*
☐ *Allen keys*
☐ *Selection of files*
☐ *Wire brush*
☐ *Axle stands*
☐ *Jack (strong trolley or hydraulic type)*
☐ *Light with extension lead*

Special tools

The tools in this list are those which are not used regularly, are expensive to buy, or which need to be used in accordance with their manufacturers' instructions. Unless relatively difficult mechanical jobs are undertaken frequently, it will not be economic to buy many of these tools. Where this is the case, you could consider clubbing together with friends (or joining a motorists' club) to make a joint purchase, or borrowing the tools against a deposit from a local garage or tool hire specialist. It is worth noting that many of the larger DIY superstores now carry a large range of special tools for hire at modest rates.

The following list contains only those tools and instruments freely available to the public, and not those special tools produced by the vehicle manufacturer specifically for its dealer network. You will find occasional references to these manufacturers' special tools in the text of this manual. Generally, an alternative method of doing the job without the vehicle manufacturers' special tool is given. However, sometimes there is no alternative to using them. Where this is the case and the relevant tool cannot be bought or borrowed, you will have to entrust the work to a franchised garage.

☐ *Valve spring compressor (see illustration)*
☐ *Valve grinding tool*
☐ *Piston ring compressor (see illustration)*
☐ *Piston ring removal/installation tool (see illustration)*
☐ *Cylinder bore hone (see illustration)*
☐ *Balljoint separator*
☐ *Coil spring compressors (where applicable)*
☐ *Two/three-legged hub and bearing puller (see illustration)*

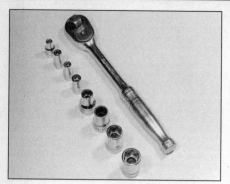

Sockets and reversible ratchet drive

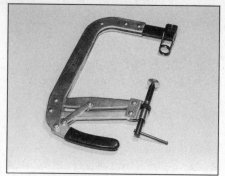

Valve spring compressor

Piston ring compressor

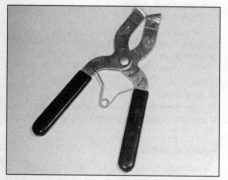

Piston ring removal/installation tool

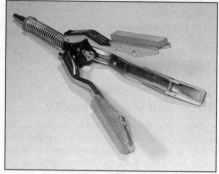

Cylinder bore hone

Three-legged hub and bearing puller

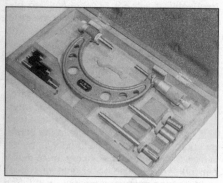

Micrometer set

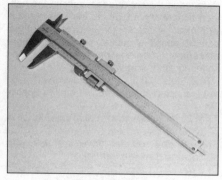

Vernier calipers

Dial test indicator and magnetic stand

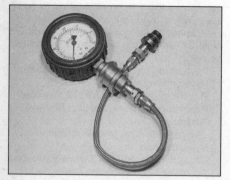

Compression testing gauge

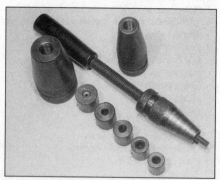

Clutch plate alignment set

Brake shoe steady spring cup removal tool

- ☐ *Impact screwdriver*
- ☐ *Micrometer and/or vernier calipers (see illustrations)*
- ☐ *Dial gauge (see illustration)*
- ☐ *Universal electrical multi-meter*
- ☐ *Cylinder compression gauge (see illustration)*
- ☐ *Clutch plate alignment set (see illustration)*
- ☐ *Brake shoe steady spring cup removal tool (see illustration)*
- ☐ *Bush and bearing removal/installation set (see illustration)*
- ☐ *Stud extractors (see illustration)*
- ☐ *Tap and die set (see illustration)*
- ☐ *Lifting tackle*
- ☐ *Trolley jack*

Buying tools

For practically all tools, a tool factor is the best source, since he will have a very comprehensive range compared with the average garage or accessory shop. Having said that, accessory shops often offer excellent quality tools at discount prices, so it pays to shop around.

Remember, you don't have to buy the most expensive items on the shelf, but it is always advisable to steer clear of the very cheap tools. There are plenty of good tools around at reasonable prices, but always aim to purchase items which meet the relevant national safety standards. If in doubt, ask the proprietor or manager of the shop for advice before making a purchase.

Care and maintenance of tools

Having purchased a reasonable tool kit, it is necessary to keep the tools in a clean and serviceable condition. After use, always wipe off any dirt, grease and metal particles using a clean, dry cloth, before putting the tools away. Never leave them lying around after they have been used. A simple tool rack on the garage or workshop wall for items such as screwdrivers and pliers is a good idea. Store all normal spanners and sockets in a metal box. Any measuring instruments, gauges, meters, etc, must be carefully stored where they cannot be damaged or become rusty.

Take a little care when tools are used. Hammer heads inevitably become marked, and screwdrivers lose the keen edge on their blades from time to time. A little timely attention with emery cloth or a file will soon restore items like this to a good serviceable finish.

Working facilities

Not to be forgotten when discussing tools is the workshop itself. If anything more than routine maintenance is to be carried out, some form of suitable working area becomes essential.

It is appreciated that many an owner-mechanic is forced by circumstances to remove an engine or similar item without the benefit of a garage or workshop. Having done this, any repairs should always be done under the cover of a roof.

Wherever possible, any dismantling should be done on a clean, flat workbench or table at a suitable working height.

Any workbench needs a vice; one with a jaw opening of 100 mm is suitable for most jobs. As mentioned previously, some clean dry storage space is also required for tools, as well as for any lubricants, cleaning fluids, touch-up paints and so on, which become necessary.

Another item which may be required, and which has a much more general usage, is an electric drill with a chuck capacity of at least 8 mm. This, together with a good range of twist drills, is virtually essential for fitting accessories.

Last, but not least, always keep a supply of old newspapers and clean, lint-free rags available, and try to keep any working area as clean as possible.

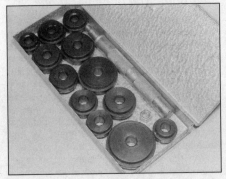

Bush and bearing removal/installation set

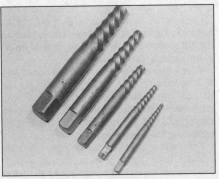

Stud extractor set

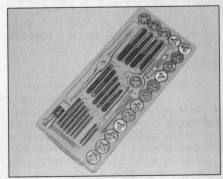

Tap and die set

Whenever servicing, repair or overhaul work is carried out on the car or its components, observe the following procedures and instructions. This will assist in carrying out the operation efficiently and to a professional standard of workmanship.

Joint mating faces and gaskets

When separating components at their mating faces, never insert screwdrivers or similar implements into the joint between the faces in order to prise them apart. This can cause severe damage which results in oil leaks, coolant leaks, etc upon reassembly. Separation is usually achieved by tapping along the joint with a soft-faced hammer in order to break the seal. However, note that this method may not be suitable where dowels are used for component location.

Where a gasket is used between the mating faces of two components, a new one must be fitted on reassembly; fit it dry unless otherwise stated in the repair procedure. Make sure that the mating faces are clean and dry, with all traces of old gasket removed. When cleaning a joint face, use a tool which is unlikely to score or damage the face, and remove any burrs or nicks with an oilstone or fine file.

Make sure that tapped holes are cleaned with a pipe cleaner, and keep them free of jointing compound, if this is being used, unless specifically instructed otherwise.

Ensure that all orifices, channels or pipes are clear, and blow through them, preferably using compressed air.

Oil seals

Oil seals can be removed by levering them out with a wide flat-bladed screwdriver or similar implement. Alternatively, a number of self-tapping screws may be screwed into the seal, and these used as a purchase for pliers or some similar device in order to pull the seal free.

Whenever an oil seal is removed from its working location, either individually or as part of an assembly, it should be renewed.

The very fine sealing lip of the seal is easily damaged, and will not seal if the surface it contacts is not completely clean and free from scratches, nicks or grooves. If the original sealing surface of the component cannot be restored, and the manufacturer has not made provision for slight relocation of the seal relative to the sealing surface, the component should be renewed.

Protect the lips of the seal from any surface which may damage them in the course of fitting. Use tape or a conical sleeve where possible. Lubricate the seal lips with oil before fitting and, on dual-lipped seals, fill the space between the lips with grease.

Unless otherwise stated, oil seals must be fitted with their sealing lips toward the lubricant to be sealed.

Use a tubular drift or block of wood of the appropriate size to install the seal and, if the seal housing is shouldered, drive the seal down to the shoulder. If the seal housing is unshouldered, the seal should be fitted with its face flush with the housing top face (unless otherwise instructed).

Screw threads and fastenings

Seized nuts, bolts and screws are quite a common occurrence where corrosion has set in, and the use of penetrating oil or releasing fluid will often overcome this problem if the offending item is soaked for a while before attempting to release it. The use of an impact driver may also provide a means of releasing such stubborn fastening devices, when used in conjunction with the appropriate screwdriver bit or socket. If none of these methods works, it may be necessary to resort to the careful application of heat, or the use of a hacksaw or nut splitter device.

Studs are usually removed by locking two nuts together on the threaded part, and then using a spanner on the lower nut to unscrew the stud. Studs or bolts which have broken off below the surface of the component in which they are mounted can sometimes be removed using a stud extractor. Always ensure that a blind tapped hole is completely free from oil, grease, water or other fluid before installing the bolt or stud. Failure to do this could cause the housing to crack due to the hydraulic action of the bolt or stud as it is screwed in.

When tightening a castellated nut to accept a split pin, tighten the nut to the specified torque, where applicable, and then tighten further to the next split pin hole. Never slacken the nut to align the split pin hole, unless stated in the repair procedure.

When checking or retightening a nut or bolt to a specified torque setting, slacken the nut or bolt by a quarter of a turn, and then retighten to the specified setting. However, this should not be attempted where angular tightening has been used.

For some screw fastenings, notably cylinder head bolts or nuts, torque wrench settings are no longer specified for the latter stages of tightening, "angle-tightening" being called up instead. Typically, a fairly low torque wrench setting will be applied to the bolts/nuts in the correct sequence, followed by one or more stages of tightening through specified angles.

Locknuts, locktabs and washers

Any fastening which will rotate against a component or housing during tightening should always have a washer between it and the relevant component or housing.

Spring or split washers should always be renewed when they are used to lock a critical component such as a big-end bearing retaining bolt or nut. Locktabs which are folded over to retain a nut or bolt should always be renewed.

Self-locking nuts can be re-used in non-critical areas, providing resistance can be felt when the locking portion passes over the bolt or stud thread. However, it should be noted that self-locking stiffnuts tend to lose their effectiveness after long periods of use, and should then be renewed as a matter of course.

Split pins must always be replaced with new ones of the correct size for the hole.

When thread-locking compound is found on the threads of a fastener which is to be re-used, it should be cleaned off with a wire brush and solvent, and fresh compound applied on reassembly.

Special tools

Some repair procedures in this manual entail the use of special tools such as a press, two or three-legged pullers, spring compressors, etc. Wherever possible, suitable readily-available alternatives to the manufacturer's special tools are described, and are shown in use. In some instances, where no alternative is possible, it has been necessary to resort to the use of a manufacturer's tool, and this has been done for reasons of safety as well as the efficient completion of the repair operation. Unless you are highly-skilled and have a thorough understanding of the procedures described, never attempt to bypass the use of any special tool when the procedure described specifies its use. Not only is there a very great risk of personal injury, but expensive damage could be caused to the components involved.

Environmental considerations

When disposing of used engine oil, brake fluid, antifreeze, etc, give due consideration to any detrimental environmental effects. Do not, for instance, pour any of the above liquids down drains into the general sewage system, or onto the ground to soak away. Many local council refuse tips provide a facility for waste oil disposal, as do some garages. If none of these facilities are available, consult your local Environmental Health Department, or the National Rivers Authority, for further advice.

With the universal tightening-up of legislation regarding the emission of environmentally-harmful substances from motor vehicles, most vehicles have tamperproof devices fitted to the main adjustment points of the fuel system. These devices are primarily designed to prevent unqualified persons from adjusting the fuel/air mixture, with the chance of a consequent increase in toxic emissions. If such devices are found during servicing or overhaul, they should, wherever possible, be renewed or refitted in accordance with the manufacturer's requirements or current legislation.

OIL CARE
FOLLOW THE CODE

OIL BANK LINE
0800 66 33 66

Note: It is antisocial and illegal to dump oil down the drain. To find the location of your local oil recycling bank, call this number free.

Buying spare parts

Spare parts are available from many sources, for example Austin Rover garages, other garages and accessory shops, and motor factors. Our advice regarding spare part sources is as follows.

Officially appointed Austin Rover garages – This is the best source of parts which are peculiar to your car and are not generally available (eg complete cylinder heads, internal gearbox components, badges, interior trim, etc). It is also the only place at which you should buy parts if your vehicle is still under warranty – non Austin Rover components may invalidate the warranty. To be sure of obtaining the correct parts it will always be necessary to give the storeman your car's vehicle identification number, and if possible, to take the 'old' part along for positive identification. Many parts are available under a factory exchange scheme – any parts returned should always be clean. It obviously makes good sense to go straight to the specialists on your car for this type of part for they are best equipped to supply you.

Other dealers and accessory shops – These are often very good places to buy materials and components needed for the maintenance of your car (eg oil filters, spark plugs, bulbs, drivebelts, oils and grease, touch-up paint, filler paste, etc). They also sell general accessories, usually have convenient opening hours, charge lower prices and can often be found not far from home.

Motor factors – Good factors will stock all of the more important components which wear out relatively quickly (eg clutch components, pistons, valves, exhaust systems, brake pipes/seals and pads, etc). Motor factors will often provide new or reconditioned components on a part exchange basis – this can save a considerable amount of money.

Vehicle identification numbers

Modifications are a continuing and unpublicised process in vehicle manufacture, quite apart from major model changes. Spare parts manuals and lists are compiled upon a numerical basis, the individual vehicle numbers being essential to correct identification of the component required.

When ordering spare parts, always give as much information as possible. Quote the car model, year of manufacture, body and engine numbers as appropriate.

The vehicle identification number is also stamped into the body on vehicles up to VIN 886518 in the boot aperture drain channel, and from VIN 886519 in the right-hand side of the bulkhead.

Additionally, a body number plate is welded to the right-hand side of the spare wheel well.

When ordering parts relating to the body, or paint, quote both the VIN and body number.

The engine number on 1.3 models is stamped on the crankcase adjacent to the flywheel housing. On 1.6 models the engine number is stamped on the cylinder block below the spark plugs.

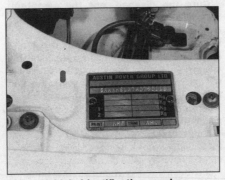

Vehicle identification number

Engine number (1.3)

Introduction

The vehicle owner who does his or her own maintenance according to the recommended schedules should not have to use this section of the manual very often. Modern component reliability is such that, provided those items subject to wear or deterioration are inspected or renewed at the specified intervals, sudden failure is comparatively rare. Faults do not usually just happen as a result of sudden failure, but develop over a period of time. Major mechanical failures in particular are usually preceded by characteristic symptoms over hundreds or even thousands of miles. Those components which do occasionally fail without warning are often small and easily carried in the vehicle.

With any fault finding, the first step is to decide where to begin investigations. Sometimes this is obvious, but on other occasions a little detective work will be necessary. The owner who makes half a dozen haphazard adjustments or replacements may be successful in curing a fault (or its symptoms), but he will be none the wiser if the fault recurs and he may well have spent more time and money than was necessary. A calm and logical approach will be found to be more satisfactory in the long run. Always take into account any warning signs or abnormalities that may have been noticed in the period preceding the fault – power loss, high or low gauge readings, unusual noises or smells, etc – and remember that failure of components such as fuses or spark plugs may only be pointers to some underlying fault.

The pages which follow here are intended to help in cases of failure to start or breakdown on the road. There is also a Fault Diagnosis Section at the end of each Chapter which should be consulted if the preliminary checks prove unfruitful. Whatever the fault, certain basic principles apply. These are as follows:

Verify the fault. This is simply a matter of being sure that you know what the symptoms are before starting work. This is particularly important if you are investigating a fault for someone else who may not have described it very accurately.

Don't overlook the obvious. For example, if the vehicle won't start, is there petrol in the tank? (Don't take anyone else's word on this particular point, and don't trust the fuel gauge either!) If an electrical fault is indicated, look for loose or broken wires before digging out the test gear.

Cure the disease, not the symptom. Substituting a flat battery with a fully charged one will get you off the hard shoulder, but if the underlying cause is not attended to,the new battery will go the same way. Similarly, changing oil-fouled spark plugs for a new set will get you moving again, but remember that the reason for the fouling (if it wasn't simply an incorrect grade of plug) will have to be established and corrected.

Don't take anything for granted. Particularly, don't forget that a 'new' component may itself be defective (especially if it's been rattling round in the boot for months), and don't leave components out of a fault diagnosis sequence just because they are new or recently fitted. When you do finally diagnose a difficult fault, you'll probably realise that all the evidence was there from the start.

Electrical faults

Electrical faults can be more puzzling than straightforward mechanical failures, but they are no less susceptible to logical analysis if the basic principles of operation are understood. Vehicle electrical wiring exists in extremely unfavourable conditions – heat, vibration and chemical attack and the first things to look for are loose or corroded connections and broken or chafed wires, especially where the wires pass through holes in the bodywork or are subject to vibration.

All metal-bodied vehicles in current production have one pole of the battery 'earthed', ie connected to the vehicle bodywork, and in nearly all modern vehicles it is the negative (–) terminal. The various electrical components – motors, bulb holders, etc – are also connected to earth, either by means of a lead or directly by their mountings. Electric current flows through the component and then back to the battery via the bodywork. If the component mounting is loose or corroded, or if a good path back to the battery is not available, the circuit will be incomplete and malfunction will result. The engine and/or gearbox are also earthed by means of flexible metal straps to the body or subframe; if these straps are loose or missing, starter motor, generator and ignition trouble may result.

Assuming the earth return to be satisfactory, electrical faults will be due either to component malfunction or to defects in the current supply. Individual components are dealt with in Chapter 12. If supply wires are broken or cracked internally this results in an open-circuit, and the easiest way to check for this is to bypass the suspect wire temporarily with a length of wire having a crocodile clip or suitable connector at each end. Alternatively, a 12V test lamp can be used to verify the presence of supply voltage at various points along the wire and the break can be thus isolated.

If a bare portion of a live wire touches the bodywork or other earthed metal part, the electricity will take the low-resistance path thus formed back to the battery: this is known as a short-circuit. Hopefully a short-circuit will blow a fuse, but otherwise it may cause burning of the insulation (and possibly further short-circuits) or even a fire. This is why it is inadvisable to bypass persistently blowing fuses with silver foil or wire.

Spares and tool kit

Most vehicles are supplied only with sufficient tools for wheel changing; the *Maintenance and minor repair* tool kit detailed in *Tools and working facilities*, with the addition of a hammer, is probably sufficient for those repairs that most motorists would consider attempting at the roadside. In addition a few items which can be fitted without too much trouble in the event of a breakdown should be carried. Experience and available space will modify the list below, but the following may save having to call on professional assistance:

- ☐ *Spark plugs, clean and correctly gapped*
- ☐ *HT lead and plug cap – long enough to reach the plug furthest from the distributor*
- ☐ *Distributor rotor*
- ☐ *Drivebelt(s) — emergency type may suffice*
- ☐ *Spare fuses*
- ☐ *Set of principal light bulbs*
- ☐ *Tin of radiator sealer and hose bandage*
- ☐ *Exhaust bandage*
- ☐ *Roll of insulating tape*
- ☐ *Length of soft iron wire*
- ☐ *Length of electrical flex*
- ☐ *Torch or inspection lamp (can double as test lamp)*
- ☐ *Battery jump leads*

- ☐ *Tow-rope*
- ☐ *Ignition waterproofing aerosol*
- ☐ *Litre of engine oil*
- ☐ *Sealed can of hydraulic fluid*
- ☐ *Emergency windscreen*
- ☐ *Wormdrive clips*
- ☐ *Tube of filler paste*

If spare fuel is carried, a can designed for the purpose should be used to minimise risks of leakage and collision damage. A first aid kit and a warning triangle, whilst not at present compulsory in the UK, are obviously sensible items to carry in addition to the above. When touring abroad it may be advisable to carry additional spares which, even if you cannot fit them yourself, could save having to wait while parts are obtained. The items below may be worth considering:

- ☐ *Clutch and throttle cables*
- ☐ *Cylinder head gasket*
- ☐ *Alternator brushes*
- ☐ *Tyre valve core*

One of the motoring organisations will be able to advise on availability of fuel, etc, in foreign countries.

Engine will not start

Engine fails to turn when starter operated

- ☐ Flat battery (recharge use jump leads or push start)
- ☐ Battery terminals loose or corroded
- ☐ Battery earth to body defective
- ☐ Engine earth strap loose or broken
- ☐ Starter motor (or solenoid) wiring loose or broken
- ☐ Ignition/starter switch faulty
- ☐ Major mechanical failure (seizure)
- ☐ Starter or solenoid internal fault (see Chapter 12)

Starter motor turns engine slowly

- ☐ Partially discharged battery (recharge, use jump leads, or push start)
- ☐ Battery terminals loose or corroded

- ☐ Battery earth to body defective
- ☐ Engine earth strap loose
- ☐ Starter motor (or solenoid) wiring loose
- ☐ Starter motor internal fault (see Chapter 12)

Starter motor spins without turning engine

- ☐ Flywheel gear teeth damaged or worn
- ☐ Starter motor mounting bolts loose

Engine turns normally but fails to start

- ☐ Damp or dirty HT leads and distributor cap (crank engine and check for spark)
- ☐ No fuel in tank (check for delivery)
- ☐ Fouled or incorrectly gapped spark plugs (remove, clean and regap)
- ☐ Other ignition system fault (see Chapter 4)
- ☐ Other fuel system fault (see Chapter 3)

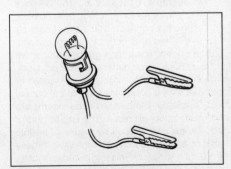

A simple test lamp is useful for checking electrical faults

Carrying a few spares may save you a long walk!

- ☐ Poor compression (see Chapter 1)
- ☐ Major mechanical failure (eg camshaft drive)

Engine fires but will not run

- ☐ Air leaks at carburettor or inlet manifold
- ☐ Fuel starvation (see Chapter 3)
- ☐ Ignition fault (see Chapter 4)

Engine cuts out and will not restart

Engine cuts out suddenly – ignition fault

- ☐ Loose or disconnected LT wires
- ☐ Wet HT leads or distributor cap (after traversing water splash)
- ☐ Coil failure (check for spark)
- ☐ Other ignition fault (see Chapter 4)

Engine misfires before cutting out – fuel fault

- ☐ Fuel tank empty
- ☐ Fuel pump defective or filter blocked (check for delivery)
- ☐ Fuel tank filler vent blocked (suction will be evident on releasing cap)
- ☐ Carburettor needle valve sticking

Crank engine and check for spark. Note use of insulated tool

- ☐ Carburettor jets blocked (fuel contaminated)
- ☐ Other fuel system fault (see Chapter 3)

Engine cuts out – other causes

- ☐ Serious overheating
- ☐ Major mechanical failure (eg camshaft drive)

Engine overheats

Ignition (no-charge) warning light illuminated

- ☐ Slack or broken drivebelt — retension or renew (Chapter 10)

Ignition warning light not illuminated

- ☐ Coolant loss due to internal or external leakage (see Chapter 2)
- ☐ Thermostat defective
- ☐ Low oil level
- ☐ Brakes binding
- ☐ Radiator clogged externally or internally
- ☐ Engine waterways clogged
- ☐ Ignition timing incorrect or automatic advance malfunctioning
- ☐ Mixture too weak

Note: *Do not add cold water to an overheated engine or damage may result*

Low engine oil pressure

Note: *Low oil pressure in a high-mileage engine at tickover is not necessarily a cause for concern. Sudden pressure loss at speed is far more significant. In any event check the gauge or warning light sender before condemning the engine.*

Gauge reads low or warning light illuminated with engine running

- ☐ Oil level low or incorrect grade
- ☐ Defective gauge or sender unit
- ☐ Wire to sender unit earthed
- ☐ Engine overheating
- ☐ Oil filter clogged or bypass valve defective
- ☐ Oil pressure relief valve defective
- ☐ Oil pick-up strainer clogged
- ☐ Oil pump worn or mountings loose
- ☐ Worn main or big-end bearings

Engine noises

Pre-ignition (pinking) on acceleration

- ☐ Incorrect grade of fuel
- ☐ Ignition timing incorrect
- ☐ Distributor faulty or worn
- ☐ Worn or maladjusted carburettor
- ☐ Excessive carbon build-up in engine

Whistling or wheezing noises

- ☐ Leaking vacuum hose
- ☐ Leaking carburettor or manifold gasket
- ☐ Blowing head gasket

Tapping or rattling

- ☐ Incorrect valve clearances
- ☐ Worn valve gear
- ☐ Worn timing chain or belt
- ☐ Broken piston ring (ticking noise)

Knocking or thumping

- ☐ Unintentional mechanical contact (eg fan blades)
- ☐ Worn drivebelt
- ☐ Peripheral component fault (generator, water pump, etc)
- ☐ Worn big-end bearings (regular heavy knocking, perhaps less under load)
- ☐ Worn main bearings (rumbling and knocking, perhaps worsening under load)
- ☐ Piston slap (most noticeable when cold)

A

ABS (Anti-lock brake system) A system, usually electronically controlled, that senses incipient wheel lockup during braking and relieves hydraulic pressure at wheels that are about to skid.

Air bag An inflatable bag hidden in the steering wheel (driver's side) or the dash or glovebox (passenger side). In a head-on collision, the bags inflate, preventing the driver and front passenger from being thrown forward into the steering wheel or windscreen.

Air cleaner A metal or plastic housing, containing a filter element, which removes dust and dirt from the air being drawn into the engine.

Air filter element The actual filter in an air cleaner system, usually manufactured from pleated paper and requiring renewal at regular intervals.

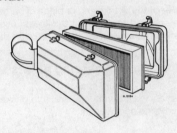

Air filter

Allen key A hexagonal wrench which fits into a recessed hexagonal hole.

Alligator clip A long-nosed spring-loaded metal clip with meshing teeth. Used to make temporary electrical connections.

Alternator A component in the electrical system which converts mechanical energy from a drivebelt into electrical energy to charge the battery and to operate the starting system, ignition system and electrical accessories.

Ampere (amp) A unit of measurement for the flow of electric current. One amp is the amount of current produced by one volt acting through a resistance of one ohm.

Anaerobic sealer A substance used to prevent bolts and screws from loosening. Anaerobic means that it does not require oxygen for activation. The Loctite brand is widely used.

Antifreeze A substance (usually ethylene glycol) mixed with water, and added to a vehicle's cooling system, to prevent freezing of the coolant in winter. Antifreeze also contains chemicals to inhibit corrosion and the formation of rust and other deposits that would tend to clog the radiator and coolant passages and reduce cooling efficiency.

Anti-seize compound A coating that reduces the risk of seizing on fasteners that are subjected to high temperatures, such as exhaust manifold bolts and nuts.

Asbestos A natural fibrous mineral with great heat resistance, commonly used in the composition of brake friction materials.

Asbestos is a health hazard and the dust created by brake systems should never be inhaled or ingested.

Axle A shaft on which a wheel revolves, or which revolves with a wheel. Also, a solid beam that connects the two wheels at one end of the vehicle. An axle which also transmits power to the wheels is known as a live axle.

Axleshaft A single rotating shaft, on either side of the differential, which delivers power from the final drive assembly to the drive wheels. Also called a driveshaft or a halfshaft.

B

Ball bearing An anti-friction bearing consisting of a hardened inner and outer race with hardened steel balls between two races.

Bearing The curved surface on a shaft or in a bore, or the part assembled into either, that permits relative motion between them with minimum wear and friction.

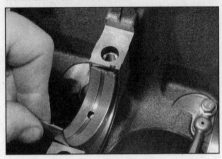

Bearing

Big-end bearing The bearing in the end of the connecting rod that's attached to the crankshaft.

Bleed nipple A valve on a brake wheel cylinder, caliper or other hydraulic component that is opened to purge the hydraulic system of air. Also called a bleed screw.

Brake bleeding Procedure for removing air from lines of a hydraulic brake system.

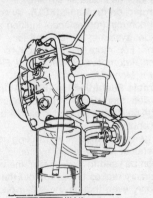

Brake bleeding

Brake disc The component of a disc brake that rotates with the wheels.

Brake drum The component of a drum brake that rotates with the wheels.

Brake linings The friction material which contacts the brake disc or drum to retard the vehicle's speed. The linings are bonded or riveted to the brake pads or shoes.

Brake pads The replaceable friction pads that pinch the brake disc when the brakes are applied. Brake pads consist of a friction material bonded or riveted to a rigid backing plate.

Brake shoe The crescent-shaped carrier to which the brake linings are mounted and which forces the lining against the rotating drum during braking.

Braking systems For more information on braking systems, consult the *Haynes Automotive Brake Manual*.

Breaker bar A long socket wrench handle providing greater leverage.

Bulkhead The insulated partition between the engine and the passenger compartment.

C

Caliper The non-rotating part of a disc-brake assembly that straddles the disc and carries the brake pads. The caliper also contains the hydraulic components that cause the pads to pinch the disc when the brakes are applied. A caliper is also a measuring tool that can be set to measure inside or outside dimensions of an object.

Camshaft A rotating shaft on which a series of cam lobes operate the valve mechanisms. The camshaft may be driven by gears, by sprockets and chain or by sprockets and a belt.

Canister A container in an evaporative emission control system; contains activated charcoal granules to trap vapours from the fuel system.

Canister

Carburettor A device which mixes fuel with air in the proper proportions to provide a desired power output from a spark ignition internal combustion engine.

Castellated Resembling the parapets along the top of a castle wall. For example, a castellated balljoint stud nut.

Castor In wheel alignment, the backward or forward tilt of the steering axis. Castor is positive when the steering axis is inclined rearward at the top.

Catalytic converter A silencer-like device in the exhaust system which converts certain pollutants in the exhaust gases into less harmful substances.

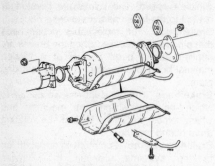

Catalytic converter

Circlip A ring-shaped clip used to prevent endwise movement of cylindrical parts and shafts. An internal circlip is installed in a groove in a housing; an external circlip fits into a groove on the outside of a cylindrical piece such as a shaft.

Clearance The amount of space between two parts. For example, between a piston and a cylinder, between a bearing and a journal, etc.

Coil spring A spiral of elastic steel found in various sizes throughout a vehicle, for example as a springing medium in the suspension and in the valve train.

Compression Reduction in volume, and increase in pressure and temperature, of a gas, caused by squeezing it into a smaller space.

Compression ratio The relationship between cylinder volume when the piston is at top dead centre and cylinder volume when the piston is at bottom dead centre.

Constant velocity (CV) joint A type of universal joint that cancels out vibrations caused by driving power being transmitted through an angle.

Core plug A disc or cup-shaped metal device inserted in a hole in a casting through which core was removed when the casting was formed. Also known as a freeze plug or expansion plug.

Crankcase The lower part of the engine block in which the crankshaft rotates.

Crankshaft The main rotating member, or shaft, running the length of the crankcase, with offset "throws" to which the connecting rods are attached.

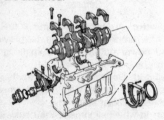

Crankshaft assembly

Crocodile clip See Alligator clip

D

Diagnostic code Code numbers obtained by accessing the diagnostic mode of an engine management computer. This code can be used to determine the area in the system where a malfunction may be located.

Disc brake A brake design incorporating a rotating disc onto which brake pads are squeezed. The resulting friction converts the energy of a moving vehicle into heat.

Double-overhead cam (DOHC) An engine that uses two overhead camshafts, usually one for the intake valves and one for the exhaust valves.

Drivebelt(s) The belt(s) used to drive accessories such as the alternator, water pump, power steering pump, air conditioning compressor, etc. off the crankshaft pulley.

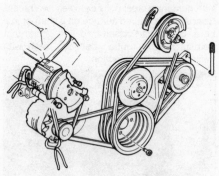

Accessory drivebelts

Driveshaft Any shaft used to transmit motion. Commonly used when referring to the axleshafts on a front wheel drive vehicle.

Drum brake A type of brake using a drum-shaped metal cylinder attached to the inner surface of the wheel. When the brake pedal is pressed, curved brake shoes with friction linings press against the inside of the drum to slow or stop the vehicle.

E

EGR valve A valve used to introduce exhaust gases into the intake air stream.

Electronic control unit (ECU) A computer which controls (for instance) ignition and fuel injection systems, or an anti-lock braking system. For more information refer to the *Haynes Automotive Electrical and Electronic Systems Manual.*

Electronic Fuel Injection (EFI) A computer controlled fuel system that distributes fuel through an injector located in each intake port of the engine.

Emergency brake A braking system, independent of the main hydraulic system, that can be used to slow or stop the vehicle if the primary brakes fail, or to hold the vehicle stationary even though the brake pedal isn't depressed. It usually consists of a hand lever that actuates either front or rear brakes mechanically through a series of cables and linkages. Also known as a handbrake or parking brake.

Endfloat The amount of lengthwise movement between two parts. As applied to a crankshaft, the distance that the crankshaft can move forward and back in the cylinder block.

Engine management system (EMS) A computer controlled system which manages the fuel injection and the ignition systems in an integrated fashion.

Exhaust manifold A part with several passages through which exhaust gases leave the engine combustion chambers and enter the exhaust pipe.

F

Fan clutch A viscous (fluid) drive coupling device which permits variable engine fan speeds in relation to engine speeds.

Feeler blade A thin strip or blade of hardened steel, ground to an exact thickness, used to check or measure clearances between parts.

Feeler blade

Firing order The order in which the engine cylinders fire, or deliver their power strokes, beginning with the number one cylinder.

Flywheel A heavy spinning wheel in which energy is absorbed and stored by means of momentum. On cars, the flywheel is attached to the crankshaft to smooth out firing impulses.

Free play The amount of travel before any action takes place. The "looseness" in a linkage, or an assembly of parts, between the initial application of force and actual movement. For example, the distance the brake pedal moves before the pistons in the master cylinder are actuated.

Fuse An electrical device which protects a circuit against accidental overload. The typical fuse contains a soft piece of metal which is calibrated to melt at a predetermined current flow (expressed as amps) and break the circuit.

Fusible link A circuit protection device consisting of a conductor surrounded by heat-resistant insulation. The conductor is smaller than the wire it protects, so it acts as the weakest link in the circuit. Unlike a blown fuse, a failed fusible link must frequently be cut from the wire for replacement.

G

Gap The distance the spark must travel in jumping from the centre electrode to the side electrode in a spark plug. Also refers to the spacing between the points in a contact breaker assembly in a conventional points-type ignition, or to the distance between the reluctor or rotor and the pickup coil in an electronic ignition.

Adjusting spark plug gap

Gasket Any thin, soft material - usually cork, cardboard, asbestos or soft metal - installed between two metal surfaces to ensure a good seal. For instance, the cylinder head gasket seals the joint between the block and the cylinder head.

Gasket

Gauge An instrument panel display used to monitor engine conditions. A gauge with a movable pointer on a dial or a fixed scale is an analogue gauge. A gauge with a numerical readout is called a digital gauge.

H

Halfshaft A rotating shaft that transmits power from the final drive unit to a drive wheel, usually when referring to a live rear axle.

Harmonic balancer A device designed to reduce torsion or twisting vibration in the crankshaft. May be incorporated in the crankshaft pulley. Also known as a vibration damper.

Hone An abrasive tool for correcting small irregularities or differences in diameter in an engine cylinder, brake cylinder, etc.

Hydraulic tappet A tappet that utilises hydraulic pressure from the engine's lubrication system to maintain zero clearance (constant contact with both camshaft and valve stem). Automatically adjusts to variation in valve stem length. Hydraulic tappets also reduce valve noise.

I

Ignition timing The moment at which the spark plug fires, usually expressed in the number of crankshaft degrees before the piston reaches the top of its stroke.

Inlet manifold A tube or housing with passages through which flows the air-fuel mixture (carburettor vehicles and vehicles with throttle body injection) or air only (port fuel-injected vehicles) to the port openings in the cylinder head.

J

Jump start Starting the engine of a vehicle with a discharged or weak battery by attaching jump leads from the weak battery to a charged or helper battery.

L

Load Sensing Proportioning Valve (LSPV) A brake hydraulic system control valve that works like a proportioning valve, but also takes into consideration the amount of weight carried by the rear axle.

Locknut A nut used to lock an adjustment nut, or other threaded component, in place. For example, a locknut is employed to keep the adjusting nut on the rocker arm in position.

Lockwasher A form of washer designed to prevent an attaching nut from working loose.

M

MacPherson strut A type of front suspension system devised by Earle MacPherson at Ford of England. In its original form, a simple lateral link with the anti-roll bar creates the lower control arm. A long strut - an integral coil spring and shock absorber - is mounted between the body and the steering knuckle. Many modern so-called MacPherson strut systems use a conventional lower A-arm and don't rely on the anti-roll bar for location.

Multimeter An electrical test instrument with the capability to measure voltage, current and resistance.

N

NOx Oxides of Nitrogen. A common toxic pollutant emitted by petrol and diesel engines at higher temperatures.

O

Ohm The unit of electrical resistance. One volt applied to a resistance of one ohm will produce a current of one amp.

Ohmmeter An instrument for measuring electrical resistance.

O-ring A type of sealing ring made of a special rubber-like material; in use, the O-ring is compressed into a groove to provide the sealing action.

Overhead cam (ohc) engine An engine with the camshaft(s) located on top of the cylinder head(s).

Overhead valve (ohv) engine An engine with the valves located in the cylinder head, but with the camshaft located in the engine block.

Oxygen sensor A device installed in the engine exhaust manifold, which senses the oxygen content in the exhaust and converts this information into an electric current. Also called a Lambda sensor.

P

Phillips screw A type of screw head having a cross instead of a slot for a corresponding type of screwdriver.

Plastigage A thin strip of plastic thread, available in different sizes, used for measuring clearances. For example, a strip of Plastigage is laid across a bearing journal. The parts are assembled and dismantled; the width of the crushed strip indicates the clearance between journal and bearing.

Plastigage

Propeller shaft The long hollow tube with universal joints at both ends that carries power from the transmission to the differential on front-engined rear wheel drive vehicles.

Proportioning valve A hydraulic control valve which limits the amount of pressure to the rear brakes during panic stops to prevent wheel lock-up.

R

Rack-and-pinion steering A steering system with a pinion gear on the end of the steering shaft that mates with a rack (think of a geared wheel opened up and laid flat). When the steering wheel is turned, the pinion turns, moving the rack to the left or right. This movement is transmitted through the track rods to the steering arms at the wheels.

Radiator A liquid-to-air heat transfer device designed to reduce the temperature of the coolant in an internal combustion engine cooling system.

Refrigerant Any substance used as a heat transfer agent in an air-conditioning system. R-12 has been the principle refrigerant for many years; recently, however, manufacturers have begun using R-134a, a non-CFC substance that is considered less harmful to the ozone in the upper atmosphere.

Rocker arm A lever arm that rocks on a shaft or pivots on a stud. In an overhead valve engine, the rocker arm converts the upward movement of the pushrod into a downward movement to open a valve.

Rotor In a distributor, the rotating device inside the cap that connects the centre electrode and the outer terminals as it turns, distributing the high voltage from the coil secondary winding to the proper spark plug. Also, that part of an alternator which rotates inside the stator. Also, the rotating assembly of a turbocharger, including the compressor wheel, shaft and turbine wheel.

Runout The amount of wobble (in-and-out movement) of a gear or wheel as it's rotated. The amount a shaft rotates "out-of-true." The out-of-round condition of a rotating part.

S

Sealant A liquid or paste used to prevent leakage at a joint. Sometimes used in conjunction with a gasket.

Sealed beam lamp An older headlight design which integrates the reflector, lens and filaments into a hermetically-sealed one-piece unit. When a filament burns out or the lens cracks, the entire unit is simply replaced.

Serpentine drivebelt A single, long, wide accessory drivebelt that's used on some newer vehicles to drive all the accessories, instead of a series of smaller, shorter belts. Serpentine drivebelts are usually tensioned by an automatic tensioner.

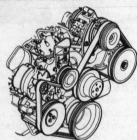

Serpentine drivebelt

Shim Thin spacer, commonly used to adjust the clearance or relative positions between two parts. For example, shims inserted into or under bucket tappets control valve clearances. Clearance is adjusted by changing the thickness of the shim.

Slide hammer A special puller that screws into or hooks onto a component such as a shaft or bearing; a heavy sliding handle on the shaft bottoms against the end of the shaft to knock the component free.

Sprocket A tooth or projection on the periphery of a wheel, shaped to engage with a chain or drivebelt. Commonly used to refer to the sprocket wheel itself.

Starter inhibitor switch On vehicles with an automatic transmission, a switch that prevents starting if the vehicle is not in Neutral or Park.

Strut See MacPherson strut.

T

Tappet A cylindrical component which transmits motion from the cam to the valve stem, either directly or via a pushrod and rocker arm. Also called a cam follower.

Thermostat A heat-controlled valve that regulates the flow of coolant between the cylinder block and the radiator, so maintaining optimum engine operating temperature. A thermostat is also used in some air cleaners in which the temperature is regulated.

Thrust bearing The bearing in the clutch assembly that is moved in to the release levers by clutch pedal action to disengage the clutch. Also referred to as a release bearing.

Timing belt A toothed belt which drives the camshaft. Serious engine damage may result if it breaks in service.

Timing chain A chain which drives the camshaft.

Toe-in The amount the front wheels are closer together at the front than at the rear. On rear wheel drive vehicles, a slight amount of toe-in is usually specified to keep the front wheels running parallel on the road by offsetting other forces that tend to spread the wheels apart.

Toe-out The amount the front wheels are closer together at the rear than at the front. On front wheel drive vehicles, a slight amount of toe-out is usually specified.

Tools For full information on choosing and using tools, refer to the *Haynes Automotive Tools Manual.*

Tracer A stripe of a second colour applied to a wire insulator to distinguish that wire from another one with the same colour insulator.

Tune-up A process of accurate and careful adjustments and parts replacement to obtain the best possible engine performance.

Turbocharger A centrifugal device, driven by exhaust gases, that pressurises the intake air. Normally used to increase the power output from a given engine displacement, but can also be used primarily to reduce exhaust emissions (as on VW's "Umwelt" Diesel engine).

U

Universal joint or U-joint A double-pivoted connection for transmitting power from a driving to a driven shaft through an angle. A U-joint consists of two Y-shaped yokes and a cross-shaped member called the spider.

V

Valve A device through which the flow of liquid, gas, vacuum, or loose material in bulk may be started, stopped, or regulated by a movable part that opens, shuts, or partially obstructs one or more ports or passageways. A valve is also the movable part of such a device.

Valve clearance The clearance between the valve tip (the end of the valve stem) and the rocker arm or tappet. The valve clearance is measured when the valve is closed.

Vernier caliper A precision measuring instrument that measures inside and outside dimensions. Not quite as accurate as a micrometer, but more convenient.

Viscosity The thickness of a liquid or its resistance to flow.

Volt A unit for expressing electrical "pressure" in a circuit. One volt that will produce a current of one ampere through a resistance of one ohm.

W

Welding Various processes used to join metal items by heating the areas to be joined to a molten state and fusing them together. For more information refer to the *Haynes Automotive Welding Manual.*

Wiring diagram A drawing portraying the components and wires in a vehicle's electrical system, using standardised symbols. For more information refer to the *Haynes Automotive Electrical and Electronic Systems Manual.*

Note: *References throughout this index relate to Chapter•page number*

Haynes Manuals – The Complete List

Title	Book No.
ALFA ROMEO	
Alfa Romeo Alfasud/Sprint (74 - 88)	0292
Alfa Romeo Alfetta (73 - 87)	0531
AUDI	
Audi 80 (72 - Feb 79)	0207
Audi 80, 90 (79 - Oct 86) & Coupe (81 - Nov 88)	0605
Audi 80, 90 (Oct 86 - 90) & Coupe (Nov 88 - 90)	1491
Audi 100 (Oct 76 - Oct 82)	0428
Audi 100 (Oct 82 - 90) & 200 (Feb 84 - Oct 89)	0907
AUSTIN	
Austin Ambassador (82 - 84)	0871
Austin/MG Maestro 1.3 & 1.6 (83 - 95)	0922
Austin Maxi (69 - 81)	0052
Austin/MG Metro (80 - May 90)	0718
Austin Montego 1.3 & 1.6 (84 - 94)	1066
Austin/MG Montego 2.0 (84 - 95)	1067
Mini (59 - 69)	0527
Mini (69 - 96)	0646
Austin/Rover 2.0 litre Diesel Engine (86 - 93)	1857
BEDFORD	
Bedford CF (69 - 87)	0163
Bedford Rascal (86 - 93)	3015
BL	
BL Princess & BLMC 18-22 (75 - 82)	0286
BMW	
BMW 316, 320 & 320i (4-cyl) (75 - Feb 83)	0276
BMW 320, 320i, 323i & 325i (6-cyl) (Oct 77 - Sept 87)	0815
BMW 3-Series (Apr 91 - 96)	3210
BMW 3-Series (sohc) (83 - 91)	1948
BMW 520i & 525e (Oct 81 - June 88)	1560
BMW 525, 528 & 528i (73 - Sept 81)	0632
BMW 5-Series (sohc) (81 - 93)	1948
BMW 1500, 1502, 1600, 1602, 2000 & 2002 (59 - 77)	0240
CITROEN	
Citroen 2CV, Ami & Dyane (67 - 90)	0196
Citroen AX Petrol & Diesel (87 - 94)	3014
Citroen BX (83 - 94)	0908
Citroen CX (75 - 88)	0528
Citroen Visa (79 - 88)	0620
Citroen Xantia Petrol & Diesel (93 - Oct 95)	3082
Citroen ZX Diesel (91 - 93)	1922
Citroen ZX Petrol (91 - 94)	1881
Citroen 1.7 & 1.9 litre Diesel Engine (84 - 96)	1379
COLT	
Colt 1200, 1250 & 1400 (79 - May 84)	0600
Colt Galant (74 - 78) & Celeste (76 - 81)	0236
DAIMLER	
Daimler Sovereign (68 - Oct 86)	0242
Daimler Double Six (72 - 88)	0478
DATSUN (see also *Nissan*)	
Datsun 120Y (73 - Aug 78)	0228
Datsun 1300, 1400 & 1600 (69 - Aug 72)	0123
Datsun Cherry (79 - Sept 82)	0679
Datsun Pick-up (75 - 78)	0277
Datsun Sunny (Aug 78 - May 82)	0525
Datsun Violet (78 - 82)	0430

Title	Book No.
FIAT	
Fiat 126 (73 - 87)	0305
Fiat 127 (71 - 83)	0193
Fiat 500 (57 - 73)	0090
Fiat 850 (64 - 81)	0038
Fiat Panda (81 - 95)	0793
Fiat Punto (94 - 96)	3251
Fiat Regata (84 - 88)	1167
Fiat Strada (79 - 88)	0479
Fiat Tipo (88 - 91)	1625
Fiat Uno (83 - 95)	0923
Fiat X1/9 (74 - 89)	0273
FORD	
Ford Capri II (& III) 1.6 & 2.0 (74 - 87)	0283
Ford Capri II (& III) 2.8 & 3.0 (74 - 87)	1309
Ford Cortina Mk III 1600 & 2000 (70 - 76)	0295
Ford Cortina Mk IV (& V) 1.6 & 2.0 (76 - 83)	0343
Ford Cortina Mk IV (& V) 2.3 V6 (77 - 83)	0426
Ford Escort (75 - Aug 80)	0280
Ford Escort (Sept 80 - Sept 90)	0686
Ford Escort (Sept 90 - 96)	1737
Ford Escort Mk II Mexico, RS 1600 & RS 2000 (75 - 80)	0735
Ford Fiesta (inc. XR2) (76 - Aug 83)	0334
Ford Fiesta (inc. XR2) (Aug 83 - Feb 89)	1030
Ford Fiesta (Feb 89 - 93)	1595
Ford Granada (Sept 77 - Feb 85)	0481
Ford Granada (Mar 85 - 94)	1245
Ford Mondeo 4-cyl (93 - 96)	1923
Ford Orion (83 - Sept 90)	1009
Ford Orion (Sept 90 - 93)	1737
Ford Sierra 1.3, 1.6, 1.8 & 2.0 (82 - 93)	0903
Ford Sierra 2.3, 2.8 & 2.9 (82 - 91)	0904
Ford Scorpio (Mar 85 - 94)	1245
Ford Transit Petrol (Mk 1) (65 - Feb 78)	0377
Ford Transit Petrol (Mk 2) (78 - Jan 86)	0719
Ford Transit Petrol (Mk 3) (Feb 86 - 89)	1468
Ford Transit Diesel (Feb 86 - 95)	3019
Ford 1.6 & 1.8 litre Diesel Engine (84 - 96)	1172
Ford 2.1, 2.3 & 2.5 litre Diesel Engine (77 - 90)	1606
Ford Vehicle Carburettors	1783
FREIGHT ROVER	
Freight Rover Sherpa (74 - 87)	0463
HILLMAN	
Hillman Avenger (70 - 82)	0037
Hillman Minx & Husky (56 - 66)	0009
HONDA	
Honda Accord (76 - Feb 84)	0351
Honda Accord (Feb 84 - Oct 85)	1177
Honda Civic 1300 (80 - 81)	0633
Honda Civic (Feb 84 - Oct 87)	1226
Honda Civic (Nov 91 - 96)	3199
JAGUAR	
Jaguar E Type (61 - 72)	0140
Jaguar MkI & II, 240 & 340 (55 - 69)	0098
Jaguar XJ6, XJ & Sovereign (68 - Oct 86)	0242
Jaguar XJ12, XJS & Sovereign (72 - 88)	0478
JEEP	
Jeep Cherokee Petrol (93 - 96)	1943

Title	Book No.
LADA	
Lada 1200, 1300, 1500 & 1600 (74 - 91)	0413
Lada Samara (87 - 91)	1610
LAND ROVER	
Land Rover 90, 110 & Defender Diesel (83 - 95)	3017
Land Rover Discovery Diesel (89 - 95)	3016
Land Rover Series IIA & III Diesel (58 - 85)	0529
Land Rover Series II, IIA & III Petrol (58 - 85)	0314
MAZDA	
Mazda 323 fwd (Mar 81 - Oct 89)	1608
Mazda 323 rwd (77 - Apr 86)	0370
Mazda 626 fwd (May 83 - Sept 87)	0929
Mazda B-1600, B-1800 & B-2000 Pick-up (72 - 88)	0267
Mazda RX-7 (79 - 85)	0460
MERCEDES-BENZ	
Mercedes-Benz 190 & 190E (83 - 87)	0928
Mercedes-Benz 200, 240, 300 Diesel (Oct 76 - 85)	1114
Mercedes-Benz 250 & 280 (68 - 72)	0346
Mercedes-Benz 250 & 280 (123 Series) (Oct 76 - 84)	0677
Mercedes-Benz 124 Series (85 - Aug 93)	3253
MG	
MGB (62 - 80)	0111
MG Maestro 1.3 & 1.6 (83 - 95)	0922
MG Metro (80 - May 90)	0718
MG Midget & AH Sprite (58 - 80)	0265
MG Montego 2.0 (84 - 95)	1067
MITSUBISHI	
Mitsubishi 1200, 1250 & 1400 (79 - May 84)	0600
Mitsubishi Shogun & L200 Pick-Ups (83 - 94)	1944
MORRIS	
Morris Ital 1.3 (80 - 84)	0705
Morris Marina 1700 (78 - 80)	0526
Morris Marina 1.8 (71 - 78)	0074
Morris Minor 1000 (56 - 71)	0024
NISSAN *(See also Datsun)*	
Nissan Bluebird 160B & 180B rwd (May 80 - May 84)	0957
Nissan Bluebird fwd (May 84 - Mar 86)	1223
Nissan Bluebird (T12 & T72) (Mar 86 - 90)	1473
Nissan Cherry (N12) (Sept 82 - 86)	1031
Nissan Micra (K10) (83 - Jan 93)	0931
Nissan Micra (93 - 96)	3254
Nissan Primera (90 - Oct 96)	1851
Nissan Stanza (82 - 86)	0824
Nissan Sunny (B11) (May 82 - Oct 86)	0895
Nissan Sunny (Oct 86 - Mar 91)	1378
Nissan Sunny (Apr 91 - 95)	3219
OPEL	
Opel Ascona & Manta (B Series) (Sept 75 - 88)	0316
Opel Ascona (81 - 88)	3215
Opel Astra (Oct 91 - 96)	3156
Opel Corsa (83 - Mar 93)	3160
Opel Corsa (Mar 93 - 94)	3159
Opel Kadett (Nov 79 - Oct 84)	0634
Opel Kadett (Oct 84 - Oct 91)	3196
Opel Omega & Senator (86 - 94)	3157

Title	Book No.
Opel Rekord (Feb 78 - Oct 86)	0543
Opel Vectra (88 - Oct 95)	3158
PEUGEOT	
Peugeot 106 Petrol & Diesel (91 - June 96)	1882
Peugeot 205 (83 - 95)	0932
Peugeot 305 (78 - 89)	0538
Peugeot 306 Petrol & Diesel (93 - 95)	3073
Peugeot 309 (86 - 93)	1266
Peugeot 405 Petrol (88 - 96)	1559
Peugeot 405 Diesel (88 - 96)	3198
Peugeot 505 (79 - 89)	0762
Peugeot 1.7 & 1.9 litre Diesel Engines (82 - 96)	0950
Peugeot 2.0, 2.1, 2.3 & 2.5 litre Diesel Engines (74 - 90)	1607
PORSCHE	
Porsche 911 (65 - 85)	0264
Porsche 924 & 924 Turbo (76 - 85)	0397
RANGE ROVER	
Range Rover V8 (70 - Oct 92)	0606
RELIANT	
Reliant Robin & Kitten (73 - 83)	0436
RENAULT	
Renault 5 (72 - Feb 85)	0141
Renault 5 (Feb 85 - 96)	1219
Renault 6 (68 - 79)	0092
Renault 9 & 11 (82 - 89)	0822
Renault 12 (70 - 80)	0097
Renault 15 & 17 (72 - 79)	0763
Renault 16 (65 - 79)	0081
Renault 18 (79 - 86)	0598
Renault 19 Petrol (89 - 94)	1646
Renault 19 Diesel (89 - 95)	1946
Renault 21 (86 - 94)	1397
Renault 25 (84 - 86)	1228
Renault Clio Petrol (91 - 93)	1853
Renault Clio Diesel (91 - June 96)	3031
Renault Espace (85 - 96)	3197
Renault Fuego (80 - 86)	0764
Renault Laguna (94 - 96)	3252
ROVER	
Rover 111 & 114 (95 - 96)	1711
Rover 213 & 216 (84 - 89)	1116
Rover 214 & 414 (Oct 89 - 92)	1689
Rover 216 & 416 (Oct 89 - 92)	1830
Rover 820, 825 & 827 (86 - 95)	1380
Rover 2000, 2300 & 2600 (77 - 87)	0468
Rover 3500 (76 - 87)	0365
Rover Metro (May 90 - 94)	1711
Rover 2.0 litre Diesel Engine (86 - 93)	1857
SAAB	
Saab 95 & 96 (66 - 76)	0198
Saab 99 (69 - 79)	0247
Saab 90, 99 & 900 (79 - Oct 93)	0765
Saab 9000 (4-cyl) (85 - 95)	1686
SEAT	
Seat Ibiza & Malaga (85 - 92)	1609

Title	Book No.
SIMCA	
Simca 1100 & 1204 (67 - 79)	0088
Simca 1301 & 1501 (63 - 76)	0199
SKODA	
Skoda 1000 & 1100 (64 - 78)	0303
Skoda Estelle 105, 120, 130 & 136 (77 - 89)	0604
Skoda Favorit (89 - 92)	1801
SUBARU	
Subaru 1600 (77 - Oct 79)	0237
Subaru 1600 & 1800 (Nov 79 - 90)	0995
SUZUKI	
Suzuki SJ Series, Samurai & Vitara (82 - 94)	1942
Suzuki Supercarry (86 - Oct 94)	3015
TALBOT	
Talbot Alpine, Solara, Minx & Rapier (75 - 86)	0337
Talbot Horizon (78 - 86)	0473
Talbot Samba (82 - 86)	0823
TOYOTA	
Toyota 2000 (75 - 77)	0360
Toyota Celica (78 - Jan 82)	0437
Toyota Celica (Feb 82 - Sept 85)	1135
Toyota Corolla (fwd) (Sept 83 - Sept 87)	1024
Toyota Corolla (rwd) (80 - 85)	0683
Toyota Corolla (Sept 87 - 92)	1683
Toyota Hi-Ace & Hi-Lux (69 - Oct 83)	0304
Toyota Starlet (78 - Jan 85)	0462
TRIUMPH	
Triumph Acclaim (81 - 84)	0792
Triumph GT6 (62 - 74)	0112
Triumph Herald (59 - 71)	0010
Triumph Spitfire (62 - 81)	0113
Triumph Stag (70 - 78)	0441
Triumph TR2, TR3, TR3A, TR4 & TR4A (52 - 67)	0028
Triumph TR7 (75 - 82)	0322
Triumph Vitesse (62 - 74)	0112
VAUXHALL	
Vauxhall Astra (80 - Oct 84)	0635
Vauxhall Astra & Belmont (Oct 84 - Oct 91)	1136
Vauxhall Astra (Oct 91 - 96)	1832
Vauxhall Carlton (Oct 78 - Oct 86)	0480
Vauxhall Carlton (Nov 86 - 94)	1469
Vauxhall Cavalier 1300 (77 - July 81)	0461
Vauxhall Cavalier 1600, 1900 & 2000 (75 - July 81)	0315
Vauxhall Cavalier (81 - Oct 88)	0812
Vauxhall Cavalier (Oct 88 - Oct 95)	1570
Vauxhall Chevette (75 - 84)	0285
Vauxhall Corsa (Mar 93 - 94)	1985
Vauxhall Nova (83 - 93)	0909
Vauxhall Rascal (86 - 93)	3015
Vauxhall Senator (Sept 87 - 94)	1469
Vauxhall Victor & VX4/90 (FD Series) (67 - 72)	0053
Vauxhall Viva HC (70 - 79)	0047
Vauxhall/Opel 1.5, 1.6 & 1.7 litre Diesel Engines (82 - 96)	1222
VOLKSWAGEN	
VW Beetle 1200 (54 - 77)	0036
VW Beetle 1300 & 1500 (65 - 75)	0039

Title	Book No.
VW Beetle 1302 & 1302S (70 - 72)	0110
VW Beetle 1303, 1303S & GT (72 - 75)	0159
VW Golf Mk 1 1.1 & 1.3 (74 - Feb 84)	0716
VW Golf Mk 1 1.5, 1.6 & 1.8 (74 - 85)	0726
VW Golf Mk 1 Diesel (78 - Feb 84)	0451
VW Golf Mk 2 (Mar 84 - Feb 92)	1081
VW Golf Mk 3 Petrol & Diesel (Feb 92 - 96)	3097
VW Jetta Mk 1 1.1 & 1.3 (80 - June 84)	0716
VW Jetta Mk 1 1.5, 1.6 & 1.8 (80 - June 84)	0726
VW Jetta Mk 1 Diesel (81 - June 84)	0451
VW Jetta Mk 2 (July 84 - 92)	1081
VW LT vans & light trucks (76 - 87)	0637
VW Passat (Sept 81 - May 88)	0814
VW Passat (May 88 - 91)	1647
VW Polo & Derby (76 - Jan 82)	0335
VW Polo (82 - Oct 90)	0813
VW Polo (Nov 90 - Aug 94)	3245
VW Santana (Sept 82 - 85)	0814
VW Scirocco Mk 1 1.5, 1.6 & 1.8 (74 - 82)	0726
VW Scirocco (82 - 90)	1224
VW Transporter 1600 (68 - 79)	0082
VW Transporter 1700, 1800 & 2000 (72 - 79)	0226
VW Transporter with air-cooled engine (79 - 82)	0638
VW Type 3 (63 - 73)	0084
VW Vento Petrol & Diesel (Feb 92 - 96)	3097
VOLVO	
Volvo 66 & 343, Daf 55 & 66 (68 - 79)	0293
Volvo 142, 144 & 145 (66 - 74)	0129
Volvo 240 Series (74 - 93)	0270
Volvo 262, 264 & 260/265 (75 - 85)	0400
Volvo 340, 343, 345 & 360 (76 - 91)	0715
Volvo 440, 460 & 480 (87 - 92)	1691
Volvo 740 & 760 (82 - 91)	1258
Volvo 850 (92 - 96)	3260
Volvo 940 (90 - 96)	3249
YUGO/ZASTAVA	
Yugo/Zastava (81 - 90)	1453

TECH BOOKS	
Automotive Brake Manual	3050
Automotive Electrical & Electronic Systems	3049
Automotive Tools Manual	3052
Automotive Welding Manual	3053

CAR BOOKS	
Automotive Fuel Injection Systems	9755
Car Bodywork Repair Manual	9864
Caravan Manual (2nd Edition)	9894
Ford Vehicle Carburettors	1783
Haynes Technical Data Book (87 - 96)	1996
In-Car Entertainment Manual (2nd Edition)	9862
Japanese Vehicle Carburettors	1786
Pass the MOT!	9861
Small Engine Repair Manual	1755
Solex & Pierburg Carburettors	1785
SU Carburettors	0299
Weber Carburettors (to 79)	0393
Weber Carburettors (79 - 91)	1784

01/10/96